· BRAVEST OF THE BRAVE ·

By the same author:

The Rest is History

BRAVEST OF THE BRAVE

The True Story of
Wing Commander 'Tommy' Yeo-Thomas
SOE Secret Agent
Codename 'The White Rabbit'

Mark Seaman

Michael O'Mara Books Limited

First published in 1997 by
Michael O'Mara Books Limited
9 Lion Yard
Tremadoc Road
London SW4 7NQ

A CIP catalogue record for this book is available from the British
Library

ISBN 1-85479-650-X

Maps by Stephen Dew

Typeset and designed by Keystroke, Jacaranda Lodge, Wolverhampton
Printed and bound in England by Clays Ltd, Bungay, Suffolk

Each one, man for man, has won imperishable praise. Each has gained a glorious grave. Not that sepulchre of earth wherein they lie, but the living tomb of everlasting remembrance wherein their glory is enshrined.

For the whole earth is the sepulchre of heroes; monuments may rise and tablets be set up to them in their own land, but on the far-off shores is an abiding memorial that no pen or chisel has traced.

It is graven, not on stone or brass, but on the heart of humanity.

Take these men for your example. Like them, remember that prosperity can only be for the free; that freedom is the sure possession of those who have the courage to defend it.

Funeral Oration spoken by Pericles, 429BC

To my mother

CONTENTS

• Maps •

ACKNOWLEDGMENTS

In the Victoria Cross and George Cross gallery of the Imperial War Museum in London, there is a showcase devoted to Wing Commander F F E Yeo-Thomas, GC, MC and Bar. For decades visitors have come to read an all too brief description of his career, to admire the dazzling array of his awards and decorations and to examine some of his wartime memorabilia. In my boyhood I was just such a visitor, little thinking that I would one day be employed at the Museum and attempt to write a life of this remarkable man.

In 1983 I was introduced to Barbara Yeo-Thomas by a mutual friend, Group Captain Ron Hockey, DSO, DFC, the wartime commander of No 138 (Special Duty) Squadron. Thereafter we became friends and she introduced me to a wide circle of 'Tommy' Yeo-Thomas's British and French friends and wartime comrades-in-arms. The more I listened to them and read the voluminous written material left by Yeo-Thomas, the more I became convinced that the popularly accepted description of him as a 'plaster saint' hero did not reflect adequately his true character and the depth of his courage. It also became clear that he and Barbara had shared a very special love story set amid the clandestine world of the resistance. As Barbara talked to me, I learnt that the pressures of the war, divided loyalties and the call of duty had put immense strain upon their relationship. Nevertheless, it was evident that it was their love that sustained them through the darkest days of fear, pain and uncertainty and formed the cornerstone of their future life together.

Consciously, I have chosen to concentrate on the war years of Yeo-Thomas's life. Details of his early life are fragmented, although, thankfully, rather more is known of his post-war activities. This book is not a history of the French resistance nor a chronicle of SOE operations. I have sought to provide a context for Yeo-Thomas's experiences, but wherever possible have left him to describe events and his feelings in his own words. It was frequently said of Yeo-Thomas that he did not suffer fools gladly and some of his judgments of others may seem harsh. However, I feel it appropriate that a man who spared himself nothing in the cause of his struggle against the Nazis should be allowed to express his own candid opinions.

I have to thank a wide range of people who have assisted me in the writing of this book. Sadly, several people, such as Ron Hockey and

Jacques Foulquier, have died since I began work on it. I hope all the others who have assisted me with their recollections and who will have the opportunity of reading the book will forgive me for not listing them all by name.

I owe a debt of thanks to Gervase Cowell, Duncan Stuart and Valerie Collins at the Foreign and Commonwealth Office for their help in providing information from the SOE Archive.

I am most grateful for the support and friendship of Toby Buchan who did so much to get the show on the road, and to my agent, Andrew Lownie. I am also greatly indebted to David Roberts and Annie Reid at Michael O'Mara whose patience must have been sorely tested as they nursed the book through to completion and publication.

As ever family, friends and colleagues have been of inestimable help in providing encouragement and the occasional welcome distraction over the years.

Last, but by no means least, is Barbara. It would not have been possible to write this book without her memories, encouragement and advice. This story is as much about her as it is about Yeo-Thomas, as he himself recognized:

All that I have accomplished that was ever any good in my life is due entirely to Barbara, whose love and devotion I can never repay.

INTRODUCTION

On 14 September 1944, as the Second World War entered its sixth year, Squadron Leader Forest 'Tommy' Yeo-Thomas wrote the most important letter of his life. It was addressed to Yeo-Thomas's superior officer, Lieutenant-Colonel L H Dismore, a senior staff officer in the secret British organization, the Special Operations Executive. In spite of the importance he attached to it, Yeo-Thomas entertained little hope that it would ever reach its intended recipient. For, at the time of writing the letter, Yeo-Thomas was an inmate of the infamous Nazi concentration camp at Buchenwald. His already parlous situation had recently become even more desperate. A few days earlier, the ss guards had taken away some of his fellow prisoners, all of whom, like Yeo-Thomas, were captured secret agents. News of the group's fate soon filtered back to their comrades: they had all been beaten and then strangled to death. Now, as he faced the prospect of his imminent murder, Yeo-Thomas wrote a farewell letter in the hope that it might eventually reach London:

> These are 'famous last words', I am afraid; but one has to face death one day or another so I will not moan and get down to brass tacks . . .

The rest of the letter outlined events that had taken place since Yeo-Thomas had parachuted into Occupied France at the beginning of the year. He told of the circumstances surrounding his betrayal and subsequent arrest in Paris in March. He went on to chronicle his torture, solitary confinement and his eventual arrival at the concentration camp in Germany. He concluded:

> The bearer of this letter will give you all the details so I will not say more – whatever he tells you is Gospel truth. He is no romancer, and he will never be able to really do justice to the horrors perpetrated here . . . I leave it to you and others to see that retribution is fierce. It will never be fierce enough.

He later tried to describe his feelings at this bleakest of times:

> I seemed to have lost all sense of feeling and to have become a

Such human characteristics and flaws do not diminish the man. They help to elevate our overall estimation of him. Supermen do not feel pain or uncertainty, nor do they make mistakes or harbour self-doubt. The very existence of these human 'failings' makes the triumph over them all the greater. Indeed, the fact that he was aware of how close he came to reaching the limits of his endurance, yet managed to retain his indomitable spirit, is just one of the reasons why he truly was the bravest of the brave.

CHAPTER ONE

· Early Life ·

Forest Frederick Edward Yeo-Thomas was born at a nursing home in Bedford Square, Holborn, London on 17 June 1901. He was the first child of John and Daisy Ethel (née Burrows) Yeo-Thomas, both British citizens but long-term residents of the port of Dieppe in northern France. The Yeo-Thomas family had lived in France for generations, first moving there in the 1850s. John Yeo-Thomas's father had originally come from South Wales where he had fallen in love with a Miss Thomas.[1] Their parents did not approve of their intention to marry and, with a stubbornness that was to be all too evident in his grandson, he left for Dieppe, married Miss Thomas and changed his name to incorporate hers. His move was not without professional success and he made a fortune selling high-grade Welsh coal to the French railways as Agent Générale of Maison Graigola-Merthyr. The newlyweds gradually settled into the Dieppois life and, in 1895, John's father went on to form and later become Honorary President of Dieppe Football Club. His son and grandson were reported to be reasonably good soccer players and, in 1964, teams in the Dieppe-Neufchâtel area still competed for a Yeo-Thomas cup. He was also a keen golfer and rose to become Vice-President of the Dieppe Golf Club.

Although the family immersed itself pretty fully into local life, Forest Yeo-Thomas later recalled the very strong British influences still present in a family that had lived in France for decades. 'We were so determined to remain British,' Yeo-Thomas said, 'that it became a fixed family rule that the children, when they came, had to be born in Britain.' He continued to describe an almost stereotypical picture of Edwardian life: 'As soon as I was old enough to stand up straight, I remember how, every evening, our meals ended with family prayers and the singing of "God Save The King". I joined in the singing almost before I knew what the words meant. We had one large photograph, I recall, of King Edward VII which, when he died, was draped in black, and for some weeks afterwards we were not allowed to talk above a whisper.' In spite of the fact that father and son tended to speak to each other in French (the latter addressed his mother in English), John Yeo-Thomas dinned into him the mantra: 'Forest, you are British – remember that always.'

A manifestation of this desire to maintain the family's 'Britishness' was to give the children an education in England. Consequently, Forest was packed off to Westcliff School at Seaford, Sussex, almost directly across the English Channel from Dieppe. However, in spite of his father's endeavours, the boy had also become deeply immersed in the French way of life and found the British public school an anathema. He would refuse to eat his porridge and at night would leave his dormitory to sit on the bank of a nearby railway line and watch the trains. His time at Westcliff was mercifully brief and lasted barely a year before his parents brought him back to France. He was sent to schools in Dieppe and Paris before attending the Collège de Dieppe in 1910. He was happy here and enjoyed its strong naval influence. The family's move from the rue Coustain, Dieppe, to Paris in 1914 had the effect of benefiting his education, and Forest was enrolled at the Lycée Condorcet and the University of Paris. Here he studied history, took his Bachelier ès Lettres and followed a variety of sporting pursuits, including football, hockey, boxing and fencing, winning the title Champion de France Universitaire d'Escrime.

However, the domestic atmosphere pervading the Yeo-Thomas household was not all sweetness and light. His mother was a beautiful spendthrift, while his father was a rather austere man whose interests were decidedly cerebral, including a personal and professional interest in lexicography. A second son, Jack, was born in 1908, who soon became his father's favourite, an emotional tie that understandably served to isolate his elder son who was already showing a strong streak of independence.

When Forest Yeo-Thomas was thirteen, the First World War broke out and the Anglo-French influences in his own life became mirrored by the military alliance between the two countries. Faced by a common enemy, the centuries-long enmity between Britain and France underwent a transformation. The taunt of *'perfide Albion'* was put to one side and replaced by the harmony of an *'entente cordiale'* that was cemented in the first weeks of August 1914 by the rapid arrival of the British Expeditionary Force (BEF). It must have been a good time to be a British boy living France as the newspapers and magazines paid tribute to the brave warriors from across the Channel. 'When the first arrivals landed at Rouen, they were received with as much rapture, said a French witness, as if they had come to conduct a service of expiation for Joan of Arc. At Boulogne, others debarked at the foot of a towering column erected in honour of Napoleon on the spot from which he had planned to launch the invasion of England. Other transports came into Havre where the French garrisons climbed on the roofs of their barracks and cheered wildly as their allies came down the gangplanks in the blazing heat.'[2] The feeling of optimism and elation was short-lived, however, and the boasts of the French soldiers that they would soon be in Berlin quickly died in their throats. The German invasion of Belgium, which had brought Britain into the war, rolled on into northern France and showed no signs of stopping. The plan, originally prepared by Count Alfred von Schlieffen, the Chief of the German General Staff, was intended to deliver nothing less than a knockout blow to France before Germany turned its attention to the threat in the east from Russia. Throughout August 1914, the French armies and the BEF retreated southwards until Paris itself was threatened and a German victory seemed assured. However, the advance lost its impetus and, instead of encircling the capital to the north, the German armies wheeled inwards leaving the way open for a French counter-attack. In September France was saved from defeat by its triumph at the Battle of the Marne but its forces were too exhausted to pursue the Germans as they withdrew to the north. A 'race to the sea' ensued in which both sides sought to secure their flanks until, as winter approached, a line of opposing trenches extended from the English Channel to the Swiss border. The war was most certainly not going to be over by Christmas and the prospect of a long, drawn-out attritional conflict loomed large.

John Yeo-Thomas was not slow to enlist in the British Army and became a staff officer, in large measure owing to his fluency in French. Similarly, Daisy volunteered to 'do her bit' and served as a nurse attached to the British Army. The Yeo-Thomases were not the first couple to find that the demands of war put a strain on their marriage, although by 1914 their relationship was already in a fragile state. They rarely saw each other and the gregarious Daisy enjoyed the rich social life that was to be found as a result of her war work. They may have survived these difficulties but for an unexpected crisis with tragic consequences. In 1917, their younger son contracted meningitis and, after a short illness, died. John Yeo-Thomas blamed the death of his favourite son on his wife for having neglected him while she continued nursing. One can only guess at the atmosphere of grief and recrimination that prevailed in the house.

It seems likely that these domestic upheavals made Forest Yeo-Thomas all the keener to enlist in the army. His father was aware of his intent and explicitly forbade his volunteering, but John Yeo-Thomas knew his son's character well enough to appreciate that his instructions would not be sufficient to deter him. He therefore notified the British and French army recruitment services in Paris of Forest's details, specifically that he was substantially under age, and ordered them to reject his application. However, the father had not reckoned on the extent of his son's ingenuity nor the entry of the United States of America into the war on 6 April 1917.

The US Army was small and ill-equipped by any standards and a sudden commitment to a major conflict halfway around the world constituted an awesome logistical challenge. The circumstances ensured that recruits only received the most cursory of examinations and, in the latter half of 1917, a young man named 'Pierre Nord', aged nineteen, was able to make a successful application in Paris to join the United States Army. Photographs of the time reveal that Yeo-Thomas barely looked his real age of sixteen, let alone the nineteen that he claimed, but, typically, he had managed to achieve his ambition. One account states that the new recruit went on to become a despatch rider but there is no record of his seeing action in France. For, with the American Expeditionary Force taking so long to be formed and its commanding officer, General John Pershing, opposed to its being dispersed piecemeal among French and British units, its opportunities for action remained limited until the German offensive of spring 1918.

The details of Yeo-Thomas's US Army service are sketchy. When completing a British military questionnaire more than twenty years later, he stated that, after the Armistice of November 1918, he had spent four months in Germany as part of the Army of Occupation. This was followed by two months in Austria and then a year and a half in Poland and Russia. During this latter period of service, he may have been part of an American military mission to Poland but, bearing in mind his adventurous nature, his presence there may have owed just as much to his desire to see action.

In 1920, and still not twenty years old, he is reported to have joined an 'American Legion' assisting the Poles in their struggle against Bolshevik Russia. In 1918, a Polish Legion was organized in the United States to provide recruits for a Polish Army that had been recently formed in France to fight on the Allied side against the Central Powers. The legion was initially made up of immigrants who had not yet been granted US citizenship and were therefore ineligible to serve in the US Army. In January 1919, the US authorities learnt 'that American citizens had joined the Polish Army and that they were being forced to go to Poland for service'.[3] There is no indication that Yeo-Thomas was pressed into service with former members of the legion, but it may offer an indication as to how he embarked upon this military adventure. The campaign's inspiration lay in Polish territorial aggrandisement rather than a defence of its new-found independence. In spite of a proposal by the Allies that Poland accept that its eastern frontier be fixed at the 'Curzon Line' (named after the British Foreign Secretary, Lord Curzon), which had been determined by international arbitration, the Poles, led by Josef Pilsudski, sought to incorporate the Ukraine into a 'Greater Poland'. Consequently, on 25 April 1920, they launched an offensive against Soviet-held

Ukraine. The next day the important city of Zhitomir was captured, followed on 8 May by the conquest of the capital, Kiev. This turned out to be the high point of Polish fortunes and in June the Bolsheviks launched a counter-attack. On 5 June, the Polish lines around Zhitomir were broken after heavy fighting, described by no less an individual than Josef Stalin, at that time Political Commissar of the Bolshevik First Cavalry Army: 'The resistance of the Poles was so desperate that our cavalry literally had to hack their way through, the result being that, of the Poles left on the field, not less than 8,000 were wounded and killed by shot or sabre.'

It seemed as if the entire Polish-Ukrainian Third Army would be encircled in Kiev, but on 13 June it broke out and retreated westwards.[4] Meanwhile, during the fighting for Zhitomir, Yeo-Thomas had been captured by the Red Army and as a foreigner was, not surprisingly, sentenced to death. Shortly before the execution was to be carried out, he seized an opportunity for escape; realizing that his guard was befuddled by drink, he strangled him and fled. It was an early example of his readiness to take violent action when the occasion demanded. Once again, there is no record of the circumstances of his flight other than a statement on his file that he travelled through the Balkans and Turkey before reaching the United States. His record shows that he left the US Army in 1922 but the circumstances remain obscure.

He returned to France to find much had changed. His parents' marriage had broken up and his father had formed a new relationship with his former secretary. John and Daisy Yeo-Thomas eventually divorced and, on 1 June 1929, the former remarried. The family fortunes had also undergone a marked deterioration as a result of the war. Following the Bolshevik Revolution, a considerable amount of money had been lost on their Russian investments and, with alimony to pay and a new wife to maintain, John Yeo-Thomas had fallen on decidedly hard times. Whether or not he had forgiven his son's disobedience, he was in no position to offer Forest much assistance and he informed him that he would have to fend for himself. Like so many thousands of other ex-servicemen, Forest Yeo-Thomas was obliged to undertake the most menial of tasks and he later admitted that he had spent some time in London, ending up selling bootlaces and matches in Piccadilly Circus. His exile was only a temporary interlude while tempers cooled and he soon returned to Paris where, towards the end of 1922, his father helped him get a job as an apprentice mechanic with Rolls-Royce, for whom John was acting as an agent. Forest Yeo-Thomas did not complete his apprenticeship owing to a 'drop in business' (although he retained a lifelong love of cars) and, instead, he decided to take up accountancy. He obviously managed to find some time away from his work and studies for he fell in love and, on 12 September 1925, married Lillian Margaret Walker. The daughter of a British father and Danish mother, Lillian was, like Yeo-Thomas, a foreigner brought up in France. However, they differed in that she adopted French nationality. In keeping with French law, a civil ceremony was conducted in Paris at the mairie of the 16ème arrondissement followed by a religious service at the Anglican church in the rue Auguste-Vacquerie.

With a wife and, before too long, two daughters (Evelyn Daisy Erica, born on 18 April 1927, and Lillian May Alice, born on 27 May 1930) to provide for, Yeo-Thomas had to apply himself to his career. He stated on one of his military files that he had been employed as senior cashier and new business manager in three banks over a period of twelve years. These appear to have been the Cambist Bankers Trust Company, the Bank of Montreal and the Chase Bank. He then acted as assistant to the general manager at Compagnie Industrielle des Pétroles until, in 1932, he joined the *haute couture* house of Molyneux in the rue Royale as general manager. Edward Molyneux was a British-born fashion designer who had managed to make a significant impact upon the Paris fashion scene. He had studied art in London and worked for the couturier Lucile before the First World War. In addition to his successful Paris house, he opened establishments in London, Monte Carlo, Cannes and Biarritz. One writer has described him as 'a modernist designer of consummate good taste, walking a fine line between the refinements of couture style and a modernist aesthetic and the ambition to be socially and culturally advanced in the age of Anita Loos and Gatsby.'[5]

Perhaps as an antidote to this intensely feminine environment, Yeo-Thomas pursued his great interest in boxing and held a part share in a gymnasium, fought as a flyweight or bantamweight and wrote occasional reports for the English magazine *Boxing* under the byline 'Eddie' Thomas.[6]

As Yeo-Thomas edged towards a relatively successful career with Molyneux and tried to come to terms with marriage and fatherhood, France was undergoing significant political and economic upheaval. Physically, economically and mentally exhausted by the sacrifices of the First World War, the nation was ill-served by a succession of inferior governments, who either papered over the obvious cracks in the fabric of French society or simply chose to ignore them. France's leading politicians revealed themselves to be incapable of exhibiting even the most basic forms of leadership. To make matters worse, their preoccupation with the façade of government was increasingly played out against a backdrop of international economic and diplomatic crises. Of course life carried on for the beau monde of *Le Tout Paris* and famous writers, painters, musicians and couturiers such as machine; I had no fear of death in any shape or form, and I felt absolutely no apprehension. Never during those days did I worry for myself; it was not a matter of courage, I just cannot explain it.

It was typical of Yeo-Thomas that his final thoughts, when facing a terrible death, should be of retribution against the Nazis who persecuted him. Similarly, it was in keeping with his character that he should dismiss any suggestion that his behaviour was courageous.

In the heat of battle, most acts of bravery are 'instinctive', buttressed by the effects of adrenalin, training, comradeship and expectations of duty. War, however, also makes demands on those who are called upon, not merely to perform one act of bravery, but to face a whole series of challenges. During the Second World War, secret agents carried out operations in enemy territory, relying for their survival upon their own skill and luck. Every day they risked capture by one of the most brutal and implacable enemies known to history. Furthermore, for those who returned to safety, there was always the possibility of a having to go yet again behind the lines. This was Yeo-Thomas's type of bravery. In contrast to the quick, spontaneous burst of heroism exhibited by members of conventional armed forces, his was a form of bravery that he was called upon to display time and time again. He volunteered to carry out operations in Nazi-occupied France, not once, but three times. Having been caught, he endured the most frightful tortures, yet refused to reveal the secrets that would have saved him from further maltreatment. Thanks to his ingenuity and willpower, he survived, against all the odds, the worst excesses of the concentration camp system. Significantly, he did not wait for liberation by the Allies but, in the closing days of the war, escaped to freedom.

Such a brief outline may seem to confirm the stereotypical image of the war hero that has been drawn of Yeo-Thomas by writers, journalists and scriptwriters. Yet to represent him as the embodiment of stiff upper-lipped heroics does scant justice to a remarkable man.

For there was a real man behind the chest full of medals and the media interviews when he talked diffidently about 'the other chaps who did not come back' and his own 'luck' at surviving. Yeo-Thomas was someone who, as a wartime colleague wrote, had become 'hooked' on the 'drug' of danger. Even allowing for the extraordinary circumstances of the time, his compulsion to return to the clandestine world of Occupied France reached the point of obsession and all but destroyed his relationship with Barbara, the woman he loved. Here was a man of humour and charm, kindness and generosity and, as the occasion demanded, ruthlessness and violence.

Molyneux were able to find rich patrons, but France was frequently teetering on the brink of political collapse. The traditional parties – who formed a succession of ineffective cabinets – proved to be more concerned with maintaining their domestic prominence than they were with addressing the major issues confronting the nation. People therefore sought expression of their aspirations (or at least representation of them) in the extremes of the Left and Right, but, in the troubled 1930s, adherence to communism or fascism inevitably resulted in association with, on the one hand, the Soviet Union and, on the other, Italy and Germany. French politics became increasingly polarized with each side remonstrating with the other about these foreign powers' involvement in national affairs.

If France appeared uncertain over domestic policies, its overriding foreign policy was crystal clear. Politicians of all parties advocated, to the point of obsession, a renunciation of any course of action that would result in another war in Europe. Consequently, successive governments of all political hues maintained the complementary policies of defence and appeasement. On 4 January 1930, following extensive discussions among the Army High Command, the National Assembly gave its approval for the construction of a massive defence line along France's frontier with Germany. Named after the War Minister, André Maginot, work began almost straightaway and, by 1936, more than seven billion francs had been invested in the defences. The Maginot Line was to extend over 200 miles from Switzerland to the borders of Belgium and Luxembourg. Although an awesome example of military engineering, it came to symbolize the entrenched perspective of French defence policy. Perhaps even more significantly, the protection it offered was only partial, on the one hand serving to discourage a German frontal assault in Alsace and Lorraine, and on the other hand leaving France vulnerable to an outflanking attack from the north through Belgium. It was a flaw that was not to go unnoticed in Berlin.

Inexorably, the game of international brinkmanship continued throughout the 1930s. Each time Hitler sought to push his demands just one stage further and each time he found to his surprise that he had been allowed to succeed. In the spring and summer of 1938 war seemed closer than ever with Nazi claims that the Sudeten region of Czechoslovakia be incorporated into the Third Reich. Appeasement, however, scored another 'victory' and, at a summit meeting at Munich in September, Édouard Daladier and Neville Chamberlain, the French and British Prime Ministers, acceded to Hitler's demands. Paris and London were delirious at the averting of war, but subsequent events were to show that the Munich Agreement had been but a stay of execution. Although it was hailed as 'peace for our time', many were later to reflect that 'time' is a relative concept.

In March 1939, Germany marched unchallenged into the remainder of independent Czechoslovakia. Even the most inveterately optimistic appeasers had to concede that there might, after all, be no limit to Hitler's 'last reasonable demands'. This intellectual acceptance of the prospect of war did not mark a fundamental revision in politicians' and generals' attitudes, but rather they bolted on unrealistic contingency plans to their increasingly redundant policies. Great Britain and France now decided to check German expansionism by guaranteeing the independence of the next country at threat, Poland. Winston Churchill, a long-time opponent of appeasement, perhaps best summed up this diplomatic and military *volte face*: 'History, which we are told is mainly the record of the crimes, follies and miseries of mankind, may be scoured and ransacked to find a parallel to this sudden and complete reversal of five or six years' policy of easy-going placatory appeasement, and its transformation almost overnight into a readiness to accept an obviously imminent war on far worse conditions and on the greatest scale . . . Here was decision at last, taken at the worst possible moment and on the least satisfactory ground, which must surely lead to the slaughter of tens of millions of people.'[7]

In the spring and summer of 1939 war beckoned, but France did not want to catch its eye. Joint French and British strategic planning continued, but with scant regard for the practicalities of waging a land war against Germany. They had tied themselves to a country on the other side of Europe that they could not readily support in the event of a German invasion. Clearly, Poland would demand an Anglo-French offensive against Germany's western frontier, but this was fundamentally contrary to existing Allied military thinking and preparation for war. Much time was devoted to speculation on whether an internal German resistance to Hitler might obviate the need to wage a war. Furthermore, if such a war did prove to be inevitable, it was hoped that an Anglo-French blockade would create such economic disruption that, as in 1918, Germany would eventually self-destruct and French and British blood would not flow in the same torrents as during the Great War. These optimistic analyses were espoused by many of the leading French generals, including Général Maxime Weygand, the former Chief of the General Staff, who affirmed in a speech given in early July: 'The French Army is stronger than ever before in its history. It has first-rate armaments, first-rate fortifications, excellent morale and an outstanding high command. No one wants war, but I assure you that if we are forced to win a new victory, win it we will.'[8]

Weygand's opinions were in large measure endorsed by his successor, Général Maurice Gamelin, who stated, on 23 August 1939, that Germany would collapse under the strain of both internal and external factors: 'The day war is declared against Germany, Hitler will collapse. Instead of defending the borders of the Reich, the German Army will have to march on Berlin in order to repress the risings there. We will then cut through Germany like a knife through butter.'[9]

As Europe slipped into war, Yeo-Thomas had plenty to worry about on his own domestic front. His marriage had not proved to be a success and, although it grieved him to leave his two young daughters, his incompatibility with Lillian resulted in their separation in 1936. He moved out of their apartment in the rue de la Pointe in the suburb of la Garenne-Colombes and went to live with his father and stepmother in the rue des Eaux in Passy. He kept in touch with his wife and his diary for 1939 reveals that he continued to meet her regularly in order to pay her maintenance. In spite of their irreconcilable differences, they could not agree on a divorce. Yeo-Thomas resisted it for, if he agreed to become 'the guilty party', he feared 'culpability' might be used to prevent his having access to the children. Sadly, when, in turn, he sought a divorce, Lillian was to deny it. Further emotional upheaval occurred on 17 July when his mother passed away. As her next of kin, he had to oversee her funeral and his diary simply records that he had to pay 20,000 francs to the undertaker.

Meanwhile, the drift towards war now seemed irrevocable. Although Parisian social and artistic life still shone as brightly as ever, there was an increasing acceptance of the apparent inevitability of the course of events. On 23 August 1939, Germany's hasty and extremely unlikely courtship of the Soviet Union was sealed by a non-aggression pact. Britain and France had sought to conclude their own arrangement with Stalin, but had been edged out by their Nazi rivals. Now Germany was free to pursue its interests with relative impunity and, on 1 September 1939, without any formal declaration of war, launched its invasion of Poland. Understandably, Poland demanded that Britain and France honour their commitments. In contrast to the rapidity with which the German tanks drove into their ally's territory, neither country seemed inclined to rush into war. Then, on Sunday 3 September 1939, Britain and France delivered ultimata demanding that Germany withdraw its forces from Poland. At 11.15am Prime Minister Chamberlain broadcast to the nation, informing the people of Britain that no adequate reply had been received from Berlin 'and that consequently this country is at war with Germany'. His speech was far from rousing stuff, with Chamberlain at pains to express his own disappointment: 'You can imagine what a bitter blow it is to me that all my long struggle for peace has failed. Yet I cannot believe that there is anything more, or anything different that I could have done, and that would have been more successful.'

However, he went on to conclude on a rather more upbeat note and the sad, tired and prematurely aged politician managed to express a statement of intent that was to constitute an almost uncanny prediction of Yeo-Thomas's wartime career: 'For it is evil things that we shall be fighting against – brute force, bad faith, injustice, oppression and persecution; and against them I am certain that the right will prevail.'

CHAPTER TWO

· WAR ·

Yeo-Thomas's first attempts to enter the war were frustratingly fruitless. The military attaché at the British Embassy in the rue Faubourg St Honoré told him that no volunteers were being accepted. He did, however, offer the concession that Yeo-Thomas could travel to England (at his own expense) and try his luck there. Yeo-Thomas was an old hand at breaking through recruitment barriers and he next tried the French Foreign Legion. However, he found them no more encouraging, for they had received orders not to accept British citizens. Not to be deterred, Yeo-Thomas returned to the embassy and pressed his services upon the air attaché, who graciously accepted him as a volunteer driver, with the proviso that he use his own car and pay for his own petrol. For three weeks Yeo-Thomas remained in limbo between civilian and military status until, on 26 September 1939, his distinguished career in the Royal Air Force began with his formal recruitment as Aircraftman 2nd Class 504896. His delight was short-lived. He was told that his duties were to be strictly those of an interpreter and was bluntly informed that he was too old to be trained to fly or even serve as an air gunner. 'This got my goat – I was as fit as a fiddle. Until the war broke out I trained in the gym every day and boxed four to eight rounds with up-and-coming boxers and I knew that I was in better shape than most men fifteen years younger than myself.' Yeo-Thomas requested an immediate transfer to serve in a British Army tank unit but was none too politely informed that, as a member of the Royal Air Force, he had no say in the matter and was simply to do what he was told.

In spite of Yeo-Thomas's desire to enter the fray, there was scarcely a fray to enter. Poland had been rapidly overrun, with Britain and France both unable and in part unwilling to intervene. Optimistic appreciations of the Polish Army's ability to defend its own frontiers were dashed as it collapsed under onslaughts, in the west from Germany and, after 17 September, in the east from the Soviet Union. With Poland now firmly under the sway of the Wehrmacht and Soviet Red Army, Anglo-French strategy ponderously unfolded, with the massive French Army gathering behind the immensity of the Maginot Line. A British Expeditionary Force reported for duty alongside its French allies and, by the end of September, over 150,000 troops had crossed the Channel and occupied their pre-planned positions on the

Franco-Belgian border. And there they stayed. The Allied master plan was steadily to build up forces, ready for an assault upon the daunting ramparts of Germany's 'West Wall' frontier defences. However, underlying this strategy was a hope that a naval blockade would facilitate a repeat of Germany's First World War collapse by economic strangulation. These uninspired strategies were further expressions of the policy of appeasement that had helped to bring about the war in the first place and, from the outset, the direction of the war signally lacked dynamism and purpose. This inertia did not go unnoticed by the citizens and armed forces of Britain and France and, encouraged by the onset of a particularly harsh winter, the conflict was soon nick-named the *'Drôle de Guerre'*, 'Sitzkrieg' and 'Phoney War'.

Yeo-Thomas's first experiences of the British armed forces were symptomatic of the general malaise. In Paris he found muddle and incompetence all around him and, in consequence, became frustrated and impatient. He did not want his contribution to the war effort to consist of driving VIPs and embassy personnel around the city and longed for the opportunity of getting into the 'real' war. Eventually matters seemed to have improved when he received orders to report to the RAF's Advanced Air Striking Force at Reims. At this time the AASF was separate from the Air Component of the British Expeditionary Force and was still under the control of Bomber Command in England. Its purpose was to establish forward bases in France for medium bombers from which they would have sufficient operational range to attack targets in Germany. In the event, this surprisingly offensive-minded rationale, which had been decided upon as early as 1938, was never implemented. 'There were no bombing raids on Germany, for the Allies had decided to refrain from this form of attack until Germany began it and the enemy dropped no bombs on France till the offensive opened.'[1]

Unfortunately, on his arrival in Reims, Yeo-Thomas found the situation as confused as in Paris and he even had difficulty in locating his new posting at the interpreters' pool in the Château Polignac. Nothing daunted, he eventually managed to find himself a room in an hotel and decided to go in search of his new job the next day. Luck was on his side and, in the morning, he happened upon Sergeant Albertella, an acquaintance from Paris who was also a member of the interpreters' pool and who was able to give him instructions to report to the château. Here, further good news awaited him and he was informed that his rank had meteorically risen from Aircraftman 2nd Class through Corporal to Acting Sergeant (unpaid). Finally, to cap it all, he found himself billeted at the home of Monsieur Veith, the local brewer. That evening his host experienced an initial period of uncertainty but suspicion of his English lodger was dispelled by

Yeo-Thomas's fluent French and immaculate manners. They soon became the best of friends and their first meeting developed into an alcoholic binge that lasted until the early hours of the following morning.

Even allowing for the conviviality of his lodgings, Yeo-Thomas's time at Reims was not a happy one. He remained without a uniform, acting as an interpreter to senior staff officers on lengthy tours, and was obliged to pay his expenses out of his own pocket. He submitted receipts but, hardly surprisingly, these were to be lost during the fall of France. His subsequent requests to the RAF for payment were met by fatuous demands for duplicate receipts to be submitted.

Yeo-Thomas's next posting was rather more to his liking and was made memorable by the eventual acquisition of a uniform. He joined the Forward Air Ammunition Park (FAAP) at Nogent l'Abesse near to Reims, where at last he found comrades-in-arms and a level of responsibility commensurate with his talents. His personality and linguistic skills made him particularly useful in liaising with the French authorities and developing better relations with the local inhabitants. This kept him fully occupied until, on 23 November, he was sent to England to attend an anti-gas course. The trip was not without incident, as Yeo-Thomas found himself having to shepherd not only his four fellow NCOs but also a dedicatedly inebriate officer across France.

His arrival in Southampton marked his first visit to England in seventeen years, but he felt little sentiment at his 'homecoming'. England was cold and bleak and Rollestone Camp on Salisbury Plain was hardly the most picturesque of places, but at least he was pleasantly surprised by the quality of his RAF instructors and there was some opportunity for trips into Salisbury. However, things did not always go smoothly and Yeo-Thomas's ruthless streak was called into action: 'We were overjoyed when a civilian employed on the camp, who went to Salisbury every weekend, offered to take us in and bring us back on the Sunday night in his car. Five of us decided to go; when all was fixed he generously informed us that we would have to pay 10/- each! Well, we were so browned off that we paid, but I was livid, and after our return on the Sunday night, I snaffled some sugar and poured about half a pound of it into his petrol tank.'[2]

His stay in England lasted less than a fortnight and he was soon back with his unit in France, but shortly before Christmas he received orders to attend another course, this time at Headquarters, Fighter Command at Stanmore in Middlesex. Yeo-Thomas's second visit was to prove even less convivial than his first. Christmas Day was spent miserably on a transport ship in the Channel and, when he reported for duty at Fighter Command the next day, he was promptly sent away for another forty-eight hours' unwanted leave. London was a miserable place: 'I don't think I have ever hated any place more than I did London that night.'

Things seemed to look up after the holiday. Although the RAF still did not know what to do with him and packed him off on another week's leave, the banks had now reopened and Yeo-Thomas was able to draw some cash. If he was going to be unhappy he would at least be able to do it in some style and he checked into a succession of luxury West End hotels, such as the Grosvenor, Cumberland and Regent Palace. The affluent sergeant certainly raised some eyebrows, but he still did not find the experience enjoyable and recalled it as 'one of the most miserable weeks of my life (not excluding my sojourn in Buchenwald)'. His misery turned to loneliness, boredom, frustration and even anger. He felt that there was little else to do but to try and blot out these feelings by means of a week-long bender.

Matters did eventually take a turn for the better. On his return to Stanmore, he was ordered to report to the Bomber Liaison Section in the Filter Room. This secret installation was the control centre into which radar stations fed their reports of hostile intruders. Yeo-Thomas could console himself with the importance of his new work, although this did not stop him resubmitting an application to train as an air gunner. Although his commanding officer was sympathetic, he was once again refused and remained downcast at his inability to find a more active posting. He soon had something to divert his thoughts, for he now met Barbara Dean, the woman who was to share the rest of his life.

Barbara was born in Kent in 1915. Her mother had died shortly after her birth and her father seemed thereafter to hold her responsible for his wife's death. Her childhood in Hove, Sussex, was consequently far from happy and was not helped by frequent clashes with her stepmother. However, the difficulties encountered in her childhood had the effect of making her fiercely independent, a quality that was to make her a match and a soulmate for Yeo-Thomas. This independence, coupled with patriotism, resulted in her volunteering for the Women's Auxiliary Air Force at the outbreak of war. However, less than four months later she was deeply regretting her decision. Although she was sounded out by her officers as to whether she would be willing to accept a commission, the boredom, pointless discipline and petty restrictions were anathema to her. The final straw came when she was put on a charge for disputing an officer's observation that her hat was crooked. It had made her determined to leave – 'I volunteered my way in and I volunteered my way out' – and she was waiting for the paperwork to be completed shortly after Christmas.

For Yeo-Thomas it was love at first sight. For a man so often

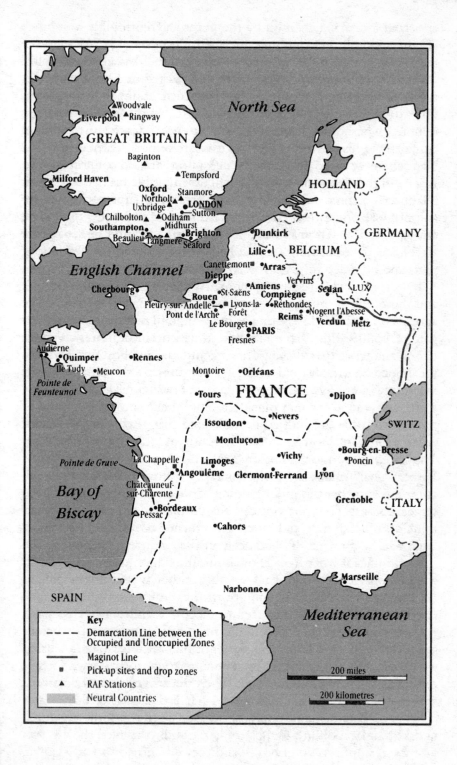

North Sea

GREAT BRITAIN

▲Woodvale
Liverpool ▲Ringway

Baginton
▲

Milford Haven

▲Tempsford

HOLLAND

Oxford
Northolt▲ Stanmore
Uxbridge▲ ▲LONDON
Chilbolton▲ ▲Odiham └Sutton
Southampton• Midhurst
Beaulieu▲Tangmere ▲•Brighton
Seaford

English Channel

Canettemont■ •Arras
Dieppe•
Cherbourg•

GERMANY

•Dunkirk

Lille• BELGIUM

•Amiens Vervins
St-Saëns• Compiègne• Sedan• LUX
Rouen• •Réthondes
Fleury-sur-Andelle• Lyons-la- Reims• •Nogent l'Abesse
Pont de l'Arche Forêt Verdun• Metz•
Le Bourget•
Fresnes• ■PARIS

Audierne•
•Quimper •Rennes
Île Tudy•
•Meucon Montoire• •Orléans
Pointe de
Feunteunot •Tours FRANCE •Dijon

Nevers•
Issoudon• SWITZ
Montluçon■
La Chappelle• •Bourg-en-Bresse
Pointe de Grave ■ Limoges• •Vichy •Poncin
•Angoulême Clermont-Ferrand Lyon•
Châteauneuf-
sur-Charente
■•Bordeaux Grenoble• ITALY
Pessac•

Bay of
Biscay

•Cahors

SPAIN
•Marseille
Narbonne•

Mediterranean
Sea

	Key
-----	Demarcation Line between the Occupied and Unoccupied Zones
———	Maginot Line
■	Pick-up sites and drop zones
▲	RAF Stations
	Neutral Countries

200 miles

200 kilometres

criticized for taking the bull by the horns, he plotted his wooing of her meticulously. He consulted Elizabeth Trouncer, a WAAF friend of Barbara's, with whom he used to chat in the underground Filter Room during long, boring watches. He even took her to dinner in the West End a couple of times but Elizabeth Trouncer 'had enough nous to realize the object of the exercise'. She told him that she doubted whether he stood a chance but Yeo-Thomas was far more confident of his prospects than his go-between and offered her a £5 bet. There was no attempt at deception and Yeo-Thomas told Elizabeth to let Barbara know straightaway that he was married. 'Well tell him to spend his weekend with his wife' was Barbara's immediate and pithy response. Moreover, she had set herself a rule not to date any airmen. Yeo-Thomas was not easily dissuaded and he sent notes via Elizabeth, explaining that he had been separated for nearly four years and intended to get divorced as soon as the war was over.

It was only on her last day in the WAAF that Barbara finally relented, and there was as much pragmatism as romance in her decision. She agreed to meet him for a drink at the Windmill pub near to the main gate of Bentley Priory, the mansion in which Headquarters, Fighter Command was situated. Apart from being intrigued by Yeo-Thomas, she hoped that he would carry her suitcases to the station. Their meeting was scarcely the most romantic of occasions. On 28 January 1940, she waited for him outside the pub believing that, in spite of the snow on the ground, custom dictated that a woman should not enter a pub unescorted. Blissfully ignorant of her presence, Yeo-Thomas waited inside, comforted by a drink and a warm fire. When Barbara finally plucked up the courage to go inside and find him, there was a further misunderstanding. Concerned at the impecunious sergeant's cash flow, she ordered the cheapest drink that she could think of, a half of mild and bitter. He returned bearing her beer and a large whisky for himself. The delay in their meeting became all the more significant when Yeo-Thomas informed her that he only had an hour before he had to go back on duty and he would not be able to take her to the station. In spite of this, they were sufficiently interested in each other and arranged to meet in London two days later. But the course of true love still did not run true and, shortly before she was due to leave home to meet him, Barbara was violently sick. It was two hours before she felt well enough to go to Leicester Square, certain that it was a fool's errand. When she arrived Yeo-Thomas was still there and at once he soared in her estimation. She also later recalled his confident and appreciative gaze when a gust of wind lifted her skirt and gave him a glimpse of her legs. By this time she was sufficiently restored to good health and they adjourned to La Coquille, a French restaurant in St Martin's Lane.

Thereafter they saw as much of each other as possible with Barbara recording in her diary, after their third date, 'liking Forest very much'. Yeo-Thomas had inherited some money on the death of his mother and was able to fuel their love affair with expensive meals and regular visits to nightclubs. After weeks of profligacy, a cheque finally bounced but, instead of being dismayed, Yeo-Thomas seemed unaccountably elated. Astonished, Barbara asked the reason for his happiness and was told that he had been determined to spend the money in order that his estranged wife would have no claim on it.

Having left the WAAF, Barbara got a job running Harridges dress shop in Sutton, Surrey. She rented a cottage nearby, which became the couple's base for weekends when Yeo-Thomas was able to get a forty-eight-hour pass from Stanmore. They were now sure of the depth of their feelings for each other and, on 9 February 1940, decided to 'get married' without the benefit of a church service. It was to be their secret bond and therefore failed to dispel the subsequent censorious comments of the moralizers with whom they came into contact. At least, as far as they were concerned, they had cemented their relationship. Yeo-Thomas also began to make arrangements to secure a divorce, but found his wife singularly un-cooperative.

In spite of the importance of his attachment to Barbara, Yeo-Thomas yearned to get back to France where he was convinced that the war was about to flare up. His wish was granted and, after a farewell meal at La Coquille, he left London on 6 April for the Bomber Liaison Section at Le Bourget airfield outside Paris. His plea-sure at returning to France was tempered by his sadness at leaving Barbara. He wrote to her every day and scrupulously recorded in his diary the arrival of her letters. After a week's separation her daily let-ters ceased and he became increasingly worried and depressed at her silence. In desperation he asked an RAF friend, who was flying to London, to telephone her on his behalf and send him a telegram confirming that all was well. Yeo-Thomas's doubts were unfounded and on the evening of his emissary's departure, he received a letter from Barbara that was followed the next day by three others that had also been delayed in the post.

Meanwhile the 'Phoney War' was about to end abruptly. Two days after Yeo-Thomas's return to France, the Germans invaded Denmark and Norway. The Danes were overwhelmed within a matter of hours, while Norway was subjected to major amphibious and airborne assaults that saw its ports and cities rapidly seized. Although Britain and France had reached an advanced stage in their own plans for a pre-emptive military intervention in Norway, the German invasion took them by surprise. An ill-coordinated series of Anglo-French

naval and land operations were mounted in support of the
Norwegians but they failed to dislodge the invaders. It boded ill
for the alliance, while the failure in Norway engendered a growing
political campaign in Westminster to dislodge the Prime Minister,
Neville Chamberlain.

The return to France did not cure Yeo-Thomas of his restlessness
and frustration. His attempts to be selected for aircrew training
continued to be unsuccessful and the novelty of his new job as part of
a direction-finding unit plotting the approach of enemy aircraft soon
palled. At the beginning of May, however, his ennui was broken. After
a two-day debate, a vote in the House of Commons showed that
Chamberlain had lost the support of ninety of his fellow Conservative
MPs. Negotiations began for the creation of a National Government
and speculation arose in Whitehall regarding his likely successor.
Matters were little better on the other side of the Channel. In March,
Prime Minister Édouard Daladier had resigned following a catalogue
of inept policies regarding the Russo-Finnish war.[3] Now his successor,
Paul Reynaud, offered his resignation to Président Albert Lebrun
because he found himself baulked in his attempt to sack Général
Maurice Gamelin, the Supreme Commander, French Land Forces.
Then, on the morning of 10 May, these internal divisions were put
into relief by reports that Germany had invaded the Netherlands,
Belgium and Luxembourg. The 'Phoney War' was well and truly over.

Fortunately, the political crisis in Whitehall was soon resolved
and on the evening of 10 May 1940, Winston Churchill, the First
Lord of the Admiralty in Chamberlain's Cabinet, was summoned
to Buckingham Palace and asked by King George VI to form a
government. As the weeks unfolded, the appointment was to have
momentous consequences. The arrival of a war leader of Churchill's
personality and powers of leadership placed in sharp contrast the
political bankruptcy of Britain's French allies.

Amid this turmoil, Barbara flew to Paris to visit Yeo-Thomas. In
spite of the international crisis unfolding around them, the two lovers
were ecstatic to see each other after their month's separation. Yeo-
Thomas was able to take Barbara to all his favourite haunts in Paris,
although on this occasion she did not get to meet his father, at whose
apartment in the rue des Eaux he was still living. When it came time
for Barbara to return to England, the situation had deteriorated such
that it was impossible to get a flight out of Le Bourget. She was
obliged to stay at an hotel near the airport while Yeo-Thomas tried to
pull strings to get her a seat home. In the end, the strings he pulled
were financial and on 19 May he bribed an official to allow her on to
a commercial flight for VIPs. Barbara hated leaving him, not merely
because of her love for him but also fearing the obvious dangers that

lay ahead as German forces advanced further into France. The aircraft took off on schedule but soon was forced to return because of German aircraft in the vicinity. Barbara tried to get off to have another chance to see Yeo-Thomas, but the cabin staff prevented her and, when the all-clear was given, the aircraft made a safe return to England.

The Allied situation at the front rapidly deteriorated. Typical of the muddled Anglo-French planning had been the contingency plan to meet an attack in the north. It consisted of an advance into Belgium to occupy a new defensive line along the River Dyle. Thus the Allied plan offered the worst of both worlds: a defensive offensive reflecting the generals' negative frames of mind, which entailed abandoning their already fortified positions along the Franco-Belgian frontier. As it transpired, the plan devised by Général Gamelin was in large measure overtaken by events and, in particular, by the speed and ferocity of the German assault. Within five days of the first attack, Holland surrendered and Belgium's much-vaunted defences were overwhelmed. The plan to fight the campaign on foreign soil soon foundered and, on 13 May, the Germans had advanced on to French soil in the relatively unprotected Ardennes sector. The French and British forces were obliged to retreat, constantly hoping that the front would stabilize long enough to enable them to prepare an effective defence line and eventually mount a counter-attack. The AASF was forced to respond to the generals' demands for attacks on the German bridgehead. On the afternoon of 14 May, Blenheim and Battle bombers of Nos 71, 75 and 76 Wings launched a series of raids on enemy positions near Sedan. Seventy-one aircraft were engaged but the attacks were a disaster. German anti-aircraft and fighter defences shot them out of the skies and forty RAF aeroplanes were lost.

On land, French and British units fared little better. They launched isolated attacks against the invader, and some even met with success but the German momentum needed more than minor counterattacks to stem the tide. On 20 May, German tanks reached the English Channel at St Valéry-sur-Somme, thereby cutting off the French 1st Army and the majority of the British Expeditionary Force. The Allied forces in this pocket fell back on Dunkirk and, faced with annihilation or capture, plans were hastily laid by the Royal Navy to mount a mass evacuation from France. On the evening of 26 May, the order announcing 'Operation DYNAMO is to commence' was issued and the rescue of the British Expeditionary Force began. The next day Belgium surrendered and, although the success of the evacuation far exceeded the dreams of its planners, it seemed that nothing could be done to prevent the whole of France being overrun.

Unlike most other members of the British forces, Yeo-Thomas was fully able to comprehend the depth of the catastrophe that was now engulfing France. The refugees who choked the roads out of Paris were as much, if not more, his fellow countrymen as were his comrades-in-arms. His duties still permitted him to live with his father and he kept in touch with his former colleagues at Molyneux's, but he found that there was little he could do to reassure them and lift the 'feeling of impending disaster'. This pessimism was soon made manifest when Le Bourget was attacked by German bombers. 'We did not see one Allied fighter and the AA [anti-aircraft fire] was poor and inaccurate. Jerry got away without any apparent losses, leaving Le Bourget a smoking shambles.'

The situation was growing increasingly chaotic. The Germans were closing in on Paris and, in the absence of specific instructions, Yeo-Thomas and his commanding officer, Flight Lieutenant James, went to the air attaché's office, only to find it empty. James therefore took the unilateral decision to follow in the tracks of the embassy staff and head for Tours. While preparations were made for their departure, Yeo-Thomas took a last look at his beloved Paris, observing both the scene and the state of mind of its inhabitants: 'In Paris crowds were besieging the stations laden with luggage and parcels, clutching children of all ages; queues were terrific and panic stricken. Cars were streaming out of the foredoomed capital piled high with the most miscellaneous collections of goods. Mattresses, beds, pillows, baby carriages, even stoves were tied with ropes and straps on the tops of cars. The roads, already cluttered up with refugees from the north and east, now became completely blocked. The whole picture was one of fear, panic, demoralisation and defeat. France was rapidly crumpling up.'

On 11 June Yeo-Thomas's unit headed for Tours. 'It was a nightmarish trip, the roads were cluttered up with refugees, cars, carts, wagons, lorries, buses, cyclists, pedestrians, women, children, pushing prams, barrows, anything that had wheels and could carry something. Old people stumble along, drawn faces, eyes that brimmed over with tears, sad eyes, hard eyes, haunted eyes, eyes full of despair, fury.'

The unit briefly resumed its direction-finding work at Tours airfield and was operating when Churchill landed there on 13 June on his last, and fruitless, visit to France to negotiate with Reynaud's government. France was on her last legs. The army was fighting a losing battle against the Germans, while Reynaud was struggling to keep control of his government. He and a few loyal supporters wished to continue the fight either in France or, if necessary, abroad. On the other hand, an increasingly vociferous group, including Général Maxime Weygand, Gamelin's successor as the French Commander-in-Chief, advocated a negotiated peace with Germany. Adding weight to the defeatist camp was the apparently unlikely figure of Maréchal Henri Philippe Pétain. Pétain had achieved immense national acclaim as the defender of Verdun during the First World War and had gained a reputation as a 'soldier's soldier' following his successful and humane handling of the French Army mutinies in 1917. Thereafter he had come to symbolize the very epitome of French military virtue. A long-time advocate of tactical defence, Pétain had been a major influence on inter-war French strategic thinking. Nor was he without political ambition and he became a significant element in French right-wing politics. On the outbreak of war, he was Ambassador in Fascist Spain and, shortly before the German invasion, had been recalled to serve as Reynaud's Deputy Premier. His appearance had constituted an important boost to national morale but, as Major-General Sir Edward Spears, Churchill's personal representative with Reynaud, commented, the eighty-four-year-old Pétain was 'still erect but so very much older, and in plain clothes which emphasized the break with the past. His face had never been other than white and expressionless. I had always known him bald; the long fair moustache, although whiter, was the same, but he seemed dead, in the sense that a figure that gives no impression of being alive can be said to be dead . . . when occasionally I looked towards him he seemed not to have heard what was being said.'[4]

Churchill only stayed for a few hours in Tours. Reynaud was succumbing to the influence of those seeking an armistice and sounded out the British Prime Minister regarding the likelihood of his accepting the possibility of a separate French peace. There was little that even the eloquence of Churchill could effect. He would not give his blessing to a French cessation of hostilities but affirmed that, 'if England won the war, France would be restored in her dignity and in her former greatness', and he returned to Britain.

Yeo-Thomas, too, was soon on his way, moving on to Limoges, but the campaign was fast drawing to a close. On 16 June, with the government now at Bordeaux, Reynaud resigned and Pétain was asked to form a government. Almost immediately he asked the Spanish Ambassador to act as an intermediary with the Germans and request an armistice. On 17 June, Yeo-Thomas heard Pétain announce on the radio that: *'Il faut cesser le combat'* ('Hostilities must cease'). This prompted the unit to press on to Bordeaux in anticipation of evacuation back to Britain. Chaos still reigned supreme but Flight Lieutenant James managed to discover that ships were still embarking personnel at the Pointe de Grave at the mouth of the River Gironde. Halfway through the sixty-mile journey, Yeo-Thomas's car ran out of petrol, but propitiously a fuel lorry soon came into sight. Flagging it down, he asked for enough petrol to get them to Pointe de Grave, but the driver refused to help and started to drive away. Yeo-Thomas's temper was already on a short fuse and he took desperate measures. He drew his revolver and persuaded the lorry driver to change his mind.

***

It was on the quayside at Pointe de Grave that Yeo-Thomas decided upon his future plan of action for the rest of the war. In short, he resolved to dedicate himself to France's liberation. At first he considered whether the best course of action was to stay behind and continue the struggle, but he recognized that this would mean his being branded a deserter from the RAF. Furthermore, he knew that the main burden of the war against Nazi Germany would fall upon Britain and that his first priority must be to carry on the fight from there. Putting words to his intent, he bought a postcard and sent a message to José Dupuis, an old friend and former teacher of his children: 'Dear José, I know what your feelings are at the present, but don't get discouraged, we will return and liberate France.' It was to be Yeo-Thomas's last act on French soil for three years apart from ripping out the clock from his car as a keepsake.

He and the rest of the party embarked upon a cargo boat and sailed for Britain. The threat of German air attack was constant and throughout the voyage Yeo-Thomas was on watch for signs of submarines or hostile aircraft. At last, after several days at sea, the ship safely reached the sanctuary of Milford Haven, and, typically, Yeo-Thomas's first experience back on British soil was to get drawn into an argument with an officious and obstreperous RAF warrant officer who tried to upbraid him for his scruffy appearance. Days without sleep had not improved Yeo-Thomas's temper and the would-be martinet was soon put in his place. His next act was to telephone Barbara and reassure her that he was safe. This was the first news that she had had of him since she had left Le Bourget in May. He then went back to the sergeants' mess, undressed for the first time in more than a week and had a bath in which he promptly fell asleep.

The next day he received orders to report to London and sent a telegram to Barbara advising her of his arrival. He found the atmosphere in the British capital markedly different from that of Paris: 'After the tenseness of the past month, the panic, the distress, the feeling of defeat, England seemed strangely calm and confident. There was apparently no anxiety. People were saying, "Well, now we are alone, no one can let us down, and we are going to win in the end." I myself had never considered that we could be defeated but I was somewhat disturbed by the complacency of the public. Anyhow, it was nice to feel that morale was so high.'

Yeo-Thomas reported for duty at No 1 Personnel Despatch Centre at RAF Uxbridge, where he met up with several of his friends from FAAP. As usual Yeo-Thomas had little patience with the prevailing inertia and confusion surrounding the RAF. For want of anything better to do, he acted as escorting NCO to parties of aircraftmen sent to London for yellow fever inoculation before being posted abroad. This served to keep him busy and provided ample opportunities for him to leave camp virtually at will. This freedom of movement came in handy for he used it to escape to the sanctuary of Barbara's cottage in Sutton.

On 16 August 1940, Yeo-Thomas left Uxbridge for RAF Odiham in Hampshire as a member of a small group of interpreters formed to help evacuated French Air Force personnel to settle in England. As ever, Yeo-Thomas was dissatisfied with service creature comforts and obtained permission to billet himself at a local public house, the White Hart: 'The licensees, Mr and Mrs Walter Dedman, were among the nicest people I ever met, and they treated me as a son.' In addition, his staying at the White Hart enabled Barbara to visit him at weekends.

All was not sweetness and light, however. He did not get on with his superior officer, Flight Lieutenant Esencourt, and they frequently argued over anything and everything. Fortunately, others at Odiham recognized his true capabilities, recommended him for a commission and, on 15 October 1940, Pilot Officer F F E Yeo-Thomas was admitted into the Royal Air Force's Intelligence Branch.

Yeo-Thomas's first posting as a commissioned officer was to No 308 (Polish) Squadron at RAF Baginton near Coventry. He arrived at the station on 2 December 1940 and quickly felt at home. Quite why a bilingual interpreter in French should have been sent to a Polish squadron remains unclear. However, Yeo-Thomas had picked up a smattering of the language during his service in Poland and French could be employed as a third language in the squadron. Many of the pilots had been blooded in war and Yeo-Thomas felt proud to be in their company. He also relished the absence of pen-pushing and square-bashing. During this period the squadron was working up to combat readiness but sustained several fatalities in air crashes flying Hurricane fighters. Yeo-Thomas, as the oldest officer in the squadron, acquired the nickname 'Papa' and on occasion acted as a father figure to the young pilots.

His relationship with Barbara was as strong as ever. He wrote to her every day, telephoned her whenever he could and impatiently looked forward to their next meeting. On 25 January 1941 he wrote in his diary: 'Barbara is the sweetest little wife in all the world – her loyalty and patience are unbelievable – I know I am the luckiest of men – all

I want is to make her the happiest of wives.' However, even his intense love for her could not totally eradicate his yearning for active service and on 30 April he grumbled: 'Time dragging on endlessly – feeling Bolshy and wish I had never joined any British force (except Salvation Army).'

In May 1941 No 308 Squadron moved briefly to Chilbolton in Hampshire before settling in the following month at Northolt to the west of London. The squadron was in action within a few hours of its arrival and continued to be in the fray for the rest of the year. The rising casualty list affected Yeo-Thomas deeply, not least because of his growing frustration as the young pilots risked their lives in battle while he remained impatiently awaiting their return: 'I got an inferiority complex, and felt ashamed of myself when I compared the safety of my duties with the dangers they ran. They were such great-hearted fellows, they knew how I felt, and they all did their best to console me, telling me that I was doing a good and important job, that I was their friend, and they trusted me, what more could I do etc, etc – But, as one by one they were reported killed or missing, so I got more and more depressed and ashamed.'

It was not much better for the pilots themselves: 'Tadeusz Schiele, who joined 308 at Northolt in 1941, arrived at the station shortly before dinner. He found three empty places at table, and noticed the sorrow of the WAAFs as they finally cleared them away. He himself had to move a dead pilot's belongings out before he could go to bed that night. The following day he went out with the squadron on a mission, from which two pilots failed to return. Again, two empty places honoured their memory.'[5]

In December the squadron moved once again, this time to RAF Woodvale, north of Liverpool. Although hailed as a model camp, on arrival they found that it was very much unfinished. 'When the station opened on December 7, the administration and living accommodation was still incomplete and the first airmen posted in found living conditions extremely primitive. Water and electricity were still not laid on to the sleeping sites to the east of the airfield and many personnel had to be billeted in Southport and Formby until facilities were improved.'[6]

Officially Yeo-Thomas had stayed behind at Northolt to clear up some squadron business but, as he confessed to his diary, really it was 'to spend an extra day with Barbara'. On 13 December he finally went north to Woodvale and was shocked by the conditions awaiting him: 'To my utter horror and disgust I found that the battle-weary squadron was expected to rest in a camp that was not even ready! The huts we were supposed to occupy had no windows, there were no means of heating them, there was no water. On the iron bedsteads provided, the usual biscuits [mattresses] were piled with two blankets for each man. Unfortunately as there were no windows, the snow had blown in and the blankets were covered with it and soaked through!'

This lamentable state of affairs would have affected Yeo-Thomas even more profoundly had he not already received some encouraging news concerning his plans to leave the squadron. He still retained the hope of finding work that would help him realize his dream of a liberated France, but up to now he seemed to lack the right connections. However, his luck turned, thanks to the friends that he had made among the French forces in England. It was while visiting some of them at their offices in St James's Square that Yeo-Thomas was introduced to Captain Eric Piquet-Wicks of the Royal Inniskilling Fusiliers. In fact, Piquet-Wicks was no longer serving with his regiment, being detached on 'Special Duties' with the Special Operations Executive, one of Britain's secret services. During the course of their conversation, Piquet-Wicks learnt a little of his background and patiently listened to him venting his frustration at not being able to put his talents to use.

Shortly after the meeting, Flying Officer Yeo-Thomas was instructed to report to Boodle's Club in St James's Street at 3pm on 8 December 1941. Here he was interviewed by Major David Keswick, SOE's Regional Controller for Western Europe. In Keswick's own words, 'he made a very favourable impression'. Furthermore Keswick concluded, 'I saw this man at the request of DRF [Piquet-Wicks], with a view to employment as DRF.1, which I think would be most suitable.' During the conversation, Yeo-Thomas took the opportunity of volunteering to be sent to France. Significantly, he also affirmed that he would rather join SOE than MI9, the secret escape and evasion organization, with whom he claimed to have had discussions.[7]

Keswick's recommendation was sufficiently encouraging for SOE to carry Yeo-Thomas's possible recruitment further with a request to MI5, the Security Service, that they search Yeo-Thomas's background for any discrepancies. On 12 December the response came back – 'No Trace' of any malfeasance, and he was one step closer to being accepted. Just as he seemed to be on the verge of achieving his ambition, a sticking point now appeared in the form of Air Ministry bureaucracy. At first it appeared that the Christmas holidays were the cause of the delay and, on 3 January 1942, Yeo-Thomas confided to his diary: 'My leave which ended today officially prolonged by me – who cares anyhow? AM [Air Ministry] is fast asleep. This is not their war.' Reluctantly, he did return to Woodvale, his humour not improved by having to organize the funeral arrangements of a member of the squadron who had been killed in an accident.

Meanwhile, the Air Ministry still steadfastly refused to release him and it appeared that there was little that SOE could do to remove the block on the transfer. In typically direct fashion, Yeo-Thomas decided to tackle the Air Ministry himself. He took five days' leave and returned to London where he met Piquet-Wicks and made personal representations to the Air Ministry. Baulked at every turn, he threatened to go to the newspapers with his story and seems to have been as good as his word, for his diary records visits to the *Daily Express* on 13 and 14 January. He even planned to have the matter taken up in Parliament if his release was not granted. Barbara was only now beginning to learn what was going on. She realized that he had had interviews for new posts but was unaware that he was seeking to join a secret organization. She now tried to talk him out of this unorthodox and potentially catastrophic scheme to achieve his transfer, but he remained adamant. On 17 January he returned to Woodvale and wrote: 'Feeling very fed up and depressed – should have been in my new job if the AM was not such a hopeless, muddling, bungling home for incapable and inefficient nitwits.' At last, on 22 January, he received a call from Piquet-Wicks informing him that the Air Ministry had finally granted his release. He spent the following week in Lancashire, kicking his heels, missing Barbara and getting drunk to drown his sorrows. Finally, on 31 January, his posting came through and he wasted no time in winding up his affairs with the squadron. It was an emotional wrench to leave so many close friends but, as events were to show, he had finally found his true métier. On 3 February 1942 he entered the shadowy and secret world of the Special Operations Executive.

CHAPTER THREE

• The Special Operations Executive •

The Special Operations Executive (SOE) was a top-secret body, created in July 1940 to foment resistance in Occupied Europe, but its origins lay in the difficult years leading up to the outbreak of war. In 1938, the War Office decided to examine the potential of irregular warfare and whether it might be exploited by Britain in any future conflict.

The assessment was initially consigned to one man, Lieutenant-Colonel J C F ('Jo') Holland, an officer with first-hand experience of unconventional warfare during his First World War service in the Balkans and the British Army's struggle against the IRA. The project soon gathered pace and, in January 1939, Holland's department, designated GS(R), was expanded to embrace two other experienced and versatile officers, Major Millis Jefferis and Lieutenant-Colonel Colin Gubbins. As the situation in Europe continued to deteriorate, the work of GS(R) became all the more significant. In April it was further expanded and renamed Military Intelligence (Research) or MI(R). At the same time, a parallel organization also concerned itself with clandestine warfare. This was Section D of the Secret Intelligence Service (SIS), also known as MI6. SIS came under the auspices of the Foreign Office and its primary concern was the gathering of secret intelligence from abroad. Consequently, whereas MI(R) was specifically interested in the theory and practice of guerrilla warfare, Section D sought to develop the potential use of sabotage and subversion in foreign countries in the event of war. This involved the creation of agent networks using both British citizens and foreign nationals and the building up of arms and explosives caches. MI(R) and Section D worked closely together during the 'Phoney War' and it was no surprise that they should, in effect, be amalgamated in the creation of SOE. This took place on 19 July 1940 when Neville Chamberlain, in his capacity as Lord President of the Council, issued a War Cabinet memorandum outlining the brief for the new organization. The document makes it clear that, if not exactly a Churchillian brainchild, the Prime Minister was intimately involved in shaping SOE: 'The Prime Minister has further decided, after consultation with the ministers concerned, that a new organization shall be established forthwith to coordinate all action, by way of subversion and sabotage against the enemy overseas.'[1]

Churchill, Chamberlain and the War Cabinet were not entirely altruistic in their decision to approve the contents of the memorandum on 22 July. For, with Britain faced by imminent invasion, insurrection behind enemy lines was of vital importance. MI(R) had initially predicted that much of its work would be concerned with the creation of secret armies in Czechoslovakia and Poland, the first victims of Nazi aggression, but the German *Blitzkrieg* of the spring and summer of 1940 had radically changed matters. As the might of Germany's victorious armed forces was arrayed against a decidedly vulnerable Britain, it was essential that the people of Occupied Europe play their part in resisting their conquerors. The 'Secret War' was now to be attritional, systematically eroding German economic strength and diverting resources away from the main battlefronts. In keeping with this aim, the fledgeling organization was bestowed neither upon the War Office nor the Foreign Office, but placed under the control of the Ministry of Economic Warfare. Another factor in this decision was the initial intention that SOE would be a civilian undertaking, appealing to the men, women and children of Europe, not the residue of defeated and largely discredited armed forces. Dr Hugh Dalton, the Minister of Economic Warfare, was one of the few Labour politicians in the War Cabinet and in a letter to Lord Halifax, the Foreign Secretary, he described the type of organization he had in mind:

> This 'democratic international' must use many different methods, including industrial and military sabotage, labour agitation and strikes, continuous propaganda, terrorist acts against traitors and German leaders, boycotts and riots.
>
> It is clear to me that an organization on this scale and of this character is not something which can be handled by the ordinary departmental machinery of either the British Civil Service or the British military machine. What is needed is a new organization to coordinate, inspire, control and assist the nationals of the oppressed countries who must themselves be the direct participants. We need absolute secrecy, a certain fanatical enthusiasm, willingness to work with people of different nationalities, complete political reliability. Some of these qualities are certainly to be found in some military officers and, if such men are available, they should undoubtedly be used. But the organization should, in my view, be entirely independent of the War Office machine.[2]

Such an affirmation was hardly calculated to excite universal approbation in Whitehall. Churchill's backing of the creation of SOE did much to suppress open criticism and it should not be forgotten that, in the summer of 1940, there was plenty to occupy the thoughts of every civilian and military department in Whitehall. However, the Secret Intelligence Service and the armed services were highly suspicious of this new organization, with its untried and unconventional stratagems. Furthermore, SOE threatened to absorb scarce resources of matériel and manpower, while at the same time impinging upon areas of operations deemed to fall within the purview of established organizations.

While labelled 'amateurs' by critical rivals in Whitehall, SOE inherited a sound core of experienced officers both from the War Office and SIS. Nevertheless, its infrastructure took a long time to develop, as did the recruitment and training of agents, the creation of wireless communications and methods for perfecting clandestine land and sea transport.

The organization was split into 'country' sections. While SOE provided planning and logistical facilities, most of its operations were carried out in association with agencies of the governments that had managed to find refuge in Britain following the occupation of their countries. The Czechoslovaks and Poles had considerable experience of such activity, but for the Norwegians, Danes, Belgians, Dutch and French this was to be a new and none too pleasurable undertaking. The various SOE country sections dealing with the Western European countries tended to consist of core staff personnel who liaised with the politicians and soldiers of their allies. Although often chosen for their linguistic fluency, proportionately few British staff were ever considered for operational duties. In the main, the agents sent into the field were selected from the members of the armies-in-exile.

Of all the countries involved, France was the exception. As the most important area of operations in Europe, it was to be served by two major sections: F (or Independent) and RF. Furthermore, two other sections, DF and EUP, were also to function there, respectively providing escape routes for agents and developing networks among the Polish community in France.[3] F Section was staffed primarily by bilingual British citizens who were sufficiently immersed in the French language and everyday life to be sent to France as undercover agents. On the other hand, RF Section was created exclusively to aid the 'Free French' in the development of resistance movements.

As a member of RF Section, Yeo-Thomas was to be closely associated with the 'Free French' movement. If SOE had problems establishing credibility in the corridors of Whitehall, this was as nothing compared with the difficulties confronting the 'Free French'. To understand it we must return to the dark days of June 1940.

The collapse of the Anglo-French forces in France had been mirrored by a similar collapse of French political will. On 14 June the

French government had fled to Bordeaux where their common purpose and political will rapidly evaporated. Agitation for an armistice
developed from a faction within the Cabinet, while external pressure
was applied by other politicians outside the government, such as
Pierre Laval, a former Prime Minister. Two days after his arrival in
Bordeaux, Paul Reynaud, the Prime Minister, resigned. The way was
now open for Pétain to make his move and the next day he
announced his intention to take the lead in ending hostilities and to
enter armistice negotiations with Germany. Pétain represented himself as the nation's favourite 'grandfather', assuming responsibility for
overseeing the armistice and assuaging the people's collective despair.
He presented himself as the embodiment of France's traditional
values and sought to offer a return to a golden age, thereby shutting
out the disasters of 1940 and the cruel reality and humiliation of
occupation.

Against this background of surrender and mutual recrimination,
the light of defiance still shone, albeit dimly, in the shape of a tall,
career army officer named Charles de Gaulle. Born in Lille in 1890,
de Gaulle had graduated from the Saint-Cyr Military Academy in
1911 and, ironically, had been posted to the 33ème Régiment
d'Infanterie commanded by one Colonel Philippe Pétain. A young
officer of promise, he served with distinction in the opening campaigns of the First World War, being wounded in August 1914 and
again in March 1915. A year later, during the battle of Verdun, he was
wounded for a third time, receiving a bayonet thrust in the thigh in
the course of a German attack on Douaumont. He was subsequently
taken prisoner and spent the rest of the war incarcerated in various
German prisoner-of-war camps, where he proved himself to be a
singularly uncooperative inmate, attempting to escape no less than
five times. On his release following the Armistice, de Gaulle served
in Poland with a French Military Mission to the recently created
Polish Army. Like Yeo-Thomas, he was present during the Russo-
Polish War, and the campaign provided him with valuable experience
which helped develop a career that might otherwise have begun to
stagnate.

During the inter-war years, de Gaulle's career was marked by a
series of staff and teaching posts that seemed set to secure a successful
move up the promotion ladder. However, his character retained a
self-assurance that was barely short of arrogance and which helped
to ensure that he left the École Supérieure de Guerre with the unsat-
isfactory classification 'bien' and the less than glowing report of
his professor, Colonel Moyrand: 'An intelligent officer, cultured and
serious-minded; he has a certain brilliance and aptitude; a strong
personality. Unfortunately, his indisputable qualities are marred by his

excessive self-assurance, his severity when it comes to the opinions of others and his 'king in exile' manner . . . furthermore, he seems [to be] better able to tackle problems on a general and theoretical level than he is at giving them detailed and practical consideration.'[4]

However, de Gaulle's career was not terminally blighted by this setback and in 1932 he was detailed to serve in the Secrétariat Général de la Défense Nationale. Never one to disguise his beliefs, he began to espouse outspoken views on armoured warfare and, in so doing, alienated his one-time patron, Pétain. Nevertheless, in 1937, de Gaulle was given command of the 507ème Régiment de Chars followed, in 1939, by the tank brigade attached to the 5ème Armée. During the 'Phoney War' he continued to propound his theories, but he did not have to wait too long to put them into practice. On 11 May, shortly after the German invasion of France, he assumed command of the 4ème Division Cuirassée and six days later launched a counter-attack against German units near Laon. After initial success, overwhelming enemy strength forced him to call off the action. He attacked again two days later but, once again, the momentum of the German advance proved too powerful and his division was forced to withdraw.

De Gaulle was rewarded for his offensives by promotion to Général de Brigade and, on 6 June, was summoned to Paris for a meeting with Reynaud. Recognizing that desperate times required desperate measures, the Prime Minister offered the supremely self-confident young general the position of Sous-Secrétaire d'État à la Défense et à la Guerre. De Gaulle accepted and immediately immersed himself in the chaotic and disintegrating world of French government. He twice visited London for conferences with Churchill and, on his return to France, tried to infuse his fellow cabinet ministers with his own conviction that the war must continue. However, not even de Gaulle's massive self-will could bolster up the collapse of French morale and the crumbling spirit of the government. His fellow generals, such as Weygand and Gamelin, became increasingly pessimistic of France's hopes of survival and therefore offered no effective alternative to the intrigues surrounding Pétain and Laval and their urging of an armistice.

De Gaulle made one more trip to London on 15 June during which Churchill offered a formal union between Britain and France. Reynaud was keen to accept, but opposition to it within the Cabinet was so strong that they did not even take a vote. De Gaulle returned to Bordeaux to learn of the resignation of the Prime Minister and that Pétain had been asked to form a government. The options for de Gaulle were limited in the extreme. To stay in France meant an acceptance of an armistice, German occupation and a government dominated by his political opponents. The only alternative was to leave for Britain and seek to continue the struggle from there. On 17 June, accompanied by a faithful aide, Lieutenant Geoffroy de Courcel, de Gaulle went to Bordeaux airport, ostensibly to bid farewell to Churchill's liaison officer, Major-General Spears. This was, in part, a deception to prevent his arrest and, as the plane began to take off, he was hoisted aboard. De Gaulle's memoirs are surprisingly reticent regarding his feelings at this time, but Churchill later recorded: 'De Gaulle carried with him, in this small aircraft, the honour of France.'

On his arrival in England, de Gaulle was given an audience with the Prime Minister who offered him every possible assistance. The first manifestation of this was the opportunity of broadcasting a message to France in reply to Pétain's announcement that he was seeking an armistice. At six o'clock on the evening of 18 June 1940, speaking from the BBC's Broadcasting House, de Gaulle made one of the great rallying broadcasts in history. He acknowledged the fact of Germany's crushing victory in the battle of France but questioned: 'But has the last word been said? Is all hope lost? Is the defeat absolute? No.'[5] Furthermore, he reminded his listeners that: 'France is not alone. She has a vast empire behind her. She can unite with the British Empire, which holds the seas, and is continuing the struggle. She can utilize to the full, as England is doing, the vast industrial resources of the United States.' He went on to invite members of the French armed forces, currently on British territory, to join him in continuing the fight, and concluded: 'Whatever happens, the flame of French resistance must not and will not be extinguished.'

In spite of its rousing sentiments, the speech made little impact at the time. Few in France were tuned in to the BBC and that organization did not have the foresight to record the broadcast for posterity. Nevertheless, his words rapidly acquired a reputation as a rousing clarion call of defiance.

Defiance was all well and good but, for the maintenance of a continuing French belligerence, de Gaulle needed legitimacy derived from recognition by the Allies and the support of his fellow Frenchmen. Less than a week after his broadcast, it looked as if political reinforcements would appear in the form of a refugee group of politicians, including Édouard Daladier, Reynaud's predecessor as Prime Minister, and Georges Mandel, the former Minister of the Interior. They fled from France on 21 June, with the tacit approval of Pétain's government, bound for French North Africa. However, the benefits of nudging a group of potential dissidents into exile were outweighed by fears that their continued resistance would compromise the armistice with Germany. Consequently Pétain's advisers had a change of heart and the politicians were prevented from disembarking from their ship, the *Massilia*, and it was ordered to sail back to mainland France. On their return, their political enemies easily represented them as cowards and traitors seeking to save their own necks; the hope of a semi-official administration to rival Pétain was destroyed.

Meanwhile, in England, de Gaulle was finding that the catatonic state induced by the German victory and the palliative power of Pétain was restricting support. As he admitted in his memoirs: 'A week after my appeal of 18 June the number of volunteers encamped in Olympia, which the British had lent us, amounted to only a few thousand.' At the end of July the number of de Gaulle's adherents had risen to barely 7000. Furthermore, his relations with the British were not proving easy, not least because this young and still relatively junior officer lacked the status enjoyed by other heads of state who were continuing the fight from exile in London. He resented his dependence upon Britain for resources and, at the same time, mistrusted British aspirations towards France's colonies. As he candidly outlined in his memoirs:

> I was starting from scratch. Not the shadow of a force or an organization at my side. In France, no following and no reputation. Abroad, neither credit nor standing. But this very destitution showed me my line of conduct. It was by adopting without compromise the cause of national recovery that I could acquire authority. It was by acting as the inflexible champion of the nation and of the State that it would be possible for me to gather the consent, even the enthusiasm, of the French and to win from foreigners respect and consideration. Those who, all through the drama, were offended by this intransigence were unwilling to see that for me, intent as I was on beating back innumerable conflicting pressures, the slightest wavering would have brought collapse. In short, limited though I was and precisely because I was so, I had to climb to the heights and never then to come down.

In spite of de Gaulle's misgivings about his Anglo-Saxon allies, it was they who imbued his movement with a legitimacy that was to prove vital in encouraging adherents. On 28 June 1940, the British Government acknowledged de Gaulle as 'leader of all the Free French'. There followed the establishment of a headquarters at St Stephen's House near Westminster Bridge and, on 24 September, a Comité National Français, which was, in effect, a government in all but name. In contrast to these encouraging developments, Anglo-Free French relations had been severely tested following a Royal Navy attack on the French naval base at Mers-el-Kébir in North Africa on 3 July. The powerful French fleet could not be allowed to fall under German or Italian control and, following the failure of negotiation, the British Government had taken the difficult decision to destroy the French warships. This action ruined any hopes of an accommodation with Pétain's government and convinced many would-be recruits to de Gaulle's cause that *'perfide Albion'* had not changed its spots. Further controversy followed at the end of September with a joint British and Free French attack on the French West African port of Dakar. This proved to be an abject failure and served as an example of the flawed trust that prevailed between de Gaulle and his British allies. But on a more positive note, several of the French colonies of Central Africa started to rally to the Free French movement. Similarly, Free French units began to play a part in the campaign in North Africa and participate in the operations to wrest control of Syria and Lebanon from Pétainist forces. Thus, by the end of 1941, the Free French had come a long way, but they remained, not entirely unrelated to de Gaulle's attitude, very much among the poor relations of Britain's allies.

This, then was the organization with which Yeo-Thomas was to deal for the rest of the war, but first he had to assimilate himself into SOE itself. On 3 February 1942, he was formally transferred to SOE under the auspices of AI 10, the Air Ministry Intelligence Section responsible for liaison with all the British secret services. He was given briefings by Lieutenant-Colonel Keswick and Wing Commander J E Redding, SOE's Air Liaison Officer, and told to report to his new job with RF section.

RF Section had been formed in May 1941 as a two-person team, comprising Captain Eric Piquet-Wicks and his secretary, Miss Pauline May. The section had originally been established at 72 Berkeley Court near to Baker Street Underground station and certainly does not appear to have featured high on SOE's list of priorities. Piquet-Wicks was half-French, spoke the language fluently and had spent much of his adolescence abroad. However, he and Yeo-Thomas never really hit it off, the latter conceding that Piquet-Wicks had a 'brilliant brain' but that his caustic wit 'made one feel like giving him a hefty kick in the pants'. In turn, Piquet-Wicks believed Yeo-Thomas 'seemed permanently to wear a chip on his shoulder'.[6] Pauline May, on the other hand, was favourably described by Yeo-Thomas as 'a strapping wench, dark-haired, with flashing eyes, quick brain and ready laughter . . . a tower of strength.'

The first joint SOE-Free French operation had taken place before the creation of the RF Section, when Piquet-Wicks was still a company commander in Belfast. At the end of 1940, the Air Ministry had requested an operation to eliminate a group of specialist pilots of the Luftwaffe's Kampfgeschwader 100 unit based at Meucon in south Brittany. F Section was unable to provide a suitable team and, consequently, the Free French were asked to help. The operation, codenamed SAVANNA, had not got off to an auspicious start and the project was not helped by the Air Ministry getting cold feet. Suffering a surprising and, some might say, hypocritical bout of moralizing, Air Chief Marshal Sir Charles Portal, the Chief of Air Staff, wrote to SOE: 'I think that the dropping of men dressed in civilian clothes for the purpose of attempting to kill members of the opposing forces is not an operation with which the Royal Air Force should be associated. I think you will agree that there is a vast difference, in ethics, between the time-honoured operation of the dropping of a spy from the air and this entirely new scheme for dropping what one can only call assassins.'[7]

In spite of these objections and various delays brought about by bad weather, the operation was finally mounted on the night of 15/16 March 1941. However, by this time, the Luftwaffe pilots had altered their routine and the five-man team of Free French parachutists discovered that their quarry was no longer susceptible to attack. The mission was consequently aborted but the enterprise had served to highlight the need for a department within SOE to help facilitate and coordinate future joint operations. Top-level talks were conducted between SOE and the Free French and the creation of just such a department was agreed.

The first fully fledged RF Section operation was to be JOSEPHINE B, a sabotage raid on the vital Pessac power station in Bordeaux. This installation was of particular importance for it supplied electricity to the nearby German U-boat base. The mission had been initially assigned to F Section but, once again, they were unable to fulfil their commitments. In consequence, the operation was next entrusted to a Polish *coup de main* party on 9 April, but the attempt ended in disaster following a series of technical calamities. The team's arms and explosives containers were prematurely released over the lower Loire, obliging the pilot to abort the operation and return to base at RAF Tangmere, near Chichester. However, the aircraft stalled on landing, crashed and caught fire; two of the crew were killed and the others injured along with the Polish parachutists. The operation was now passed to a three-man team from the Free French parachute company. They were dropped 'blind' (without a reception committee) on the night of 11/12 May 1941, but they found that their target was a tougher nut to crack than had been anticipated. It was, therefore, not until the night of 7/8 June that they were able to launch their attack, reinforced by a member of the JOSEPHINE B team who had remained in France. The operation proved a great success with six of the eight transformers destroyed, resulting in widespread power shortages throughout south-west France.

In spite of this excellent start, RF was still in its infancy when Yeo-Thomas joined it. In August 1941 its numbers had been swelled by the arrival of two new recruits: Lieutenant Herbert O'Bryan Tear (always known as 'OBT') to act as Piquet-Wicks's assistant, and Lieutenant Seeds to act as the liaison officer with the French training school at Inchmery near Southampton. The growth of the section did not radically improve matters and an indication of the amateurishness of both RF and their Free French counterpart is provided by a chapter of accidents that took place in December. One of the students at Inchmery, Lieutenant Michel Pichard (of whom more later), blew off three fingers of his right hand while practising with explosives. The next day, Lieutenant Seeds sought to restore the confidence of the rest of the students by giving his own demonstration. Unfortunately, Seeds's expertise and luck proved even inferior to Pichard's, while the damage was greater – his accident blew off his entire left hand. A replacement RF officer, Lieutenant R A Johnson, not surprisingly made a highly critical report of the school but it was to be another four months before Inchmery was closed down and RF/Free French training was integrated within the rest of SOE.

Yeo-Thomas had long bemoaned the absence of a real challenge and he was certainly to find it with RF. In August 1941, the section had moved from Berkeley Court to 1 Dorset Square, the former offices of Bertram Mills's Circus. One of the section's heads described it thus:

It was a large Georgian house and its inhabitants were entirely occupied in liaison with the Fighting French. In peacetime the building had been the office of Mr Bertram Mills. Downstairs we had our operations room with maps showing our dropping zones and the whereabouts of our parties. The top floor contained a flat where we fitted up in English clothes the French men and women who had arrived the night before by Lysander or Hudson, and satisfied ourselves of the authentic Gallic appearance of those about to cross the Channel. The rest of the house contained the training staff, the despatching officers who went with those going to or coming from the field, a small intelligence unit and the secretaries. On the *piano nobile* was a large room in which Mr Bertram Mills himself had sat. Innumerable dirty rhomboids on the wall showed where had hung the signed photographs of the lion tamers, the jugglers and the men on the flying trapeze.[8]

Yeo-Thomas was thrown in at the deep end and recorded: 'I had to absorb a lot in a short time, and the set-up was so complex that there were moments when I thought I would go mad.' One of his first priorities was to be introduced to the Free French organization with which RF was to liaise. Yeo-Thomas's diary reveals that on his fourth day with the section he lunched at the Five Hundred Club with Piquet-Wicks and 'Bienvenue'. The latter was, in fact, Capitaine Raymond Lagier of the Bureau Central de Renseignements et d'Action Militaire (BCRAM) – the Free French secret service. Lagier was in charge of its AM (Action Militaire) Section and was the primary BCRAM liaison officer with SOE. He therefore featured large in Yeo-Thomas's work and became a good and trusted friend. Lagier was one of a small group of staff officers under the command of Lieutenant-Colonel André Dewavrin, the head of the BCRAM.

Dewavrin was a career officer born in 1911, who had enjoyed a distinguished academic schooling at the École Polytechnique and the École Militaire et d'Application du Génie. In 1938 he was made Assistant Professor of Fortifications at the École Spéciale Militaire de Saint-Cyr. After volunteering for active service, he served with distinction during the Norwegian campaign of 1940 and only returned to France on 17 June, disembarking at Brest at almost the same moment as de Gaulle was flying into exile. Dewavrin was also soon on the move again, the remnants of the French Expeditionary Force to Norway being evacuated, not as anticipated to North Africa but to Southampton. In England Dewavrin was prey to a mass of conflicting emotions, including dismay at France's collapse, fear for loved-ones at home and a suspicion of Britain's long-term intentions. So pronounced was his uncertainty that, when his unit was ordered to North Africa, he travelled to Barry Docks in South Wales to embark with them, but, following a last-minute discussion with his commanding officer, Dewavrin decided to stay in Britain and join de Gaulle. On 1 July he reported to St Stephen's House where he received an immediate interview with de Gaulle. Following a brief series of curt questions, he was informed that he was now head of the 2ème and 3ème Bureaux of the Free French headquarters, the precursors of the BCRAM.

In spite of a complete absence of experience in clandestine matters, Dewavrin had been charged with the running of de Gaulle's intelligence service and, at the same time, had responsibility for operational planning. Understandably, he had mixed emotions at the appointment. The sheer size of the task was compounded by the limitations of the available resources, but he quickly began to recruit a coterie of officers bearing his own characteristics of youth, enthusiasm and inexperience. He drew heavily upon the contacts he had made during the Norwegian campaign and was able to call upon the services of Lieutenants Lagier, Duclos and Beresnikoff.

It was essential that these men adopt *noms de guerre* to protect their families in France from any retribution following a leak of information as to their activities in England. Dewavrin decided that the names of Paris métro stations would be as good as anything and therefore he became 'Passy', Lagier was 'Bienvenue', Duclos was 'St Jacques' and Beresnikoff became 'Corvisart'. This small band initially was housed at de Gaulle's headquarters at St Stephen's House and then followed him to 4 Carlton Gardens. However, as the organization grew, and the need for secrecy became paramount, it acquired its own premises, first at 3 St James's Square, then, as early as March 1942, at 10 Duke Street, a mere stone's throw from SOE's headquarters in Baker Street. Such was the shortage of suitable agents that, in August 1940, Duclos and Beresnikoff were sent on a mission to France. It should be noted that a feature of Dewavrin's organization was the number of its senior staff officers who took part in missions in occupied territory. This was not necessarily the most secure of practices, but it certainly ensured a first-hand knowledge of operational conditions and won the respect of the agents whom they trained and briefed in England. Yeo-Thomas soon became good friends with his opposite numbers in the BCRAM and the significance of their hazardous return to France made him all the more determined to experience an operational mission himself.

Soon after his appointment, Dewavrin had recognized the need to seek the assistance of SIS and the novice was soon able to call upon the advice of one of the most experienced, wiliest and most devious members of the British intelligence community. This was Claude Dansey, the Assistant Chief of SIS, whose reputation has been widely described as, at best, cynical and, at its worst, positively malevolent. However, Dewavrin was to be unstinting in his praise:

> I was fortunate to have a teacher who saved me from many a pitfall and trap: he was Sir Claude Dansey, the assistant head of the Intelligence Service . . . He was one of the pillars of that famous organization for almost thirty years. He saw everything, he knows everything. To me, at first, he was a master beyond compare; he soon became a friend. He had a shrewd and sceptical intellect, he was admired for his merit and feared by his subordinates for his stinging or scornful comments. He formed generations of officers in this so fascinating of professions; one

where you receive more blows than praise, a profession that brings you into contact with the best and the worst of the human race, rarely with those who are mediocre and afraid of risk or adventure.

Good old 'Uncle Claude', how can I thank you enough? You were always there to curb the ventures that were too risky. You always pointed out the snags and dangers along the way – spotted immediately by your greatly experienced eye. You knew, a little better every day, how to teach me to weigh up the risks against the gains that my enthusiasm would anticipate and often magnify. It took me many years and today I am convinced that, thanks to you, catastrophes were avoided that would have cost a great deal of French blood, and the highest quality at that – what you would call 'vintage 1940'.[9]

The feeling was mutual as Sir Frank Nelson, SOE's Executive Director recorded in June 1941: 'The success of this virtually new Section of the Free French Intelligence will depend upon the personality and capabilities of de [sic] "Passy", and I am certainly well-impressed by this man, who has been specially recommended to me by the ACSS [Dansey] and his satellites in C [SIS] who have worked closely with him since June 1940.'[10]

Whatever Dewavrin's debt of gratitude to his mentor, 'Uncle Claude' was not solely inspired by an altruistic desire to help his young protégé. SIS was keen to exploit the Free French connections with Occupied France and to seek to recruit agents of its own from among the refugees seeking to join the ranks of de Gaulle's supporters. Dansey sought to resist allowing Dewavrin's organization 'first pick' of potential recruits, stating that neither SOE nor SIS could be expected to 'act as a press-gang for the Free French Services'.[11] Needless to say, this poaching of talent became a source of much heated debate but, in the main and it must be said, quite surprisingly, the nature of cooperation between SIS and the BCRAM was relatively harmonious.

In contrast to his frequently alleged antipathy towards SOE, it was Dansey who effected an introduction in May 1941 between Dewavrin and Sir Frank Nelson, the Executive Director of SOE. Shortly afterwards, further introductions were made at a dinner hosted by Nelson, where Dewavrin met Brigadier Colin Gubbins, now the Director of Operations, H N Sporborg, the Regional Controller for North-West Europe and Major Maurice Buckmaster, the future Head of F Section. It was at this meeting that Sporborg proposed the creation of a SOE section dedicated specifically to Free French needs, which later became the RF Section.

Yeo-Thomas had joined SOE to find a more active employment and he may well soon have been regretting his decision. Piquet-Wicks almost immediately went absent on sick leave, diagnosed by Yeo-Thomas thus: 'He suffered from lung trouble, and unfortunately tried to neutralize the weakening effects of his illness by taking massive doses of whisky . . . as a result he got no better and eventually had to take a long rest.' Within a fortnight of joining the section, Yeo-Thomas began to note in his diary comments such as 'On duty alone – very hectic day but managed to cope with everything. Only had 20 minutes off for lunch. Home – quite fagged out.' To make matters worse, on 15 February 'OBT' was posted on a parachute training course while Piquet-Wicks's absences began to grow more frequent: 'PW did not come to work. Had a hectic day all on my own' (19 February), 'PW did not put in an appearance – still coping' (20 February) and 'Busy day – PW off again – What a life' (21 February). 'Life' was not all black, however, and, on that same day, the increased burden of responsibility was at least recognized with news of his promotion to Flight Lieutenant. He spent much of his time selecting agents, vetting the candidates and overseeing their training in association with Lagier and his opposite numbers in BCRAM. He was also in constant touch with the air liaison staff of SOE, arranging the transportation of agents into and out of enemy territory by parachute or small aircraft. He was, therefore, particularly pleased at the success of his first operation when, on 1 March 1942, two agents were brought back from France by aircraft on Operation CRÈME. However, there were times when his work saw him caught up in the Baker Street politicking and inter-section rivalry. On 29 May 1942, Yeo-Thomas travelled down to Tangmere to see off Gaston Tavian, an agent departing on Operation SHRIMP, and to greet an incoming Free Frenchman. He returned home from Sussex with barely enough time to have a bath and change of clothes before reporting at Norgeby House, Baker Street for a ten o'clock meeting with Brigadier Gubbins. The circumstances surrounding the meeting are unclear, save for a reference in Yeo-Thomas's diary to 'a memo' and the fact that he did not find the interview a pleasant experience:

30 May 1942
Oh boy, what a rocket!! Like kids at school before headmaster except that headmasters are well educated. Brig is more like a bloated crab on a greasy ball – no chance to say anything – one is just condemned without a hearing. There are some pretty lousy, sneaky, double-dealing bastards in this racket. Having less & less respect for the British in general.

31 May 1942

Very busy day spent at office – making up reply to memo that caused rocket. Waste of time as it is obviously intended to use us to cover up underhanded work of a couple of sneaks. Tripe all of them!!

If Yeo-Thomas was sometimes less than happy at work, his home life was a source of continued contentment. In July 1941, Barbara had taken a small flat at 5 Queen Court, Guilford Street, in Bloomsbury, near to where Yeo-Thomas had been born. She had initially continued to work in Sutton but soon switched jobs to a shop in the West End. Queen Court became their base with Yeo-Thomas staying there at every possible opportunity during his periods of leave from No 308 Squadron. On his transfer to SOE, he saw the realization of two ambitions: a job in which he could help France and the opportunity of a domestic life with Barbara. In order to share more fully Yeo-Thomas's love of France, Barbara began to study French and sought to become involved with the Free French cause. On 14 February, she joined the Amis des Volontaires Français, an aid organization for the Free French, which was staffed primarily by British citizens.

It was soon evident that Piquet-Wicks's health and drink problems were never going to get better and that he was becoming an increasing liability to the section. He was regularly absent for long periods and, however loyal his staff, his shortcomings could not be disguised indefinitely. On 21 April Yeo-Thomas wrote in his diary: 'Both operations failed – no committee found – general depression – usual lack of understanding on our Ops side. PW ill in afternoon – Pauline [May] made *faux pas* by telling Sporborg.' The breach was getting wider and even encouraging petty acts of revenge. On returning home late from a party with his Free French friends, Yeo-Thomas admitted: 'Phoned PW at 3am to wake him up – hooked receiver up without saying a word' (20 June). Barbara was no more impressed with the head of RF Section and had recorded in her diary on 25 April: 'Bumped into Piquet-Wicks – snooty bastard.' By the end of July, matters had got even worse and Yeo-Thomas confided in his entry for the 26th: 'Very busy day. PW due in at 12.30 – never came. In the end phoned me up at 5.30 from 83/85 [Baker Street] – had been celebrating birthday – I was mad.' Relief was at hand. SOE was not blind to the need for action to be taken regarding RF Section and in August replaced Piquet-Wicks with Lieutenant-Colonel J R H Hutchison.

Hutchison had served in the cavalry during the First World War and was a veteran of two evacuations, Gallipoli in 1916 and France in 1940. In peacetime, he had been a successful businessman involved in shipping and insurance brokerage and was an effective and personable officer. He did not have Piquet-Wicks's linguistic ability and, as his eventual successor recalled, he was prone to the occasional gaffe: 'His own French was fluent but not very idiomatic. I remember when his last day in the office had come the look of surprise on the face of the Frenchman to whom he was introducing me when he observed, *"Écoutez, mon cher, aujourd'hui c'est mon chanson de cygne."* ("Listen, my dear, today it is my song of the swan.")'

However, he was a decidedly more solid and reliable figure than his predecessor and it was hoped that his maturity and experience would help the development of the section and enhance its relations with the French. He had been recommended to David Keswick and, over coffee at Boodle's, was asked if he 'would like to join the false nose brigade?'[12] A meeting with Brigadier Gubbins followed and, in spite of having little understanding of the job offered to him, he accepted the challenge of heading RF Section. Piquet-Wicks offered the rather jaundiced description:

> A wiry little Lieut-Colonel wearing 1914–18 war ribbons and the Territorial Decoration appeared from nowhere announcing his leadership and control of the section. He wore an old-fashioned World War I greatcoat, and he had a passion for one-word instructions written on pink slips that he would pin to every report, memo or cable that came his way. His eyes darted briskly and busily. He seemed happiest when dictating, and sat, red-faced and ferret-like, while he punctuated his remarks, and occasionally himself, with one of the pins that were forever to hand. Colonel Sir J R H Hutchison, despite his many idio-syncrasies and his surprising lack of understanding of the French, was however soon to prove his great courage [Hutchison later volunteered to go into the field].[13]

A general reorganization of the section followed with Piquet-Wicks remaining with RF until his health collapsed completely and he spent a considerable time in a military hospital. Johnson took charge of operations, 'OBT' assumed control of equipment and Yeo-Thomas took responsibility for planning and briefing of agents. All three men also carried out conducting-officer duties as required, accompanying agents to the holding stations and airfields and receiving newcomers from France.

In spite of the evident responsibility of his duties and the respect and comradeship he felt for both his French and British colleagues, Yeo-Thomas remained dissatisfied. All the same resentments and jeal-ousies that he had been prey to when serving with No 308 Squadron once more came to the fore. These had begun to manifest themselves as early as June 1942 when he recorded in his diary (albeit at the time of his fracas over the memo): 'Hectic day – one damned thing after another. Fed up with the whole business & would much prefer to be in the field where one <u>does</u> meet <u>real men</u> not <u>dug-ins</u> & slackers.'

However, agents were exclusively provided by Dewavrin's BCRA (in the summer of 1942 the 'Militaire' was dropped). There was no need for RF Section to send a British agent into the field, especially one who exhibited such a special aptitude for creating and maintaining links between the British and French services. Yeo-Thomas clearly recognized that he could not wait to be approached for operational duties and therefore cast around for a suitable mission of his own.

With hindsight the 'master plan' that Yeo-Thomas devised seems positively harebrained. That he was able to have it seriously considered for adoption by the leading figures in SOE reflects either his powers of persuasion or the gullibility of several of the leading lights at Baker Street. In short, he proposed a buccaneering enterprise that would see him infiltrated into the South of France in order to seize the luxury yacht MY No.5, belonging to his former employer, Edward Molyneux.[14] Yeo-Thomas secured Molyneux's approval for the operation and put forward his plan to Hutchison. An appreciation dated 3 November 1942 and submitted to Robin Brook, SOE's newly appointed regional controller, makes interesting if fanciful reading. Bearing all the hallmarks of Yeo-Thomas's indefatigable enthusiasm, the scheme was a nonsense. The plan concedes that it was not known precisely where the yacht was berthed and whether it was currently seaworthy. Furthermore, for the operation to be 'viable', it would be necessary to infiltrate Yeo-Thomas and a wireless operator by sea, along 'with fuel and lubricating oil and any other vital stores, together with certain anti-aircraft weapons'. Yeo-Thomas affirmed that, in spite of having no experience of sailing or navigation, he would locate a crew and sail the yacht to Gibraltar.

The core of the argument in favour of the operation appeared to be that the vessel might be of some use: 'The duties to which a vessel with such a useful speed could be put for the general purposes of the country and *probably* [author's italics] for SOE do not need to be emphasized.' Furthermore, it would be cheap: 'The yacht is the property of a wealthy British subject who is prepared to hand it over to SOE FFC Section [RF] for any purpose for which it may be used without compensation and without pay.' Miraculously, Hutchison's proposal was passed by Brook and the head of SOE's Naval Section for further development of operational details under the codename SEAHORSE. On 20 November a meeting of SOE's Western European Working Committee was held at Norgeby House, Baker Street to discuss SEAHORSE. From the minutes of the meeting, no one present appears to have called the RF Section's bluff. On the contrary, there does not seem to have been even a faintly dissenting voice. The plan to infiltrate Yeo-Thomas by sea was dispensed with and it was arranged that he undergo a parachute training course beginning on 29 November in order that he be dropped to an RF reception committee near Lyon. Yeo-Thomas was able to claim that F Section had agreed to lend him a wireless operator for the duration of his mission, thereby exhibiting a new and surprising aspect of inter-section co-operation. It still appears that the operation's very limited rewards were generally masked by the even more limited demands it was making on SOE's resources. When asked for his equipment requirements, 'D/RF.2 [Yeo-Thomas] stated that no special equipment would be required except 3 "Mae Wests" [life jackets].' The provisional date for the operation was fixed as 16 December.

Glimmerings of doubt began to emerge from the Head of SOE's Naval Section who, on reading the minutes of the meeting, was moved belatedly to raise some pretty fundamental questions, such as: 'What do we want Yacht No. 5 for?' and 'Is it certain that the value of the operation justifies the risk to the personnel concerned?' It seemed as if Yeo-Thomas had been rumbled, but Hutchison proved a loyal ally and wrote back reiterating that the yacht was worth having and, if circumstances did not permit its capture, then 'the officer who is proceeding to France had many other tasks which he can usefully per-form'. The last week of November was a hectic one for Yeo-Thomas with briefings at Dorset Square to learn Playfair cipher conventions from Captain Benn of the Codes and Cipher Section. This system would enable Yeo-Thomas to encipher messages to be transmitted by wireless or, if needed, to hide messages within apparently innocent plain text correspondence. As the project continued to build up momentum, on 29 November Yeo-Thomas left London, Barbara and RF Section for Cheshire to undertake his parachute training.

Ringway airfield, near Manchester, was, at the end of 1942, the centre of all military parachute training but SOE had its own instruc-tion centre, STS 51, near to the airfield. Yeo-Thomas arrived in the early hours of a Sunday morning and was up at seven o'clock for an hour and a half of physical training, which he found particularly tax-ing after a year of office work. This was followed by practice jumps through the exit hole of a dummy fuselage and swinging on parachute harnesses. The next day, after another one and three-quarter hours' physical training, Yeo-Thomas was ready to make his first real descent. His thoughts at the prospect of facing this challenge show a refresh-ing candour, belying the stereotype of the implacable hero: 'You damned fool, why ever did you undertake such a silly job – in a few minutes you'll have to jump through that hole and it doesn't appeal to you a bit, you are scared stiff and you'll have to force yourself to do it, Twerp!' It greatly helped when he saw that his fellow jumpers looked as apprehensive as he and, typically, when he completed his descent, his immediate reaction was to want to do it again. Over the next three days, he was to get several more opportunities to jump. He found descents from balloons surprisingly unnerving, while his night jump 'went off very well', and he admitted: 'I now felt perfectly confident.' The least pleasurable of his experiences was the water jump, which went without a hitch until he dropped into the lake at Tatton Park. It was freezing cold and his waterproof suit soon began to leak, saturating his battledress trousers. He managed to extract himself from his parachute harness and freed his inflatable dinghy. However, the CO_2 gas bottle with which he had been supplied was not sufficiently full to inflate it and the hand pump would not connect properly to the valve. After fifteen minutes' hard and freezing work, there was sufficient air in the dinghy for him to get in it, but this merely accentuated the tear that he discovered in its bottom. Water seeped in as fast as he could bale it out and he barely made it to the bank before it was completely swamped. Apart from being frozen stiff, there were no ill effects and he returned home the next day in good spirits 'to Barbara and happiness'.

While Yeo-Thomas completed his parachute training, the section set about compiling false identity papers and a suitable cover story for him. SOE's forgery department was asked to furnish a French identity card, demobilization certificate, driving licence and ration cards. Wherever possible the cover story fitted Yeo-Thomas's own personal experience and even the name, 'François Yves Thierry', shared the same initials as his own. Similarly, his cover story claimed that 'Thierry' had done his military service with the French Air Force at Le Bourget and was employed in the clothing trade.

As Yeo-Thomas was subjecting himself to the rigours of parachute training, the planning staff at Baker Street finally cottoned on to the impracticality of the SEAHORSE scheme. On 1 December the Operations Section informed Brook that Gubbins had ruled that: 'Under existing conditions, and in view of the unsuitability of the craft for SOE purposes, he does not consider that its attempted seizure is justifiable as the primary objective for the operation.'

The door had not been slammed in Yeo-Thomas's face completely, however, for if 'some other important task' was found and approved, then the seizure of the yacht might be considered as a means of exfiltrating the party. The ever reliable Hutchison sent off a memorandum the next day. He still did not completely accept the rejection of the yacht scheme but now proposed an alternative and more

realistic mission for Yeo-Thomas: 'MI6 have recently sent a representative (Manuel) [Dewavrin's second-in-command] for a general look
round in France; and I believe something similar will be useful for us,
particularly in view of the new arms situation. D/RF.2 [Yeo-Thomas]
might well make a tour in company with the heads of the resistance
movements in order to satisfy himself as to the condition of the
weapons, their numbers, etc., etc.'

Hutchison's request had much to commend it but perhaps Baker
Street were now justifiably suspicious. Gubbins's response on 4
December argued that a man of Yeo-Thomas's value should not be
wasted on an irrelevance and he should be held in reserve for the
important work that lay in the future. While these disappointments
were surrounding him, Yeo-Thomas went on leave with Barbara to
visit her family in Brighton. His diaries do not record any anxiety at
the baulking of his plans, while official files do not give an indication
of his response to this rejection. Christmas passed without incident
other than that he spent an enjoyable lunch with his friends at
the BCRA. Work was still being carried out on perfecting his false
documentation but now apparently without purpose. However,
Hutchison and his friends in the Free French had taken the matter in
hand and at the turn of the year it was decided that Yeo-Thomas
would join a two-man BCRA mission to northern France to assess the
state of the resistance movements. At last Yeo-Thomas was on his way
home.

CHAPTER FOUR

· The First Mission — Operation SEAHORSE ·

The France to which Yeo-Thomas was so impatiently preparing to return had changed immensely since he had left from Pointe de Grave more than two and a half years earlier.

As might have been expected, Germany treated its overwhelming victory in June 1940 as expiation of its humiliating defeat in 1918. Deep resentment of the peace settlement imposed by the victorious Allied powers had formed an important part of the Nazi Party's ideology and it was inevitable that Hitler would give this built-up grievance full rein. Consequently, the armistice negotiations became part-conference, part-theatre. Général Charles Huntziger, the commander of the 2nd Army, was the unfortunate who had been ordered to lead the French delegation and duly presented himself to the German representatives 'at the Loire bridge near Tours'. He was then driven deep behind enemy lines, arriving on 21 June at Réthondes in the forest of Compiègne, fifty miles north-east of Paris. The immediate significance of the location was not lost on him, for it was here in November 1918 that Allied officials had received the German peace emissaries. After the war, the site and the railway car in which the negotiations had taken place were transformed by the French authorities into a museum. Now, little more than twenty years later, the Germans had decided to use the same coach in order to exact their retribution. Hitler had chosen to witness personally this sublime moment of German revenge and, in the opinion of the American journalist William Shirer, revealed a 'burning contempt for this place now and all that it has stood for in the twenty-two years since it witnessed the humbling of the German Empire'.

Generaloberst Wilhelm Keitel, the Chief of the German High Command, read out the swingeing terms of the armistice agreement and handed copies to Huntziger for relaying to his superiors in Bordeaux. For more than twenty-four hours, Pétain's cabinet bickered over the details, their conversations with Huntziger's delegation being dutifully 'tapped' by a German Army signals unit. Finally the order came through, instructing Huntziger to sign. At 8.50pm on 22 June, the armistice was concluded, although the ceasefire did not formally come into effect until 12.35am hours on the 25th. Hitler had not attended the formal signing, preferring to remain at his headquarters near Bruly-de-Pêche. On 23 June, he undertook a lightning

tour of Paris, which was enough to provide several photo opportunities for the Nazi propaganda machine and to enable him to savour the
sights of the vanquished city.

While Hitler was being whisked around the tourist spots of the
capital, Pétain and his government were attempting to come to terms
with the conditions that had been imposed upon them. The most
obvious was that France had been dismembered. The northern
départements of the Nord and Pas de Calais were taken away from
French control and placed under the administration of the German
Military Governor of Holland and Belgium. Italy's belated entry
into the war on Germany's side enabled it to create a fifty-kilometre
demilitarized zone in French territory, as a prelude to realizing its
ambitions regarding the acquisition of Haute Savoie and the Côte
d'Azur. The most extreme geographical division, however, was the
splitting of France into two separate zones. The northern regions,
including Paris and the entire Channel and Atlantic seaboards,
were occupied by German forces and the French administration was
ordered to comply with its conquerors' instructions. Meanwhile,
central and southern France, comprising approximately forty per cent
of the country, was left to Pétain's government to administer as a
'Free' zone.[1] The Occupied Zone (*Zone Occupée* [ZO]) contained
by far the greater proportion of France's industry, its most fertile
land and the majority of its population, and was therefore prey to the
voracious economic demands of Germany. An armistice commission
was established to regularize what, in effect, became the systematic
plundering of French agriculture and industry. In addition, the terms
of the armistice included the payment of a daily tribute of 400 million
francs to defray the costs of the German occupation forces. The two
zones were to be delineated by a closely guarded demarcation
line that meandered from the foothills of the Pyrenees to the Swiss
border. Although in contravention of the agreement between the two
nations, a further territorial 'adjustment' was soon imposed. The
'shuttlecock' provinces of Alsace and Lorraine, which had already
changed hands twice in the last seventy years, reverted back to
Germany once again and were annexed as provinces of the Third
Reich. As a consequence, some 400,000 of its population, who were
considered to be irredeemably French, were expelled from their
homes and sent to the Unoccupied Zone.

The armistice agreement was primarily concerned with the apor-
tioning of territory and economic matters. It was not a peace treaty,
for the Germans stated that this more lasting conclusion of hostilities
would have to await the defeat of Britain which, in June 1940, was
assumed to be not too far away. It was therefore essential that the
prisoners of war already in German hands at the conclusion of the

armistice should remain in captivity. Other, more fortunate members of the armed forces were demobilized, but almost two million Frenchmen remained behind barbed wire. Paradoxically, the new government was permitted a token army of 100,000 men, but all its artillery, tanks and heavy equipment were handed over to Germany.

With Paris and the logical alternative, Bordeaux, inconveniently situated in the Occupied Zone, the French government needed a 'capital'. Pétain's cabinet initially moved to Clermont-Ferrand, but this owed more to the personal preference of Pierre Laval than to the city possessing adequate facilities as the centre of a national administration. The most immediately suitable choice in the Unoccupied Zone was the city of Lyon, but the dominant and potentially troublesome figure of its Mayor, Édouard Herriot, loomed too large for comfort. Instead, in the first week in July, the spa town of Vichy, with its abundant hotels and tranquil ambiance was chosen as the seat of government. It should not be forgotten that, for most Frenchmen and women, the Vichy Government was now *the* legitimate embodiment of the state. France's defeat was seen by many as the ultimate manifestation of the bankruptcy of French politics, which had earlier brought the nation to the verge of civil war during the 1930s. At least with Pétain in power and his assumption of responsibility for France's future, there appeared to be an end to factionalism and the promise of a new beginning. In fact, the new beginning was to be characterized largely as a return to the past. Vichy propaganda evoked an image of a 'golden age' that was essentially an amorphous rejection of 'new' values, such as communism, and a return to the traditional props of the state, such as family and religion. Parliamentary democracy had for decades produced weak, ineffectual governments that had finally reached their nadir during the crises of May and June. Now a fresh start was offered, born of a *Révolution Nationale*, which was supposed to touch every corner of French life. In place of the French Republic's resounding *'Liberté, Egalité, Fraternité'*, Pétain's National Revolution advocated the stolid virtues of *'Famille, Travail, Patrie'* ('Family, Work, Fatherland'). In keeping with the national feeling of shock and dislocation, Vichy offered a dream-like vision of the future, defined in Pétain's rambling radio broadcasts: 'You have suffered. You will suffer still more . . . Your life will be a hard one. I shall not rock you to sleep with words of deceit. I hate lies – they have done you so much harm in the past. But the earth – the earth does not lie. It remains your refuge. The earth is our homeland. A field that goes fallow is a piece of France that has died . . . Do not expect too much from the State, which can only give what it receives. Rely on yourselves for the present, and, for the future, rely on your children whom you will have brought up with a sense of duty.'

If the country was to be fed platitudes, they needed to be imbued with the clear distinction of being government platitudes. Soon after its move to Vichy, Pétain's political legitimacy was bolstered by some highly effective manoeuvring carried out by his *éminence grise*, Pierre Laval. The core of the elected French Parliament remained intact but, like the army before it, proved powerless to stem the tide of events. The National Assembly voted on 10 July by 569 votes to 80 (with 17 abstentions) to give all powers to Pétain and sanctioned his authority to create a new constitution for the French State. This carte blanche was even endorsed by the likes of Herriot who was moved to comment: 'Let us all rally round the Marshal.' Such sweeping powers would have turned the head of the mildest of politicians but, for a man of Pétain's self-regard and ambition, it was a dream come true. On 11 July, Pétain declared himself the Head of the French State, employing the regal '*nous*' ('we'). As the French Republic was now deemed to be discredited and redundant, the office of President was felt to be no longer necessary and, similarly, the Assembly was, in effect, scrapped.

Whatever his grandiose aspirations, Pétain was enough of a realist to appreciate that his position was dependent upon the tacit support of Germany. On 24 October 1940, he met Hitler at Montoire, near Tours, after which the Marshal announced in a speech that he intended pursuing a policy of collaboration with Germany. In this he was supported, albeit in very different ways, by his two closest aides, Laval and, after his dismissal on 13 December 1940, Amiral Jean-François Darlan, the Commander-in-Chief of the French Navy. Laval was a wily and experienced politician who had served between the wars in various cabinet posts, including that of Prime Minister. He had been an advocate of appeasement and, in the face of German might, decided that France's best interests lay in cooperation rather than obstinate denial of the realities of German power. He enjoyed an uneasy relationship with Pétain, the two men having no significant empathy but finding themselves unable to do without each other. However, this did not prevent Laval's dismissal as Vice-Premier in December in a coup engineered by his cabinet rivals. After a brief interregnum, in February 1941 Admiral Darlan was appointed to replace him. In part inspired by his fervent Anglophobia, Darlan sought to ally France's interests specifically with those of Germany and promote closer military ties between the two countries. Following a meeting with Hitler in May, he approved a series of protocols that saw French military bases, transit facilities and intelligence offered to German forces in the Mediterranean and Middle East. However, so far-reaching were his recommendations that even his colleagues in the Cabinet deemed them to be too collaborationist and the terms were not implemented. Closer Franco-German bonds were formed, however, only a month later when Germany invaded the Soviet Union. Vichy's anti-communist beliefs allowed it to offer support to a campaign that was represented as an anti-Bolshevik crusade. It was now possible for Frenchmen working in munitions factories, or even those who took the extreme step of fighting along-side the Wehrmacht as members of the Légion des Volontaires Français, to portray themselves as French patriots.

The Vichy regime was not merely acting as a cipher for its German masters; it gave expression to many of the autocratic policies that had been touted by French right-wingers for decades. Anti-Jewish laws were promulgated as early as 1940 and, under Darlan, even an Anti-Jewish Police was created. At the same time, anti-Semitic propaganda was widely disseminated by the regime throughout both the Occupied and Unoccupied Zones. Freemasonry, long a bane of the far right, was portrayed as a national menace and some 7000 arrests of members were made by the Vichy and German authorities. By the time Laval was recalled to office in April 1942, the complexion of the Vichy state had changed and, with the shift in the course of the war, its relations with Germany had also altered. Instead of appearing the undisputed victor of the conflict, Germany was becoming increasingly beleaguered, faced by the prospect of a long and total war. Vichy's hopes of an association between the two countries, with France as the most favoured nation within the 'New Order' in Europe dominated by the Third Reich, were fast evaporating. Now, Germany merely wanted French subservience. In recognition of this shift of emphasis, the Vichy Government conceded its own vulnerability, and Laval was obliged to affirm his administration's position in a radio broadcast on 22 June 1942: 'I believe in Germany's victory, and I want this German victory, because, without it, Communism will establish itself everywhere in Europe.' In this same speech, Laval introduced a policy named *La Relève* ('the Relief'), where one French prisoner-of-war was repatriated for every three workers volunteering for employment in Germany. In spite of a massive propaganda campaign, the programme failed to elicit the required response and, in February 1943, the Vichy Government enacted the Service Obligatoire du Travail (STO) (Mandatory Work Service). Similar to national conscription, the law made every man between the ages of eighteen and fifty liable for compulsory labour service in Germany.

However, there were others who needed no coercion to serve the Führer. As the war progressed, more and more authority was vested in Germanophile fascists, such as Philippe Henriot, Marcel Déat, Joseph Darnand and Jacques Doriot. These men were at the centre of a series of increasingly collaborationist movements that embraced volunteers wishing to fight on the Eastern Front in the Légion des

Voluntaires Français and even the Waffen-SS itself. In addition, they controlled extreme political groups, such as the Parti Populaire Français, the Service d'Ordre Légionnaire and the Milice.

The fascists had greater opportunity to express their beliefs after the German occupation of Vichy France on 11 November 1942. This was Hitler's reaction to the confused and equivocal Vichy response to the Allied landings in French North Africa that had taken place three days earlier. In Vichy and Algiers, there was an almost total absence of a coherent policy. As soon as a member of the government issued an order, a contradiction was rarely slow to follow. Darlan, more by luck than judgment, found himself at the centre of events in Algiers as the landings began, for he was there visiting his sick son who was suffering from poliomyelitis. Meanwhile, Laval was summoned to Munich and, after being berated by Hitler, was informed of the German invasion of the Unoccupied Zone. Back in North Africa, Darlan signed an armistice with the Allies, only to be instructed by Pétain to oppose the landings. Then, in a subsequent and secret message, the Marshal told him to: 'Act for the best. You have all my confidence.'[2] Amid this muddle, some Vichy units engaged the Anglo-American invasion forces, while, on the other hand, the Armistice Army in France did not oppose the German forces as they moved into the Unoccupied Zone.

The constant ebb and flow of power politics after June 1940 should not disguise the fact that, for most of the population in both the zones, the routine of everyday life continued. Politics remained an important element of French society but, in the main, the people's energies and preoccupations remained the perennial ones of work and home life. The very fact that defeat had made life more difficult left little energy for agitation against the new regime. The ramifications of occupation and the rule from Vichy touched France in a host of different and frequently contrasting ways. For the farmer who continued to live on his land in an isolated part of the country, apparently little had changed. The absence of a son, however, in a prisoner-of-war camp or a shortage of seed had grave repercussions. For the bulk of the population living in the towns and villages, new regulations and economic hardship made life ever more difficult. It was an increasing problem just to move around the country; a plethora of paperwork was needed to cross the demarcation line, to enter the coastal forbidden zones and even to be out after dark. Furthermore, France's railway system became monopolized by Germany's military and economic needs and, as the war progressed, timetables were subject to disruption, following Allied bombing and sabotage by the resistance. In spite of these difficulties, travel became essential in the search for food to compensate for its absence in the shops and to augment the meagre rations allowance. In response to these shortages, city-dwellers took matters into their own hands and at weekends there was a regular exodus from the towns to the country. At the same time, there developed a flourishing black market in which most of the nation indulged in some capacity. This widespread participation in illegal activity set an important precedent and initiated countless thousands into a secret world of opposition to the authorities.

Officialdom in Occupied and Unoccupied France had many faces. An immense bureaucracy was needed to supervise the constant round of new laws, decrees and regulations imposed by the Vichy and German authorities. The various police forces that existed under the Republic in the main continued much as before, except that they were now obliged to engage in the enforcement of severe political and racial laws. Furthermore, as resistance grew, they were augmented by specialist 'counter-terrorist' units, such as the Groupes Mobiles de Réserve (GMR). The zealots of the extreme fascist organizations were always on hand to lend assistance in this regard, and on 31 January 1943 Laval approved the establishment of a Milice Française, which was to be 'composed of volunteers morally ready and physically capable, not only of supporting the new state by their action, but also of cooperating in the maintenance of order.' Although initially restricted to the southern zone, eventually it was allowed to carry out its counter-resistance work throughout France.

Repression was far from being the sole obligation of the Vichy authorities, however. The Germans maintained a substantial garrison in France, which, in November 1943, comprised forty-six divisions in spite of the pressing needs of other fronts. Their presence owed much to the fear of an Allied invasion and France's suitability as a place where German units might refit and retrain. The most effective forces of repression were the German security forces and, in particular, the Abwehr (military intelligence), the SS's Sicherheitsdienst (SD, the intelligence service) and the Gestapo (the security service). The specific roles of the latter two organizations have been much debated. According to an official historian of SOE, however, 'arguments about the distinctions and resemblances between the Gestapo and the SD are as valueless as the old disputes about how many angels can dance on the point of a pin. The practical point is that they worked, from an Allied agent's point of view, as one.'[3] Although often represented as having a permanently anatagonistic relationship, these two organizations *did* work together in France. Individuals and specific departments were frequently at loggerheads, sometimes over the brutal techniques employed by the SD and Gestapo. However, operational necessity saw the Abwehr and Sicherheitsdienst engaged in numerous successful joint endeavours against the resistance and

Allied Intelligence. The Abwehr's primary aim was the combating of enemy intelligence-gathering and, although the SD was also engaged in this task, its role was also to root out subversion and therefore particularly concerned itself with the repression of resistance movements. The SD was more than willing to use any form of coercion to achieve its results and its headquarters in the major towns and cities of France became feared symbols of Nazi oppression. Highly effective use was made of French agents, it being recognized that operatives with local knowledge offered the best means of carrying out surveillance and penetration of resistance groups. The public fear of the apparent omniscience of the German security forces, allied to the dire consequences awaiting those captured by them, was a major factor in the creation of a climate in which the risks of joining the resistance far outweighed the advantages.

Nevertheless, resistance did soon emerge from the ashes of defeat, albeit one that took a relatively long time to develop. At first, greater opportunities lay in the Unoccupied Zone where Vichy's control was far from absolute and efficient. As early as the summer of 1940, men and women began to consider the possibilities of opposition to the new state of affairs in France. Few could, or even wished to, leave France and join de Gaulle, and therefore they turned to resistance 'at home'. The most obvious means of registering opposition was to publish newspapers and journals that offered an alternative political perspective to that provided by the the media under German and Vichy control. One group with a broadly based political agenda was Combat, which produced, from December 1941, a clandestine newspaper, which had a circulation of over 30,000 within a year. More direct forms of resistance followed with intelligence-gathering, the forging of false papers and even sabotage. Another organization, Libération, based its support upon the remaining vestiges of pre-war trade-unionism. Meanwhile, a group with a left-wing, Catholic agenda, produced its own illegal newspaper, *Franc-Tireur*, and began to develop a wide range of contacts throughout the Occupied Zone.

In the Occupied Zone, opposition to Vichy and German rule was perhaps more focused, as a consequence of the harsher prevailing conditions, but, for the same reasons, it was more difficult to build up resistance networks. Minor acts of civil disobedience occurred soon after the signing of the armistice, such as giving misleading information to German soldiers on the métro, but these constituted merely temporary and highly personal palliatives.

By the end of two years of occupation, three main groups of resisters had formed in the Occupied Zone. These were Libération-Nord, Organisation Civile et Militaire (OCM) and the Front National. Libération-Nord was primarily left-wing in complexion, drawing much of its support from among socialists and trade unionists. Like most of the movements, its newspaper was an essential element in its activities and, in spite of its illegality, was to reach a circulation of 50,000. In 1941, its representatives made contact with de Gaulle and, the following year, one of its leaders, Christian Pineau, went to England for consultation. In contrast, the Organisation Civile et Militaire was more conservative in its political outlook and, as its name suggests, drew upon serving or retired soldiers and civil servants for its members. The influence and access to information enjoyed by many of its members became of particular importance to Dewavrin's organization, which undertook to help finance its activities. The Front National was also well named, for it set out to encompass as broad a cross-section of political persuasions as possible on both sides of the demarcation line. After the invasion of the Soviet Union in June 1941, it absorbed a strong communist element that propelled it into the front rank of resistance movements. However, the dominance of communists among its leadership engendered ill-feeling with some other more right-wing groupings.

Clearly de Gaulle and the BCRA needed up-to-the-moment reports on the state of this resistance activity and, furthermore, the opportunity for high-level talks with resistance leaders. As plans for a future Allied invasion of Europe developed, the political situation in France assumed ever greater importance. Resistance was clearly growing, but, in many ways, its structure remained ill-defined and uncoordinated. Reports from both the Occupied and Unoccupied Zones revealed a wide range of groups adhering to a diverse series of political agendas. The efficiency of these groups, or, more precisely, their potential, demanded an appropriate assessment. It was to this end that de Gaulle ordered Dewavrin to undertake Operation ARQUEBUSE.

Yeo-Thomas's work with SOE and his own personal interest ensured that he met many of the representatives of the resistance groups that made their way to London. He also maintained close professional and personal connections with those members of Dewavrin's staff who undertook operational missions in France. He often socialized with his BCRA comrades-in-arms and his diaries recall frequent dinner and drinks parties with them. These occasions helped to reinforce the French dimension of his personality, but sometimes had the effect of annoying Barbara. Jealousy of Britain's primacy in the war effort and shame at France's collapse sometimes manifested itself in outbursts of Anglophobia. On one celebrated occasion, Barbara's patriotism would not allow her to sanction their communal running down of all things British and she threw Yeo-Thomas and his French guests out of *her* apartment. They realized that they had gone too far and Yeo-Thomas confessed that he had joined in largely to tease her. If Yeo-Thomas was able to offer adverse comments on Britain, he would not tolerate ill-considered criticisms by others. At one nightclub he overheard Free French officers talking indiscreetly and disrespectfully about Britain and the British. In perfect and forceful French he reminded them that they were guests in the country and suggested that they leave the premises. They did as they were told.[4] Not all of their social events with the French were sources of acrimony. Yeo-Thomas and Barbara were invited to a dinner party at a BCRA apartment in Courtfield Road. The atmosphere was convivial with three of his best friends present: Fredérique Scamaroni, Bruno Larat and Alain de Beaufort. The Frenchmen were some of Dewavrin's closest aides and each was about to go into the field. Larat and de Beaufort were to undertake missions concerning air supply to the resistance, while Scamaroni was to be sent on an operation to his native Corsica. A fourth officer, Paul Marchal, was also staying with them while he awaited his flight to Occupied France. The party was a jolly affair, with Larat's and de Beaufort's fiancées making up the group. Of the five men at dinner, Yeo-Thomas was the sole survivor of the war.

In January 1942, de Gaulle sent to France his most important emissary to date. Jean Moulin, a forty-three-year-old career civil servant, was to become, arguably, the greatest figure in the French resistance. Before the war, his rapid promotion had marked him out as something of a high-flyer and, in 1939, he had been appointed Préfet of the Eure-et-Loir *département*, one of the youngest administrators in France to hold such a rank. He had stayed at his post under the Vichy regime for as long as he could bear it, but he was eventually dismissed in November 1940 for refusing to implement instructions to dismiss left-wing mayors of local communities. Having taken time to collect his thoughts and survey the possibilities of resistance in the Unoccupied Zone, he acquired false papers and made his way to neutral Portugal. In Lisbon he made contact with SOE, who did what they could to arrange his passage to England where, after some delay, he arrived in October 1941. Whatever hopes SOE entertained of recruiting him for their own purposes were dashed by the instant bond between Moulin and de Gaulle. Here was a man with sufficent patriotism, character, political weight and personality to represent the leader of the Free French in France. With the assistance of RF Section, Dewavrin arranged Moulin's training in the methods of clandestine life. He was to need all the skills he could be taught, for, after his return to France on the night of 1/2 January 1942, he was to spend the next fourteen months travelling throughout the country in near constant fear of recognition and arrest. He sought and, in large measure, succeeded in gaining the confidence of the burgeoning resistance groups in order, as de Gaulle had instructed, to forge them into an effective whole. Eventually, on 13 February 1943, he was withdrawn to England for a rest and consultation. He brought with him Général Charles Delestraint, who had the distinction of being one of de Gaulle's former commanding officers and, more significantly, was Moulin's nominee as leader of a future 'Secret Army' of resisters created out of the unification of the various groups.

Moulin had concentrated much of his attention upon the resistance in Vichy France, and de Gaulle therefore ordered Dewavrin to focus his mission upon the situation in the Occupied Zone. To assist him in this undertaking, he selected a relatively new and controversial member of the BCRA, Pierre Brossolette.

Brossolette had been born in 1903 and was therefore of a similar age to Yeo-Thomas. His political beliefs were distinctly left-wing and, during his pre-war career as a journalist and radio broadcaster, he had been a vehement opponent of his government's appeasement of Germany's territorial demands. He had served in the French Army during the Battle of France and, following his demobilization in August, lived with his wife and two children in Paris. His political convictions precluded a return to journalism and, to make ends meet, he bought a bookshop and stationer's in the rue de la Pompe. However, a man of such strongly held beliefs could not remain passive for long and in September he began writing for underground journals. It was therefore a natural progression in the winter of 1940/41 to join a resistance group, comprising intellectuals who worked at the Musée de l'Homme. He wrote and edited its clandestine publication, *Résistance*, and his shop became a dead-letter drop and secret meeting-place for the members of the network. It was not long, though, before the German security forces closed in and arrested many of its members, with Brossolette fortunate to remain undetected and at liberty. He was not daunted by this narrow escape and developed other far more influential contacts with an intelligence-gathering network named La Confrérie Notre Dame (CND). Its leader, Gilbert Renault (codenamed 'Rémy'), became a legendary figure both in French and British circles, being respected and admired by his controllers in the BCRA and SIS. Renault recalled in his memoirs that his first meeting with Brossolette did not take place under the most auspicious of circumstances. In November 1941 an intermediary 'suggested that I meet Pierre Brossolette, a well-known journalist about whom he gave an attractive account. Before the war, I was a reader not of the *Populaire*, but of *Action Française*. Brossolette's opinions and mine were thus far apart. I had heard accounts of Brossolette which made him out to be a climber, and by no means an attractive one. Consequently, at first, I refused to meet him. But afterward I reproached myself. We had no right, I argued to myself, to take personal opinions into consideration. Our duty was to welcome all men of good will from wherever they came, if they were sincere. I asked Paco[5] to invite Brossolette to lunch. From the first moment, I was conquered by his live intelligence and the kind of inner flame with which he seemed to be lit. I asked him to take on the compilation of a press review which we were adding to our despatches. He agreed.'[6]

After working for six months for La Confrérie Notre Dame, it was decided that Brossolette, now bearing the first of many codenames, 'Pedro', should be sent to England. In the company of Jacques Robert ('Rewez'), another leading BCRA agent, he made his way to St Saëns, near Rouen. In the early hours of 28 April 1942, they were picked up by a Lysander aircraft flown by Squadron Leader A M 'Sticky' Murphy of the Royal Air Force's No 161 (Special Duty) Squadron. The flight went without a hitch except that a bottle of perfume carried by Robert leaked and Murphy's 'pleasurable anticipation' at meeting his unknown passenger on landing proved to be sadly misplaced.

In London, the favourable impression that Brossolette had made on Renault was extended to Dewavrin, who found himself greatly impressed by the short, thin man with a shock of black hair marked by an unusual flash of white. As Dewavrin later wrote:

> Of all the men I have met in my life, Brossolette was, without question, the one who made the strongest impression on me. His mind shaped and assimilated ideas at such a rate that few were able to follow his breakneck speed. A great deal of sensitivity hid behind his scathing comments and he gave me the impression of being able to understand and to predict everything, and of being one of those rare personalities capable of combining a highly intuitive understanding of the human condition with an exceptional ability to analyse and reason. Like many above-average men, he provoked in his wake currents of envy and hate among the mediocre or cowardly, incapable of appreciating the brilliance of his extraordinary intellect.[7]

Brossolette's stay in London was not to be of long duration. The BCRA planned to have him develop links between London and the resistance movements in the Occupied Zone, but more personal matters took a hand. Reports from Paris revealed that the Germans had raided his shop and interrogated his family. They appeared to have accepted the cover story that he had prepared with his wife before his departure and seemed satisfied with the explanation that his absence was due to his having run off with another woman. The

Germans' inquiries made it vital that Madame Brossolette and the children leave France. Such was Brossolette's haste that he refused to undertake an SOE parachute training programme and, on 7 June 1942, made his first jump from an aircraft over Burgundy, near Saint-Alban. On reaching Paris it was clearly too dangerous for him to return to his home and he therefore stayed with friends, making initial contact with his wife through 'cut-outs', the intermediaries who, if caught, would help to protect the security of both of the Brossolettes. Meticulous arrangements were made for their flight and, as it was too risky for him to travel with his family, he left them in the care of helpers who escorted them to the Mediterranean coast where a boat secretly embarked them and took them to Gibraltar, arriving in July. Brossolette followed on 4 September, being taken off a beach near Narbonne by a Polish-manned felucca, *Seadog*. This SIS-sponsored operation, codenamed LEDA, nearly ended in disaster when French customs officials stumbled upon the scene, and only six out of the ten passengers were embarked.

Brossolette and his family were eventually reunited in England, where he soon gained a reputation as one of the leading intellectuals among the Free French.[8] Brossolette, now using the alias 'Commandant Bourgat', was soon at work bringing his writing and broadcasting talents to bear on behalf of de Gaulle. Ironically, his anonymity did not extend to the BBC and, on 22 September, he broadcast to Occupied France using his own name.

Whereas Brossolette was an integral part of the BCRA mission, bearing his own codename BRUMAIRE, it might at first have been assumed that Yeo-Thomas's presence was that of a makeweight. However, on the contrary, Dewavrin specifically wished to have a British officer accompany the mission in order to arrest an evident deterioration in relations between SOE and the BCRA in London and France. Furthermore, 'I was concerned that the statements we would have to make on our return to London could not be disputed or accused of lacking objectivity if, as I supposed, they were to be translated by our Allies at a political level into a fairer appreciation of what Général de Gaulle truly represented in France, and translated on a military level into more numerous parachute drops.'[9]

Dewavrin already had a high opinion of Yeo-Thomas and had no doubt that he could pass for a Frenchman, later commenting that 'Yeo-Thomas had lived in France for almost thirty-five years and spoke French without a trace of an accent, using slang and jargon with more assurance than I could have myself. For Brossolette and I he was not only a colleague we valued as much for his intelligence as for his calm and resolute courage, but he was also a treasured comrade who soon became a very dear friend.'[10]

Dewavrin's desire to have Yeo-Thomas join him is made clear by a note addressed to Hutchison on 4 January 1943, in which he promised to give the SOE representative complete freedom of action and the same facilities as those extended to Brossolette: 'In other words, Lieutenant YT will be treated by our comrades exactly in France as they would treat one of their own, just as it should be between brothers-in-arms fighting for the same cause.' The only proviso that Dewavrin stipulated was that the results of the mission would not be exploited by SOE until de Gaulle had given his permission.

Time was of the essence, and it was essential that Yeo-Thomas receive as much specialist training as possible before the team left England. Having completed his parachute training, he was next sent on a week's crash course at Special Training School 36, SOE's agent-finishing establishment at Beaulieu, near Southampton. Here he was schooled comprehensively in agent tradecraft. He learnt how to make clandestine contacts, to select the most secure meeting-places and how to detect and carry out surveillance. The stereotypical subjects of disguise and secret inks were not overlooked and great importance was attached to the agent's personal security. Briefings were given on the wide range of German counter-espionage organizations awaiting him in France, and the importance of maintaining a sound cover story was strongly emphasized. To be prepared for a situation where all else had failed, he was taught techniques of how to resist interrogation. Overall, he clearly impressed his tutors but, in his finishing report, they also recorded with great perspicacity some of his flaws:

> . . . is quite intelligent and practical, with a wide knowledge of the world and of people, yet nevertheless his approach to problems is sometimes naive and lacking in subtlety. He has a strong character, is direct, single-minded, determined and completely sure of himself. He has a pleasant personality and is a good mixer. It is possible that some people might find his complete self-assurance a little irritating.
>
> He has good powers of leadership and would be most effective in charge of those less intelligent than himself.

He returned to Dorset Square on 11 January, where the first of several drafts of the operational instructions for his mission was drawn up. Meanwhile SOE's impressive backroom staff continued to carry out their meticulous preparations. DF Section furnished him with contact addresses in Paris, Lyon, Marseille and Lisbon should he need assistance in escaping from France or be in urgent need of money. It was hoped that he would only need to call upon these contacts as a last resort, for he was to be provided with 300,000 francs (concealed in an especially made toilet case) for his immediate needs. Meanwhile the Code Section kept him up to date with a variety of codes to cover wireless messages, letters and even BBC broadcasts that would warn him if any of his DF escape routes had been compromised. He had retained the 'Thierry' alias, from the original plan to steal the yacht, but the Forgery Section, assisted by the Free French, continued to work on perfecting his documentation. Yeo-Thomas bought a complete set of clothing for the operation purchased for the not inconsiderable sum of £50 5s 10d. He made sure his clothes were tailored with a French cut so that they would not attract suspicion in France, where shortages and clothes rationing made smart clothes a rarity. He even made two trips to an SOE-approved dentist to ensure that no dental problems would flare up when in France. Should he encounter any difficulties that proved rather more threatening than toothache, he took the opportunity of practising snap shooting with a .32 Colt automatic pistol at the London Transport rifle range, which was conveniently situated under Baker Street Underground station.

Barbara had known for a long time of Yeo-Thomas's plans to return to France. They had discussed it often and whatever her own fears for his safety she had too much respect for him and their relationship to try and prevent him from going. He had explained that he could not continue to send men to risk their lives in France when he had not experienced this himself. Obviously, as the preparations built up, she realized that the day was not far off. However, it would appear that she did not receive the news from Yeo-Thomas himself for, on 1 February, she recorded in her diary: 'Went to Harrods to buy flowers. Met St Jacques [the BCRA officer, Duclos] Heard of T. departure.'

Hardly surprisingly, the news hit her badly and the next day she wrote: 'Feeling very miserable re Tommy Rabbit's departure.'[11]

At least Barbara could console herself with the fact that Yeo-Thomas was not the first of the team to leave, for it had been decided that Brossolette would head an advance party. Now even more conspicuous following his broadcast, Brossolette tried to conceal his identity by growing a moustache and changing his hairstyle. He left on the night of 26/7 January 1943 in a Lysander flown by the celebrated pilot, Wing Commander Percy Pickard, and landed near Issoudon in central France. He then made his way to Paris to renew some of his old contacts and await the arrival of his colleagues. In contrast, Yeo-Thomas and Dewavrin were to be sent in by parachute and had to wait for the next 'moon period' when the pilot of the aircraft would have a better chance of accurately locating the drop zone. The delay was frustrating, but Yeo-Thomas remained in good heart: 'Strange as it may seem, and almost unbelievable, I was not in the

least bit nervous at the idea of thrusting my head in the lion's jaw –
on the contrary, the nearer I got to the date of departure, the cooler
and more confident I felt.'

At last, on 21 February, Yeo-Thomas and Dewavrin were told to be
on stand-by. A seemingly interminable wait of a few days followed
before they were told that the operation was on for the night of the
25th. Yeo-Thomas and Barbara went for a farewell lunch and at three
o'clock he left her to collect Dewavrin for the drive up to Tempsford
airfield, near Bedford. Their first stop was a holding station near to
the aerodrome where they were given a final check of their belongings
by the Conducting Officer. They changed out of their uniforms and
put on their 'French' clothes while their pockets were scrutinized for
any incriminating documents. More sinister was the issuing of their
suicide pills, known as 'L' tablets, which they were assured would take
effect within five or six seconds after being swallowed. Yeo-Thomas
hid his in his waistcoat pocket while Dewavrin secreted his in a hollow
signet ring. The Frenchman may have had a more exotic hiding-place
than Yeo-Thomas, but he was to regret it. In keeping with SOE
procedure for agents going into the field, the two men were given
an excellent dinner by the commanding officer of the station. After
the meal, Dewavrin washed his face and hands, only to find that
the water had leaked into the ring and reacted with the cyanide pill.
His eyes and lips swelled up almost immediately and this accidental
poisoning almost threatened to force the cancellation of the operation. Dewavrin would have none of it, but took special care to wrap
a replacement tablet securely in cellophane.

After this scare, a car came to fetch them and drive them to the
airfield, where they were kitted out with their 'striptease' jumpsuits,
helmets, parachutes and a variety of survival aids. Another car then
arrived to collect them and drive them out to the runway where
a Halifax bomber awaited them. The aircraft took off shortly after
midnight and, although it encountered German anti-aircraft fire over
the French coast, it reached its approximate pinpoint near Orléans
without too much trouble. However, the pilot found the drop zone
obscured by cloud and, in spite of circling for half an hour in the
hope of spotting a signal from the ground, he was obliged to abort the
operation. They made a safe return to Tempsford, arriving at 4.30am
and went to bed for a few hours' sleep. There was little that they could
achieve by staying at Tempsford and, 'very anxious because if we did
not get off soon, we would have to wait until the next moon period,
and lose practically a month', they returned to London. Yeo-Thomas
may have been disappointed but, as Barbara understatedly wrote in her
diary, she was 'very happy to have him back' so unexpectedly. The
details of rearranging the flight were left to the BCRA, SIS and the

RAF, while Yeo-Thomas and Barbara enjoyed this unexpected time together. On the morning of 26 February, they were told that the flight was on again for that night. They had another farewell lunch, went shopping for a new hat for Barbara and then the car arrived to take Yeo-Thomas back once more to Tempsford. Barbara had little time to reflect upon his departure, for soon after he had left she went to the dentist and had a tooth extracted.

SIS provided Flying Officer Luce to act as Dewavrin's Conducting Officer, while the faithful Hutchison completed the party and performed the same duty for Yeo-Thomas.[12] This time everything went like clockwork and the captain of the Halifax, Pilot Officer Foster, managed to locate the new drop zone near Lyons-la-Forêt in Normandy without difficulty. The two agents were told to stand by, hooked up their static lines (for the automatic opening of their parachutes) and, as the red light on the bulkhead switched to green, Dewavrin slipped out of the hole in the fuselage, followed by Yeo-Thomas.

Yeo-Thomas's first experience on landing did little for his confidence. A man appeared from out of the darkness and, clasping him by the hand, asked *'C'est vous, Shelley?'* ('Are you Shelley?') Unhesitatingly, Yeo-Thomas answered in the affirmative, although he had no idea why he was being addressed in this manner. Only subsequently did he learn that this was the codename that had been bestowed upon him by SIS. The four-man reception committee had been laid on by Olivier Jacques Courtaud ('Jacot') of Renault's Confrérie Notre Dame and they had unilaterally added to Yeo-Thomas's growing list of *noms de guerre*.

When they had collected their various packages, Courtaud informed them that they had a fifteen-kilometre bicycle ride to their safe house. If challenged by anyone, they were to pretend to be revellers returning from a wedding celebration. To prevent this cover story being compromised in the event of a search, they handed over their pistols to the reception committee. This security measure proved to be a waste of time for, when they eventually reached their sanctuary (after a bike ride that saw Yeo-Thomas's five-feet-eight-inch-frame unevenly matched against a bike built for a giant), they found that Dewavrin had picked up, not his own case, but one carrying a positive arsenal of guns and explosives.

Not for the last time was Yeo-Thomas to reflect upon the bravery, hospitality and generosity of his French hosts. Roger Vinay, the Lyons-la-Forêt pharmacist, and his wife, Denise, welcomed them with a feast of French cooking that belied the food rationing of the time: 'These people who risked everything, day after day, night after night, week in week out, looked upon us as heroes, as St Georges falling from heaven to slay the dragons, and tried to express their gratitude by giving us the sort of food that they never had themselves. When we realized this, later on, we felt very small and humble and were filled with awe and admiration for these people.'

The next day Yeo-Thomas and Dewavrin were taken to Rouen to catch the train to Paris. It was an unsettling experience for the Englishman to see France under occupation. He had to learn the new ways of rationing, not to ask for a *'café crème'* when no cream was available, to remember that 'meatless days' made anyone asking for such food liable to interrogation, and, of course, to respect the wide range of travel restrictions, and carry the necessary identity papers. These were everyday routines that Yeo-Thomas would quickly have to recognize but he still had much to learn in the art of dissimulation. As he and his colleagues killed some time in a café, Courtaud noticed the look of open contempt and hostility Yeo-Thomas was showing towards some nearby Germans. He wasted no time in warning him to keep his feelings in check. It was a lesson well learnt, according to Yeo-Thomas: 'I swallowed my drink and my wrath and deciding that I must control myself better, acquired a pose of studied indifference to the Hun.'

The journey to Paris passed without any incident and they arrived at 8.30pm. Although both men knew the city well, Courtaud was still acting as their guide and he led them to an apartment in the rue de la Faisanderie where Brossolette was waiting for them. The apartment belonged to Claire Davinroy, a schoolteacher and long-time friend of Brossolette's, and was a highly unusual location for so secret a reunion. The block of flats was almost exclusively occupied by members of the Gestapo and, paradoxically, was a secure haven for, as Yeo-Thomas later wrote: 'We therefore could hardly be safer, for who would suspect Allied agents of chosing such an environment.' After a brief council of war, it was decided that Dewavrin would stay with Brossolette, while Yeo-Thomas was taken to a nearby flat belonging to Roland Farjon, the son of Roger Farjon, a distinguished French politician and former Vice-President of the Senate.

The next day Yeo-Thomas left the Farjons' early in the morning and spent a couple of hours reacquainting himself with the sights and sounds of Paris. He was shocked by the all-pervading drabness that surrounded him: the absence of taxis and non-military traffic, the empty shops, the bedraggled passersby and the appalling coffee and liquid saccharine served in the cafés. He could not resist the urge to move towards the Passy métro station from whence he might observe his father's apartment, hoping to catch a glimpse of him for the first time in two and a half years. His walk also provided him with the first test of his false identity papers when he suddenly found himself faced by a line of French police and German troops blocking the street ahead.

> They worked in couples, one German, one French . . . I showed my card. It was opened, my photograph and description glanced over, then I felt two pairs of eyes going over me, whilst I tried to look unconcerned and at ease. The suspense was terrific, was there anything wrong? . . . had they any suspicions? . . . the seconds seemed like centuries . . . then my identity card was returned to me, and I heard the German say, *'Gut'* . . . the suspense was over and I was safely through my first experience of checking up by the police. This gave me enormous confidence. Obviously my card was a first-class forgery, it must have been, I could trust in it.

This examination passed without the slightest suspicion, though Yeo-Thomas was disconcerted to find that an identical experience awaited him around the corner in the place Victor Hugo.

At eleven o'clock, he made his rendezvous with Brossolette and Dewavrin at the Porte Maillot. They immediately went to an apartment in the avenue des Ternes, the home of Hélène Peyronnet, Brossolette's cousin. This was to become something of a headquarters for the three agents, serving as a refuge and secure meeting-place where they could take their meals and discuss their plans without fear of being overheard. Nevertheless, they each needed their own safe house and, by the end of the day, Madame Peyronnet had found them lodgings with trusted friends. Yeo-Thomas was allocated a flat in the rue Casimir Pinel in Neuilly that belonged to the actress Jeanne Helbling, while the other two were to share an apartment in the rue Marcel Renaud.

Dewavrin had many matters to attend to of a purely intelligence nature and, while he set about these tasks, his colleagues concentrated on making contact with the agents responsible for the parachute grounds and the storage of weapons and explosives. Yeo-Thomas had already met several of these men, such as Michel Pichard, Jean Ayral and Jean-Pierre Deshayes, in England, and there was therefore an existing trust and respect upon which he could build.

On 2 March, they had their first interview with a representative of a resistance group. This was Colonel Alfred Touny, of the Organisation Civile et Militaire (OCM). This proved to be only an initial contact and, two days later, a full meeting was convened at Claire Davinroy's flat where Touny brought his main assistants, including Roland Farjon, Yeo-Thomas's erstwhile host. The discussions with this influential and well-organized group went smoothly and Touny promised to supply the emissaries from London with all the details that they requested.

Meanwhile, they had also met up with Colonel Henri Manhès (with whom it was originally intended that Yeo-Thomas should travel to France). This proved to be a far less satisfactory encounter, with Manhès's personal bravery failing to compensate for his grandiose schemes for resistance action or, in the opinion of Yeo-Thomas, for the questionable attitude of his assistant, Pierre Meunier. It was clearly going to be an uphill struggle to pull a variety of dedicated and strong-willed resisters into line. Brossolette's acerbic tongue often gave offence and there was a resentment among others that the ARQUEBUSE-BRUMAIRE mission was undoing the arrangements already put in place by Jean Moulin. As an observer of these French arguments, Yeo-Thomas gained the impression that Manhès had only reluctantly agreed to the very specific instructions that the resistance's action programme was to be coordinated from London. However, the latter had little time to reflect on his disappointment, for within twenty-four hours, he was arrested. Yeo-Thomas's recognition of Manhès's bravery was not misplaced, for although tortured he did not give anyone away.[13] After making a report to Dewavrin, Meunier sensibly went to ground but was later to emerge and play a full part in subsequent discussions.

The agents' next contact was very different and obliged Yeo-Thomas's to display an ability to subdue his own political beliefs in the interests of his mission. The OCM effected an introduction to Georges Beaufils, known as 'Joseph', a representative of FANA, the intelligence branch of the Front National. 'In spite of having diametrically opposed ideas,' Yeo-Thomas 'got on quite well' with Beaufils and agreed to help create direct wireless communication between FANA and London.[14]

The resistance was now starting to develop and Yeo-Thomas was delighted to be playing a part. The OCM reported that some of their groups were ready to receive supply drops. Consequently, Michel Pichard, a trained organizer of air drops, was attached to them and later reported that suitable dropping grounds had been surveyed and met with his approval. As good as his word, Yeo-Thomas sent a message to London via a BCRA wireless, requesting that supply drops be arranged for these new grounds. To his great delight, four successful operations took place in March, greatly boosting morale and, although by now it scarcely needed it, substantially elevating Yeo-Thomas's reputation among the resisters.

The list of contacts grew longer when, on 7 March, Jacques Lecompte-Boinet, the leader of the Ceux de la Résistance movement, paid a call. A somewhat retiring, professorial figure, Lecompte-Boinet

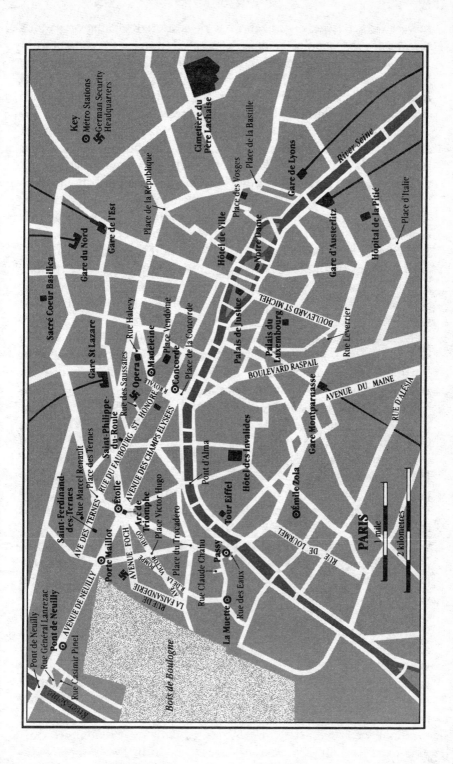

represented a large organization with scattered groups in various regions of the Occupied Zone. He accepted the need for control from London 'and arrangements were rapidly made to implement our instructions'. The next resistance leader beating a path to the men from London was Roger Coquoin of Ceux de la Libération. Once again, this well-connected organization recognized the need to co-ordinate its efforts with London's plans. Primarily based in the Paris area, it also claimed supporters in influential bodies, such as the police, fire brigade, *Garde Mobile* and road transport administration.

Less impressive was Libération, whose primary role was the gathering of intelligence. Neither its leader, Brunschwig, nor its military wing created a great impression on Yeo-Thomas: 'It was mainly of a civil nature but has now turned its attention to paramilitary matters. It is, however, far behind the other groups in this respect and, during conversations with its heads, the paramilitary chief very frankly informed us that he had only been in this position for three weeks and could not say what his troops numbered, what their quality was or where they were located.'

A far more substantial introduction now followed from Beaufils who arranged for them to meet Pierre Ginzburger, the leader in northern France of the Front National. Far from being a discreet briefing at which they would outline the London directive, Yeo-Thomas, Brossolette and Dewavrin found that they had been invited to attend a meeting of the organization's Comité Directeur. An elaborate route was taken to a villa near Sceaux in the south of the city that must surely have pleased the security-conscious Yeo-Thomas. Here they were surprised to discover an astonishing collection of people, ranging from communists to Catholic priests. Although Ginzburger took great pains to extol the martial exploits of the communists' Francs-Tireurs et Partisans, Dewavrin and Brossolette were given ample opportunity to propose that the Front National join in the growing association of resistance groups. Never a man for public-speaking, Yeo-Thomas did not address the meeting, leaving his French colleagues to deliver the necessary oration.

However, their work did not solely consist of high-level meetings with the leaders of organizations. They also regularly met with agents already sent from London and 'gave them fresh instructions, encouraged them, listened to their reports on progress made, complaints on various subjects, etc'. These meetings were held at locations throughout Paris and the exhausted agents walked miles to their appointments in order to avoid the risks attendant on using the métro. When the meetings were over, the work continued with the encoding of outgoing and incoming wireless messages brought by the couriers.

Amid all this work, Yeo-Thomas found the time to call on his old friend, José Dupuis. Before he left England, he had sent her an obliquely worded message over the BBC: *'De Tommy à José, nous boirons bientôt du bon vin de Chenin.'* ('From Tommy to José, we will soon drink some good Chenin wine.') She became Yeo-Thomas's first recruit in his own, exclusive *réseau* (network) that he had decided to create to give himself a core of reliable helpers. She was also able to tell him that his father had been arrested by the Gestapo and questioned about his son's whereabouts. In the light of his obstructive attitude, John Yeo-Thomas had been sent for four months to Fresnes prison in the southern suburbs of Paris. The good news was that he had been released as a result of his age and poor health, although he had returned home to find that his apartment had been looted by the Germans in his absence. His son resolved that, if José Dupuis felt that the risk was acceptable, he would visit him at the conclusion of his mission.

Yeo-Thomas's caution was well founded, for he had already had a brush with the ever present danger of enemy agents. Jean Ayral, one of the men sent to France with the help of RF Section, had been compromised and had to leave the city. However, he needed to be briefed by Dewavrin and Brossolette before making for the safety of the provinces. Yeo-Thomas therefore offered to meet him at a neutral rendezvous and escort him to his colleagues and, if he was being followed, to draw off his hostile companions. With his Colt .32 tucked under his arm and his 'L' tablet in his pocket, Yeo-Thomas set off for the meeting outside the Church of St Ferdinand des Ternes. Ayral, who was well known to him from his stay in London, arrived on time, but as they walked along the street, he explained that he was sure that he was being followed. A series of simple stratagems confirmed Ayral's suspicions, and it was therefore imperative that Yeo-Thomas entice their tail to follow him. Ostentatiously, he pretended to pocket a message and, at the place des Ternes, the two agents split up. The agent followed the Englishman who promptly led him a merry dance around the backstreets of St Philippe du Roule before losing him and heading back to meet his friends.

The ARQUEBUSE mission now awaited the arrival of de Gaulle's two emissaries, Moulin and Delestraint, who had returned to France on 21 March, but had been preoccupied by affairs in the south. In order profitably to occupy their time while they waited, Dewavrin and Yeo-Thomas decided to leave the capital and continue their survey of the resistance in the provinces. While the Frenchman went north, the Englishman, accompanied by Pichard, headed for the *départements* of the Nièvre, Cher and Allier. Things got off to a particularly bad start when, as the train for Nevers pulled out of the station, a one-time acquaintance from Yeo-Thomas's pre-war life entered his compartment. To make matters worse, he remembered that this unwanted travelling companion had held strongly pro-German and anti-British opinions. After a long period of scrutiny, the newcomer asked if they had met before and Yeo-Thomas affirmed that they most certainly had not. A lengthy conversation ensued about the surprising incidence of 'doubles'. Thankfully, Yeo-Thomas was able to maintain his defences until, with great relief, he left the train at Nevers.

The situation in the region proved to be most encouraging. Pichard introduced him to a remarkable resistance leader named Courvoisier ('Napoléon') who escorted the two men around the area for three days. The resistance boasted a strong element among the local *gendarmerie* and Yeo-Thomas was asked to give them a pep-talk: 'I had weighed the dangers carefully and considered that I was justified, as the moral effect would be considerable, particularly because a British officer who spoke of de Gaulle as the only leader of the French, would exert more influence, and help to combat the deplorable consequences of the 'Giraud affair' which very nearly wrecked French Resistance.[15] The talk was a great success, and my right hand ached for days afterwards from the vigorous handshakes I got.'

The trip was not all hard work, however. While visiting members of the reception committees in the Pouilly area, Yeo-Thomas and Pichard were asked to taste some of the local wines. In principle this was an act of public relations well within their capabilities until their host then explained that there were twenty-one wines to taste. This mammoth task competed, they found themselves obliged to visit the cellars of two more resisters. There had been no training for this at SOE's schools, but Yeo-Thomas handled it manfully and 'on the way back to Nevers we stuck our heads out [of the van] and managed to get back in fairly good shape'. However, their rural expedition proved to be merely a warm-up for the main event.

Our headquarters in Nevers were situated in the house of a 'Charcutier' . . . and when we reached there we found preparations going on for a feast in our honour . . . no getting away from it either! So we had to face another ordeal. The old boy who owned the business, a small, thin, grey-haired man of about sixty-five, but as active and chirpy as a cricket, disappeared into the cellar, reappearing with a basket containing half a dozen bottles covered with cobwebs, among them a bottle of pre-war Pernod. We had to partake of it . . . we then slogged through a terrific dinner, washed down with white wine, red wine, champagne and ending with coffee and liqueurs.

I felt like a Python by the time it was over. It was then about

10pm, Pichard and I were catching the 5am train to Paris. We were worn out! Then to our dismay, another of the Area leaders turned up. He was the 'Forestry Officer' of the region, and a most active and invaluable official. He insisted on us coming to his house where a couple of his assistants were waiting to meet us. So we went, and since he was an Alsatian, we had to partake of Alsatian wines and Mirabelle. We managed to stagger to the 'Hairdressing Saloon' where we were to spend the night, just before curfew, at 11.55pm. This had been a most exhausting day, our heads ached and we had the most appalling attack of indigestion you could imagine. How we managed to get through the day, I shall never know, we were almost killed by hospitality.

Yeo-Thomas recovered sufficiently to make his way back to Paris but he did not stay in the city long. His next task was to travel to the Unoccupied Zone and interview leading politicians and military men. He was bound for Lyon to make contact with Édouard Herriot, the former Prime Minister, leader of the Radical Party, President of the Chamber of Deputies and Mayor of Lyon. Herriot had played an equivocal role following the fall of France, but it was felt that a politician with such credentials should be sounded out as to his current opinions. However, Herriot had been placed *en résidence surveillée* (house arrest) by the Vichy authorities the year before, and Yeo-Thomas had to make do with Jules Jullien, Herriot's friend and former Ministre des Postes, Télégraphes et Téléphones. The interview was none too illuminating and merely confirmed that the pre-war politicians had little to offer the resistance. Nothing daunted, Yeo-Thomas left Lyon for Grenoble to contact Jules Jeanneney, the former President of the Senate. However, Yeo-Thomas found him in a poor physical condition and, although he was willing to come to Britain, his family demanded that they accompany him.

The succession of failure continued when he tried to make contact with an army colonel in whom Dewavrin was interested. It transpired that the officer was dogmatically loyal to Pétain and, after a heated argument about the nature of loyalty, Yeo-Thomas took his leave and returned to Paris.

After so unproductive an excursion, it was particularly good for Yeo-Thomas to rejoin his friends. The bond between the three men had now grown very strong and Yeo-Thomas has left a very evocative record of their life at this time:

When I look back on those days, I can picture the daily talks we had. They always took place in the evenings, in the flat occupied by Passy and Brossolette in rue Marcel Renaud, in a small back room where there was a wood-burning Mirus stove. Heating was a problem as fuel of any description was scarce . . . electricity and gas were so reduced and rationed that electric or gas radiators were impossible to use. We managed to get a little wood in the blackmarket, and our greatest luxury was a fire in this room at nights. Col Passy would sit in an old armchair on one side of the stove, I would sit in another armchair on the opposite side, whilst Brossolette would sprawl full-length on the floor between us, as close as he could to the stove, as he was very fond of warmth and suffered much from the cold. I might add that the armchairs, being Louis XVI, were not very comfortable. We would discuss everything for hours. When he had gone over all the problems we had to deal with, we would either fall silent and think our own thoughts, or we would talk about our loved-ones, our plans for the future if we survived, the shape of things to come. Sometimes, Brossolette, who was a historian, would hold forth, and we would listen enthralled. We got on famously together, in spite of the abysmal fundamental differences in our upbringings. We had a common ideal, and each of us relied upon the two others . . . brothers could not have been closer than we were. There grew between us a bond that nothing short of death could break.

However, the three were doing far more than dreaming. On 23 March 1943, a crucial meeting took place at Jeanne Helbling's flat. Representatives of most of the leading resistance groups assembled to thrash out a declaration of common principles that could be submitted to their directing committees for approval. Three days later, they reconvened and the document was signed by Brunschwig (Libération Zone Nord), Lecompte-Boinet (Ceux de la Résistance), Coquoin (Ceux de la Libération), Touny (OCM) and Ginzburger (Front National).

At last, on 30 March, Moulin arrived, although Delestraint was to remain in the south for more than a week. Sadly, it was not long before Brossolette and Moulin were at daggers drawn, their specific differences of opinion over policy being exacerbated by a clash of personalities, and by often mischievous rumour-mongering by their adherents. At one point, Dewavrin feared that the intense nature of their argument would have Claire Davinroy's Gestapo neighbours intervening. In spite of their personal enmity, the two men managed to effect a united front (or at least the appearance of one) when they met with the representatives of the various groups. At last, with the arrival of Delestraint, another full meeting of the various delegates was convened on 12 April and, in spite of some not unexpected intransigence on the part of the Francs-Tireurs et Partisans, the meeting was deemed to be a success.

The work of the ARQUEBUSE/BRUMAIRE/SEAHORSE mission was drawing to a close, but there still remained time for discussions with representatives of the trade unions, including Louis Saillant of the Confédération Générale du Travail (CGT) and Gaston Tessier of the Confédération Française de Travailleurs Chrétiens (CFTC). They also spoke to a small group of young resisters who had published an illegal newspaper, *Défense de la France*, and recommended that they join Ceux de la Résistance, from whom they could anticipate receiving funds from London to continue their work.

On a personal note, the conclusion of the mission meant that Yeo-Thomas could now take the risk of seeing his father. He disguised himself with a pair of glasses and, following the instructions of José Dupuis, rang the front door bell five times to signal that he was a friend. Their reunion was apparently without emotion until, safely ensconced in the drawing-room, Yeo-Thomas's father enquired: 'What the bloody hell have you been doing for the last two years, you ought to have been over here ages ago.' The apparent irascibility probably masked a more sensitive emotion and the two men spent quite some time catching up with each other's news, while remembering not to disclose any secrets that might unnecessarily endanger the other. The son gave the father money, cigarettes, tea, coffee and sugar before taking his leave.

Having sent word to London of their wish to be exfiltrated, on 14 April Yeo-Thomas received a message that they were to be picked up by Lysander near Lyons-la-Forêt the following night. It was to be a double aircraft operation for their party now included 'Jargon', a wireless operator, and Captain John Ryan, a downed American pilot, who had made contact with members of the CND.[16]

Elaborate precautions were taken to protect the airman from having to respond to any questions during their journey to Normandy and all went well until Yeo-Thomas, of all people, suffered a surprising lapse of concentration. To celebrate their safe arrival at the Pont de l'Arche station on the outskirts of Rouen, Yeo-Thomas ordered beers for Ryan and himself at the station buffet. However, when the time came to pay, he could not find his wallet and spat out the Anglo-Saxon, 'Where the hell is my bloody money?' Fortunately, the noise in the station prevented his outburst being noticed and they safely caught their train to Fleury-sur-Andelle. There they encountered the bane of Yeo-Thomas's clandestine life – bicycles – and pedalled to Lyons-la-Forêt where they were looked after by the same reception committee that had received them. Yeo-Thomas and

Ryan hid up throughout the next day until that evening they were taken to the landing ground (codename 'Pamplemousse'), where they met up with Dewavrin, Brossolette and 'Jargon'. The two Lysanders appeared right on time and, in less than two minutes, Yeo-Thomas, Ryan and 'Jargon' were in the air. A quarter of an hour later, the second Lysander landed and picked up Dewavrin and Brossolette.[17] The flight lasted barely an hour and they touched down at Tangmere at 1.30am. After a few drinks with their pilots, Flying Officers McCairns and Vaughan-Fowler, they were driven back to London.[18] Yeo-Thomas merely records being 'happy and tired' about his return and that Barbara 'was anxiously awaiting him'. She had received advance notice of his imminent return the day before with a telephone call from the Free French that was later confirmed by Johnson of RF Section. However, any privacy surrounding their reunion was to be short-lived. Yeo-Thomas arrived home at 6.30am and, half an hour later, Johnson called round for him. It was business as usual.

CHAPTER FIVE

• The Second Mission — Operation MARIE-CLAIRE •

Yeo-Thomas seemed to shed the strain of his two months in France pretty quickly. Lunching with Barbara and Johnson on his first day back in London was particularly pleasant as he reflected: 'It was quite relaxing not having to be constantly on the alert, not having to worry about being followed.' This was to be just the first of a constant round of celebratory meals and drinks parties with Barbara, his friends in the BCRA and colleagues in SOE. These culminated in a special dinner hosted by Robin Brook and Hutchison at the Mayfair Hotel where the guests of honour, Yeo-Thomas, Dewavrin and Brossolette, were joined by Manuel and Lagier of the BCRA.

It was not all play, however, and Yeo-Thomas had to make verbal presentations to Hutchison, Brook and Gubbins before writing his formal report. This was completed a fortnight after his return from France and was supplemented by a special note to Robin Brook concerning his misgivings regarding Moulin's attempts to maintain control of the 'Secret Army' and of Delestraint. It would be easy to interpret this critique as a continuation of the arguments that had taken place in Paris between Moulin and Brossolette. While it cannot be denied that Yeo-Thomas had formed a close personal attachment to Brossolette and identified himself closely with his friend's opinions, his assessment is demonstrably his own. He was particularly concerned that the strength of Moulin's personality was dominating the debate: 'I had the impression, which I found afterwards was shared by all the heads of the groups, that Général Vidal [Delestraint] was absolutely under Rex's [Moulin's] thumb. During the general meeting, at which I was present, Général Vidal was hardly able to say a word as directly he opened his mouth, Rex cut him short.'

While Yeo-Thomas praised the 'undoubted abilities of Rex as a civil administrator and organizer', he questioned the wisdom of having so forceful a character intervening in the creation of the 'Secret Army'. Furthermore, he felt that Moulin's experience of the resistance in the former Unoccupied Zone did not ideally equip him to analyse the situation in the north. Yeo-Thomas therefore proposed that London nominate a chief-of-staff for the 'Armée Secrète' and send him to France in order to dilute Moulin's influence and provide a better balance.

Brook was pleased with the report, as was Sir Charles Hambro, Nelson's replacement as executive head of SOE, who commented to

Sir Desmond Morton, Churchill's adviser on matters relating to France, that Yeo-Thomas was level-headed and sensible, 'although you will see from his report that he is pro de Gaullist.' On the other hand, Yeo-Thomas was not quite so impressed with his superior and noted in his diary that their meeting was a 'lot of balls'. This observation may have been less a reflection on Hambro and more an expression of Yeo-Thomas's increasing frustration at the inability of staff officers to appreciate the realities of life at the sharp end:

> It was impossible for people who had not lived the clandestine life of an agent, to realize how sensitive one became. They could not always appreciate that seemingly simple things were frequently very complicated and difficult to do. One of the most difficult things to make them understand was the slowness and precariousness of communications. Our Home W/T stations were constantly complaining about our operators in the field, and our decoding section also moaned about coding errors or mutilations. It was not because they did not want to understand but because they were quite incapable of realizing what it meant to, first of all encode a message, then tap it out, all the time keeping one's eyes and ears attuned to the possible approach of danger, in the shape of a raid or a D/F car.

On Thursday, 20 May 1943, Yeo-Thomas was summoned to an audience with Général de Gaulle who had asked to see the British officer who had featured so largely in Dewavrin's report on the ARQUEBUSE mission. It was the first meeting of the two men and, according to Yeo-Thomas, the General shook his hand, congratulated him, thanked him and asked him a few questions. Yeo-Thomas was 'very much struck by his rather gruff way of speaking' and that 'he seemed bigger than ever, and I had to look up at him, feeling rather like a Pigmy'. Stature was not all, however, and Yeo-Thomas noted in his diary that de Gaulle 'was a big man in every way'.

In spite of his newfound 'celebrity' status, Yeo-Thomas was soon immersed in the everyday life of RF Section. His diary is full of allusions to 'busy days', including the entry of 26 May: 'Miss Block ill – two secretaries away ill – Kay Moore on leave – PW in hospital – Hutch and Storrs away – Johnny away. What a life.'

It was therefore perhaps not surprising that Yeo-Thomas should have sought a return to 'active' duty. In spite of his promise to Barbara that he would only once undertake a mission to France, he was clearly agitating for just such a course of action. On 31 May, Hutchison wrote to Brook requesting 'a ruling on a possible further visit by RF/P [Yeo-Thomas] to the *Zone Occupée* at a fairly early date'. He added that

Yeo-Thomas was 'quite anxious to undertake the mission again'. The operational objectives were ostensibly to update the information gleaned from the SEAHORSE mission and formulate an assessment of the capabilities and requirements of the resistance groups. It was also felt that French morale had been uplifted by the first trip and that the second visit of a British officer 'would have equally happy results'. The impression left by the memorandum is of Yeo-Thomas manipulating Hutchison into recommending him for another mission, which was not strictly necessary. The drudgery of office work at Dorset Square must have lain heavily upon a man who had experienced the rush of adrenalin brought on by clandestine life. Hutchison was singularly sympathetic to Yeo-Thomas's feelings, for he, too, desired a more active role in the war.[1] He was therefore later able to write with some feeling of the driving force behind his colleague:

> Gradually I came to realize that to many people danger is a drug. Dostoevsky, in *Possessed*, writes of a sect of Russians to whom danger had become a physical craving. 'The conquest of fear was what fascinated them,' he explains, and I am sure that for some people this is true. It has excitement and a sense of achievement and there have been many cases where our volunteers, having courted danger and overcome it, had the greatest difficulty in settling down to humdrum dangerless life. They longed to get back into a task where the peril was even greater. Tommy Yeo-Thomas, the 'White Rabbit', was such a case. When he came back from a mission to France, he thought restlessly of how he could justify another, although each time that he went the risks were greater, for on each visit some more traces must inevitably be left behind. Yet he still wanted to go and such was his experience and his efficiency that he persuaded the authorities to let him do so.[2]

Such was Yeo-Thomas's desire to re-enter the fray that his fertile brain came up with a scheme that made his plan to seize Molyneux's yacht seem positively mundane. On 18 June 1943, he submitted a proposal to 'dispose' of Grossadmiral Karl Doenitz, the Commander-in-Chief of the German Navy. Yeo-Thomas had noted that Doenitz made frequent journeys, protected by only a small escort, between his headquarters in Paris and outstations in Cherbourg and Angoulême. He concluded that, with the assistance of Gilbert Védy of Ceux de la Libération, it was 'quite feasible to hold up the three cars, dispose of the escort, capture Admiral Doenitz alive, and bring him back to England'. SOE did not share Yeo-Thomas's view of the plan's feasibility and it was not adopted.

At a time when he felt frustrated and restless, the Free French's decision to award him the Croix de Guerre avec Palme should have been the cause of some gratification, but this apparently joyous event ushered in another clash with Whitehall officialdom. The Air Ministry had to approve the award of the decoration before Yeo-Thomas could wear the ribbon on his tunic. After some delay, the approval was denied on the grounds that de Gaulle did not have the right to make such an award. As the French began to question why Yeo-Thomas was not displaying the medal, Hutchison took up the cudgels on his officer's behalf and maintained that the Admiralty had set a precedent of acceptance of the medal. Nevertheless, the bureaucrats fought on with a stubbornness that would have made them assets on the battlefield rather than as pedants in the corridors of Whitehall, and it was only on 18 October 1943 that the Air Ministry issued its formal approval.

British recognition of Yeo-Thomas's service was equally mismanaged. He and Barbara took a holiday in the West Country and, on 19 June, were delighted to receive telegrams from his SOE and BCRA colleagues congratulating him on the award of the Military Cross. Hutchison wrote to him two days later that 'the Section is pleased and proud', but the pleasure and pride were to be short-lived. The Section Head had appeared to have confused a 'recommendation' for the decoration with its award and his premature announcement to Yeo-Thomas and all concerned was to cause further embarrassment as the Air Ministry pondered over its decision.

Yeo-Thomas was now as much a part of the Free French world as any of de Gaulle's staff. He and Barbara took special care to welcome newcomers to England, such as Valentin Abeille, who had recently escaped from France by Lysander. He was invited to dinner and called at their flat with a folded newspaper held mysteriously behind his back. When asked if he would like to put it on the table, he declined. When Yeo-Thomas suggested that he put it in his pocket, he also refused, and eventually admitted that he had torn the seat of his trousers when getting into the plane and had no other clothes. Once he had finished laughing, Yeo-Thomas gave him a pair of his own that ensured Abeille was decently dressed, even if the trousers stopped halfway up his leg.

While Yeo-Thomas continued his battle with the paperwork of Dorset Square and lectured at SOE's training schools on the experience of life in enemy territory, Moulin and Delestraint were continuing the work in France. On 27 May 1943, they had convened the first meeting of the Conseil National de la Résistance, marking a major step in the establishment of an effective and truly national resistance. The euphoria at this achievement was soon to be rudely shattered. On 9 June, Delestraint was arrested at La Muette métro station in Paris. Robert Moog and Jean Multon, two Frenchmen in the pay of the Abwehr and SD, had discovered a secret 'letter box' in Lyon used by René Hardy, the leader of the Résistance-Fer railway sabotage organization. They intercepted an uncoded message to Hardy, asking him to meet Delestraint at La Muette and consequently were able to arrest the former at Chalon-sur-Saône en route to Paris. They then went on to Paris and captured Delestraint and three of his aides. Moulin was in Lyon when he received the news of this disaster and called a meeting of leading members of the nascent 'Secret Army' to discuss the crisis.

If the arrest of Delestraint had been a calamity, events that soon unfolded in the Lyon suburb of Caluire were to prove positively catastrophic. On 21 June 1943, eight of the most prominent members of the French resistance met at the house of Dr Frédéric Dugoujon. Scarcely had the last of them arrived when a squad of SD men led by SS-Obersturmführer Klaus Barbie burst in. At first it seemed as if Moulin might escape detection for, as 'Jacques Martel', he was sitting in the doctor's waiting room when the Germans entered. But everyone found in the house was deemed to be suspect and, along with the others, he was taken for interrogation to Barbie's headquarters in the former École du Service de Santé Militaire.[3] For two days the men captured at Caluire maintained their silence, but eventually one of them broke and Barbie turned his attention to 'Jacques Martel'. Moulin remained resolutely silent under the most extreme torture and, when seen by Christian Pineau, another prisoner, he was barely recognizable: 'Imagine my stupefaction, my horror, when I recognized the man stretched out on the bench as none other than Max [sic] Moulin. He had lost consciousness; his hollowed eyes seemed to be sunken in his head. There was a filthy bluish wound on his temple. A soft, rasping sound escaped from his swollen lips.'[4]

Frustration, desperation and sadism drove Barbie to continue the torture of his captive until Moulin passed into a coma. Perhaps realizing that he had gone too far, Barbie drove with Moulin to Paris in order to report to SS-Stürmbannführer Karl Boemelburg, the head of the SD's counter-espionage branch. Moulin, however, was already on the brink of death and incapable of being any possible use to his persecutors. He was sent by train to Germany 'for further questioning' but died en route at Metz on 8 July.

The man left to deal with the crisis precipitated by the arrest of Moulin was Capitaine Claude Bouchinet-Serreulles, a young French Army officer who had served in London as one of de Gaulle's aides-de-camp. He had pressed his superiors for a more active posting and had succeeded in gaining a transfer into the BCRA. After a crash course learning the skills of clandestine life,[5] he was landed in France

by an RAF Hudson aircraft on operation KNUCKLEDUSTER on the
night of 15/16 June 1943, with orders to act as Moulin's assistant.
Events were rapidly to overtake him. He made his way to Lyon,
arriving there on the 19th and, on the same day, holding his first
meeting with his superior. It was to prove a tense and far from happy
street-corner rendezvous. Moulin appeared tired, nervous and,
understandably, preoccupied with the ramifications of Delestraint's
arrest. Furthermore, he had expected Serreulles two months earlier
and clearly felt that his arrival then would have obviated much of his
present predicament. To complete the lack of harmony, Moulin was
suspicious of the influence of Dewavrin and resented what he felt was
an attempt to interfere in his work. In spite of this rather frosty
conversation, Serreulles was at least able to brief Moulin upon recent
events in Algiers, where the Comité Français de Libération Nationale
(CFLN) had been formed. The two men dined together the following night and met a third time on the morning of the 21st, when
Moulin announced that he wished Serreulles to attend the meeting to
be held that afternoon at Caluire.

Serreulles's mission had not had a particularly auspicious start. It
would have had an even worse ending had he made his fourth rendezvous with Moulin, for he would then have found himself caught
up in the disaster at Dr Dugoujon's. The circumstances of Serreulles's
escape were in keeping with the remarkable string of lucky breaks that
characterized his clandestine career. At 1pm he arrived, as instructed,
at the top station of a cable railway overlooking the city. When, after
waiting for twenty minutes, there was still no sign of his contact he
aborted the rendezvous. Meanwhile, at the bottom cable station,
Serreulles's contacts awaited him until, at 1.45pm, they in turn gave
up and proceeded to the fateful Caluire meeting. The subsequent
German raid and wholesale arrests could have done little for even the
strongest-nerved of agents, let alone a young staff officer on his first
mission, and one who was described by Henri Frenay of the Combat
organization as 'still wet behind the ears as far as the underground
was concerned'.

Two months after Serreulles's arrival in France, while he was
attempting to set up his own organization in Paris, another leading
figure appeared on the scene. This was Jacques Bingen, like Serreulles
a senior member of de Gaulle's headquarters and a one-time head of
the Free French Merchant Navy. He, too, had sought a transfer to
more active duties and, in the spring of 1942, joined the BCRA.
Bingen had hoped to work with Moulin in France, but the arrests at
Caluire forced an alteration to his plans. On the night of 15/16
August 1943, he was landed by Lysander as the accredited CFLN
delegate for the former Unoccupied Zone. It was an awesome

responsibility for these two novices in the secret world to try to make some order out of the chaos that followed Moulin's disappearance.

Resistance activity in France had by no means ground to a halt, however, and agents of the Bureau d'Opérations Aériennes (BOA) maintained regular contact with London, advising on the status of landing grounds, drop zones and reception committees. However, confounding the BOA's endeavours was an overall resistance organization that was at best confused and, at worst, shambolic. Even the military leaders appointed by de Gaulle, the Délégués Militaires Régionaux (DMR), reported that they could achieve little in their endeavours to create the 'Secret Army' for lack of cooperation from the separate resistance movements. In contrast, Serreulles and Bingen were sending long wireless messages to London, affirming that all was well and progressing to plan. These two conflicting assessments aroused concern in London, and indicated that Yeo-Thomas and Brossolette would have to carry out a new fact-finding mission to identify the true state of affairs.

As early as 13 July, Dewavrin had proposed to SOE that Yeo-Thomas be made available for a joint mission with Brossolette. Later that day Hutchison sent a memo to Robin Brook, summarizing the basic reasons for the operation, and adding some suggestions of his own. At this stage, the main purpose was to assist Serreulles in implementing Moulin's plans 'in the setting up of the organization in the north, along the lines recently agreed, of regionalizing paramilitary and especially D-Day activities'. Further objectives were to include liaising with the Front National, providing an updated analysis of resistance in the Occupied Zone, and compiling a damage assessment following the arrest of Moulin. Hutchison concluded by agreeing to Brook's suggestion that Yeo-Thomas's absence from SOE Headquarters in Baker Street should be explained by claiming that he had been sent on a liaison mission to the United States.

Weeks of briefings and discussions ensued before, on 6 September, Yeo-Thomas received his orders for the mission, which was code-named MARIE-CLAIRE. But this was far from the end of the arrangements for, crucially, it was by no means certain that Brossolette would be able to accompany him. His comrade-in-arms and close friend had left for Algiers on 13 August, and it was doubtful whether he would be free to take part in the mission. Brossolette's most likely replacement was Lieutenant-Colonel Paul Marchal (variously codenamed 'Morinaud', 'Hussard', 'Moncey', 'Riquet', 'Moreau' and 'Masséna'), a choice that Yeo-Thomas, in his own words, 'was not all that keen on'. Although unquestionably courageous, Marchal was too well known in France to escape attention; furthermore, Yeo-Thomas felt that the Frenchman's recklessness could only increase the likelihood of his being recognized. Significantly, his opinions had been expressed to Hutchison at an earlier meeting, long before there had been any question of his having to collaborate with Marchal. In the end, however, the problem was avoided with Brossolette's recall and departure from North Africa on 19 September and the reunion in London of the two friends.

If the personnel were confirmed, a host of others details still awaited resolution. SOE allocated the codenames 'Marie-Claire' and 'Marie-Claire II' to Yeo-Thomas and Brossolette respectively, while the BCRA nominated them 'Magino' and 'Briand'. SOE's Documents Section was also kept busy creating a fresh set of papers in the name 'Tirelli' to add to Yeo-Thomas's existing 'Thierry' collection. Meanwhile, the Codes Section initiated him in the use of SOE's new and very secure system of one-time pads. Using keys printed on silk which, once used, were to be destroyed, he could look forward to a much more reliable means of encoding his messages than hitherto. Obviously the pads posed a problem of concealment but this was resolved by incorporating them into the lining of a leatherbound pocket chess set. It was decided not to send the party in by parachute but deliver them by Lysander aircraft. They were to be taken to a landing ground south of Angoulême, where a reception committee would be waiting.

At 1am on Saturday, 18 September 1943, Yeo-Thomas was informed that both the RAF and the reception committee in France had confirmed all the arrangements. The operation was on for that night. Hardly surprisingly, Barbara was, in Yeo-Thomas's words, 'rather nervous at the idea of my departure', and she persuaded him to have his photograph taken at Mannells of Baker Street as a keepsake. The session completed, they went to lunch at one of their favourite restaurants, La Coquille, where they were both 'rather quiet', although he did his best to cheer Barbara up. They returned to their apartment where he completed final checks of his papers until, at 4.30pm, an SOE car arrived to collect him, leaving Barbara to note starkly in her diary, 'feeling terrible'. Brossolette, sporting pepper-and-salt dyed hair and without his moustache, and Hutchison were picked up by the car and the party left London for Tangmere, taking a customary detour for drinks at the Spread Eagle Hotel in Midhurst.

At Tangmere, the agents took dinner with their pilot, Flight Lieutenant Peter Vaughan-Fowler, an old friend of Yeo-Thomas, who had been one of the Lysander pilots who had picked him up at the conclusion of his last mission. Even at this stage, there remained an element of uncertainty about the operation because of adverse weather reports from the station meteorologist, but Vaughan-Fowler, after consultation with his flight commander, Wing-Commander Guy

Lockhart, felt that the mission should be attempted. So, their meal over and the final checks completed, Yeo-Thomas and Brossolette bade farewell to Hutchison and climbed aboard the aeroplane. Crammed together in what was originally the gunner/observer's cockpit, along with a selection of parcels, packages and suitcase radios, the two men could not anticipate a comfortable flight. The weather conditions had not improved, with thick cloud and fog keeping the flight in jeopardy even after take-off. A different threat appeared as they crossed the French coast when anti-aircraft shells began to explode around them. Alerted by radar or sound locators, the German batteries were firing blind into the fog and cloud, but they were sufficiently threatening to oblige Vaughan-Fowler to carry out a series of evasive manoeuvres.

After almost an hour-and-a half's flight, a break in the cloud allowed them to regain sight of the ground, and Vaughan-Fowler glimpsed a large town which he identified as Poitiers. This greatly buoyed up Yeo-Thomas's spirits, and he was further encouraged at 1.25am by the sight of the landing lights laid out by the reception committee in a field near La Chapelle. Confirmation that it was safe to land came with the flashing of a Morse recognition signal so, having circled the field, Vaughan-Fowler began his approach. Hard though it is to believe, Yeo-Thomas was later to claim that the landing was so gentle that he did not know when they had touched down. Scarcely had the aircraft come to a halt than it was surrounded by members of the reception committee. Yeo-Thomas jumped out and started to catch the packages as Brossolette threw them down to him. Brossolette then joined him and, after a few brief words of greeting, was replaced in the Lysander cockpit by the return passenger, André Mercier, a leading member of the communist resistance. The chief of the reception committee, Jean Lapeyre-Mensignac (codenamed 'Clo' or 'François'), presented Vaughan-Fowler with a bottle of champagne and, with no more ado, and with the fog descending, the latter took off. Even though the unloading of the baggage had been held up when a suitcase became wedged in the cockpit, the Lysander had been on the ground for less than five minutes. Yeo-Thomas warned Lapeyre-Mensignac that a second Lysander was about to land, and moments later it appeared through the mist. Flying Officer Jimmy McCairns had considerably greater difficulty in landing, but managed to deliver his passengers and packages and take off again in less than three minutes. Yeo-Thomas recognized one of the new arrivals as 'Dunois', a young sabotage instructor whom he had helped to brief in England.

Apart from the mist, thus far all had gone perfectly, but a logistical problem soon loomed. The only transport for the agents, their baggage, and the entire reception committee was a rather dilapidated

Citroën motor car. This oversight became all the more important when it was revealed that the safe house that was their intended destination was some forty miles distant. A compromise of sorts had to be arranged and it was decided to take the bulk of the baggage, less the agents' suitcases, to a ruined house some fifteen miles away. In the meantime, Yeo-Thomas and Brossolette remained behind with a bodyguard, and tucked into the iron rations and flasks that SOE had provided.

At 3am, after an hour-and-a-half's wait, the car returned, but even without the luggage it was still a tight fit to cram nine armed men into it. Nevertheless, the human sardine tin set off, with Yeo-Thomas reflecting on precisely how the occupants would extract themselves, let alone offer a defence, if challenged for breaking the curfew. After a very uncomfortable forty-five-minute drive, an enforced stop was made when a tyre burst, just as they were passing through a village. The last vestiges of secrecy now vanished, with agents hiding in doorways and guards posted on the approaches, while the noisy process of changing the wheel took place. Hardly surprisingly, one of the inhabitants opened his window to see what was happening. Confronted with Yeo-Thomas's Colt pistol, his curiosity quickly evaporated – his shutters were hurriedly closed and his light extinguished. The agents could only hope that neither he nor his neighbours were moved to summon help from elsewhere. Before any further threats had to be made, however, they removed the wheel at last, only to discover that the spare tyre was flat. True to form, there was no pump; the sole remaining decision was whether driving fast or slow would be the best course of action. Throwing caution to the wind, they decided to press on as quickly as possible. The weight of the nine occupants did little for the tyre's condition, and the bumps in the road grew ever more pronounced until, with the car running on the wheel rim, they finally reached the safe house.

Safely ensconced and enjoying a substantial meal, Yeo-Thomas and Brossolette learnt from Lapeyre-Mensignac that this had been his first Lysander reception and that he had received scarcely any supply drops. Although disappointed at this news, this was neither the time nor the place for a debate on the difficulties of clandestine air supply and the two agents excused themselves and asked to be shown to their room. Warm feather beds awaited them and they were able to enjoy in comfort what remained of their first night in enemy territory.

Waking at ten o'clock, they devoured a breakfast made memorable by freshly baked white bread and a bottle of very potent Pinaud des Charentes. Fortified, they discussed with Lapeyre-Mensignac how to get to Paris. He recommended that they take the 6.30 train that evening from Châteauneuf-sur-Charente (fifteen miles away) to

Angoulême, followed by the Paris train at 1.30 the next morning. This settled, they spent the rest of the day eating and drinking with their hosts, acquainting them with the latest events in Britain. At 4pm, after fond farewells, they were taken by gig to Châteauneuf-sur-Charente.[6]

The only difficulties encountered in getting to Paris were those that regularly confronted even the most innocent of travellers in Occupied France. Early curfew at Angoulême meant that the two agents had to wait on the station platform, sitting on their cases and avoiding the downpour issuing from a leaky roof. They got little respite on the train for, finding it already packed with passengers, they had to stand all the way to Paris. Arriving at the Gare d'Austerlitz, they wasted no time in confirming the availability of their safe house. Using a simple system of passwords arranged during their last mission, they telephoned Madame Peyronnet and, on receiving the all-clear, went to her apartment at the rue des Ternes.

Their first priority was to contact Serreulles and Michel Pichard, now the senior air operations officer for the Northern Zone. Brossolette sent a message to Serreulles using a dead-letter drop that had been arranged during his last mission in Paris. Yeo-Thomas followed the same method by calling at the restaurant Chez Bosc, near the Madeleine, and leaving a verbal message for Pichard stating that he wished to arrange a meeting. The responses were quick in coming. Serreulles agreed to see the two agents at ten o'clock the next morning at his safe house in the rue de la Pompe. Pichard, however, had duties outside Paris and was unable to meet Yeo-Thomas until the following Friday, 24 September.

Most of the rest of the day was spent renewing contact with their sub-agents in the city and preparing fallback safe houses in case their lodgings at the Peyronnets' became compromised. José Dupuis was instructed to recruit couriers and locate safe houses. The Peyronnets' sixteen-year-old daughter, Poucette, became a useful courier, and she in turn introduced Suni Sandöe, a Danish teacher, into the circle. Sandöe's apartment in the rue Claude Chahu became an important rendezvous, as did that of a friend of Madame Peyronnet, Diana Provost. Other members of this feminine *réseau* were two sisters, Denise Martin and Nicole Bauer (re-christened 'Maud' by Yeo-Thomas), and their friend Jacqueline Devaux.

Yeo-Thomas's and Brossolette's combined experience of clandestine life clearly stood them in good stead. They had quickly established a tight cell of loyal, independent followers, willing to carry out a variety of tasks. The succession of safe houses gave the security of a choice of havens, each stocked with food, arms, money and clothes. Nor should the importance of the close personal friendship between the two men be overlooked. Vastly different in character, they neverthe-less bonded in a highly effective partnership, as Yeo-Thomas was to recall: 'By now, Brossolette and I formed a perfect team. We had learned to like each other, we both trusted each other implicitly, we never tried to hide anything, we planned everything together. I admired my companion whole-heartedly. We shared everything like twins. We shared a common ideal and all our energy was combined and directed towards a final victory.'

At 10am on Tuesday, 21 September 1943, Yeo-Thomas and Brossolette called on Serreulles. The meeting did not get off to a good start when Serreulles explained that his office was less than 100 yards down the street from their present meeting-place. Their discomfiture was all the greater when Serreulles scorned their expressions of con-cern. The meeting never recovered from this unfortunate beginning, as is clear from Yeo-Thomas's observations in his subsequent report to SOE: 'We found him in a most dangerously self-satisfied frame of mind, inclined to resent our arrival on the scene and determined to make things as difficult as possible for us both. In the course of our conversation, we found Sophie [Serreulles] quite unable or unwilling to answer many of our questions.' Both in the preface to his report and in a post-war account, Yeo-Thomas was insistent that he held no personal animosity towards Serreulles – 'on the contrary [I] had the greatest respect for his courage', notably regarding the Frenchman's first, abortive flight to France when Serreulles had been wounded in the aircraft by German anti-aircraft fire. Acknowledgment of Serreulles's bravery, however, could not alter the fact that Yeo-Thomas was dismayed by his performance since assuming command. He was also displeased by reports that Bingen, ostensibly the head of the organization in the former Unoccupied Zone, was spending too much of his time in Paris. After two hours' conversation, and with little constructive to show for it, Yeo-Thomas and Brossolette asked that they meet with Serreulles again the next day, but that this time Bingen and Marchal, who had arrived in Paris on 14 September as head of the 'Secret Army' in the Occupied Zone, should also be present. Understandably fearing the lax security of their host, the agents stipu-lated a complex system of cut-outs, warnings and fall-back rendezvous. They then left to spend the rest of the day reactivating members of their cell and making other checks on the availability of safe houses.

The meeting next day consisted of another fruitless conversation with Serreulles and Bingen, for there was still no sign of Marchal. As Yeo-Thomas reported:

After two hours of listening to Necker [Bingen] who is a specialist in diluted vagueness, we had not the faintest idea of what he had been talking about, and we very much doubted whether he had either. In spite of our efforts to get replies to our questions concerning the progress made on the paramilitary side, we failed utterly; the only pronouncement of any consistency that we were able to obtain was that we had grossly overstated the dangers of clandestine work and that we were both timid and possibly scared. Overconfidence oozed from every pore and our friends openly showed us that they considered our insistence on the security angle quite childish.

The absence of Marchal was now more than an inconvenience; indeed, it was becoming positively worrying. In an attempt to make some progress and to find out information for himself, Yeo-Thomas requested that Serreulles provide him with contacts among the Délégués Militaires Régionaux (DMR) and Bureau d'Opérations Aériennes (BOA) officers. Serreulles agreed, promising that the system of couriers that he had established would convey the information to him.

It must have come as no surprise to the now somewhat sceptical agents when Serreulles's courier failed to appear at the Peyronnets' at the agreed time of 4pm. There were any number of explanations, and not all of them sinister but, since a strict condition of the rendezvous was punctuality, Yeo-Thomas and Brossolette assumed that the message would be passed to them the next day. Consequently, they settled down to a relaxed evening with their hosts. At 10pm, Madame Peyronnet answered a ring at the door to find the building's concierge and the courier on the doorstep. The whole incident was to epitomize the abject lack of security surrounding Serreulles's organization. Ignoring instructions to abort the meeting if he was delayed, the envoy had decided to press ahead. He had not bargained for the concierge, whose duties included questioning any visitor attempting to enter the building after she had shut the front door at 8pm. The agent explained that he was calling on a *'Monsieur Shelley'*, which increased the suspicions of the concierge, who knew that there was no resident of that name. The courier affirmed that the gentleman he was calling on was staying on the third floor and the concierge accompanied him to the Peyronnets', where two refugees from Nantes, Messieurs 'Thierry' and 'Boutet', were house guests. Fortunately, the concierge was prepared to forgo asking any further questions and returned to her lodgings. Late, and having compromised Yeo-Thomas's cover, the courier compounded his errors by handing the SOE agent a type-written note addressed to 'Shelley', which contained names of resisters and details of rendezvous. Such abject tradecraft confirmed all of Yeo-Thomas's worst fears and was to fuel the next day's disagreements with Serreulles.

At 9pm on Friday 24 September, Yeo-Thomas and Brossolette met Michel Pichard and at last had the consolation of renewing contact with an old friend who could give them a fresh perspective on the crisis. Pichard's opinion proved to be a precise endorsement of Yeo-Thomas's own views: 'We were informed [by Pichard] that he was thoroughly fed up with Sophie [Serreulles], that he was quite unable to get any sense or assistance out of him, that his funds were always late in delivery and that instead of aiding the efforts of the BOA, Sophie put every obstruction in the way and had fostered antagonism between the movements and the BOA.'

Resisting the temptation to treat this corroboration of his own analysis as conclusive, Yeo-Thomas determined to seek reports from other trusted operatives such as Jean-Pierre Deshayes ('Rod'), Jacques Guérin ('Ampère'), Jean-François Clouet des Pesruches ('Galilée'), Jean Lapeyre-Mensignac ('Clo'), Guy Chaumet ('Mariotte') and Albert de Touba ('Soldat').

After leaving Pichard, the two agents went on to another meeting at the safe house in the rue de la Pompe, at which neither side – for that was how their relations were measuring up – accepted the other's stance. Criticisms of Serreulles and Bingen were met by smiles and assurances that Yeo-Thomas and Brossolette 'had exaggerated the dangers of underground work, and that really it was fairly simple!' This was followed by a two-hour briefing from Bingen that 'left us as wise as we were before'. The four men could not even agree upon implementing London's instructions to send two members of Serreulles's organization, Daniel Cordier ('Alain') and Pierre Péry ('Nard') to England. True to form, the meeting achieved little and ended with more requests from Yeo-Thomas and Brossolette for contacts with the DMRs, BOA and Marchal, and a response from Serreulles that this would take some time to arrange.

Tensions were clearly rising. The fraught and acrimonious relationship with Serreulles and Bingen, together with an abiding fear over security, convinced Yeo-Thomas and Brossolette that it was time to switch safe houses. The final straw was reached when Serreulles's courier again failed to appear at the Peyronnets' at the appointed time. At 11pm the two agents moved out, Brossolette going to stay with Claire Davinroy and Yeo-Thomas seeking sanctuary with Jacqueline Devaux. The next day, Saturday 25 September, Yeo-Thomas and Brossolette met at the place du Trocadéro and set out to conduct a full review of their situation. 'Maud' was contacted by Yeo-Thomas and instructed to make general enquiries, and specifically to check on the safety of the Peyronnets. She reported back to him at 6pm in the place Victor Hugo and informed him that his premonition of danger had been well founded. Her investigations had revealed that Serreulles's courier had been arrested and that the Peyronnets' address had been found on him. Consequently, at six o'clock that morning, the Gestapo had raided the apartment in the avenue des Ternes, missing the two agents by seven hours. The address was not necessarily incriminating in itself, and the courier, the Peyronnets and the concierge all stuck to their stories of being merely very small cogs in some black-market deal. Typically, Yeo-Thomas and Brossolette had left no compromising material behind and, so far as could be assessed, the Gestapo accepted the explanations given to them.

Any relief that might have been felt at the Peyronnets' safety was dispelled the next day in the face of even more dramatic revelations. Meeting Serreulles and Bingen, Yeo-Thomas and Brossolette learnt that the office in the rue de la Pompe had been raided by the Gestapo and several of its staff and many of its files seized. In spite of this catastrophe, Yeo-Thomas thought Serreulles seemed 'quite unmoved, in fact complacent'. Clearly, given the nature of their relationship, Yeo-Thomas was not disposed to consider this as an exhibition of Gallic sang-froid. The principal difficulty, however, lay not merely with Serreulles's attitude, for the seizure of his files threatened to have disastrous consequences.

In his report to SOE, Yeo-Thomas outlined details of this latest clash: 'We asked him [Serreulles] what had happened and were astounded to hear that four months' couriers and telegrams in both directions, and lists of names 'en clair', had been taken. It had never occurred to us that anyone could be foolish enough to keep such documents in the office where they worked, especially when that office was known to at least sixteen people. We were both infuriated and pointed out to Sophie [Serreulles] the gravity of the situation, but he did not seem to grasp it at all.'

If Serreulles did not grasp the significance of recent events, Yeo-Thomas determined that London would. Refraining from personal criticisms of the Frenchman that he must have been sorely tempted to make, he focused upon the current danger and his acceptance of responsibility, and had the following telegram sent:

Deux du vingt-six stop Secretary and liaison agents of Sophie [Seurrelles] arrested by Gestapo, also Hard ['Nard' – Pierre Péry] stop couriers and telegrams in and out past four months captured, also list names prominent people and pseudos regional officers dash Massena [Marchal] missing presumed enemy hands dot In view gravity situation, are taking all precautions prevent further damage dash nothing concerning operations compromised dot Request also send instructions to Sophie and Baudet

[Bingen] insisting extreme care dot Acknowledge by IDOFORM to me stop.

Unfortunately, at this most crucial moment wireless communication with London was severed. Yeo-Thomas passed the message to Pichard for transmission by one of his wireless operators but, hard pressed by the Germans, the 'pianist' had to go to ground, and only transmitted it on 14 October. In the meantime, the two agents set about warning prominent figures such as Senators Jeanneney and Farjon who, it seemed, had been implicated by the disaster. It was equally important that Yeo-Thomas and Brossolette look to their own security precautions. Once again they changed safe houses, the Frenchman going to stay with Suni Sandöe while Yeo-Thomas, now using his 'Tirelli' identity, moved in with Jeanne Helbling. The MARIE-CLAIRE mission, which had struggled from the outset, now found itself menaced by the dire failures of security, but the conscientious creation of their own self-contained operational cell stood the two agents in good stead, and brought the consolation of reliable associates with, should the need arise, an ample number of bolt-holes.

It proved difficult to acquire information through this screen of security, however, especially since the Serreulles/Bingen set-up was so heavily compromised. Slowly the story of what became known as *L'affaire de la rue de la Pompe* began to emerge. Serreulles was to maintain that the disaster stemmed from the arrest of Marchal, which had a knock-on effect that led the Germans to his closest aides and, ultimately, to himself. Jacqueline d'Allincourt, Serreulles's finder of safe houses, soon followed Marchal into captivity, and they were then rapidly joined by Hugues Limonti ('Germain'), the chief of the team of couriers, and Laure Diebold ('Mado'), the principal secretary. Serreulles had arrived at his office at 9.15am on 25 September only to find the Gestapo awaiting him, but the luck that had been with him in Lyon did not desert him and, 'after ten minutes of explanation, I was fortunate to be able to withdraw with their apologies'. While Serreulles was simply to ascribe his escape to the Germans' extreme stupidity, another of his associates was not so fortunate. Pierre Péry, whose return to London his superior had refused, was arrested on his arrival at the office. By 7 October 1943, Serreulles was able to offer an explanation of *l'affaire* and sent a communiqué that sought to minimize the dire consequences of the seizure of his documents: 'There really were very few of them since they were held in two suitcases but they were of high quality.' He continued with an outline of his own endeavours at damage limitation, but signally failed to make mention of the MARIE-CLAIRE mission's interventions. Unaware of Serreulles's justifications, Yeo-Thomas and Brossolette received news of Marchal's arrest and his suicide by swallowing his 'L' tablet. It emerged that he had been captured as early as the morning of Thursday 23 September, a fact that raised grave questions about the lack of attention paid to the gathering of intelligence in Serreulles's organization.

Thrown rather more onto his own resources, Yeo-Thomas had to expand his network of agents and, on the recommendation of his long-time friend and confidante, José Dupuis, interviewed and recruited three potential sub-agents, André Lemonnier ('Horace'), Edmond Vacher ('Ernest') and Bernard Josseaume ('Agenor'). In contrast to the loyalty of his female helpers, two of the men proved to be serious disappointments.

In September, the nineteen-year-old Lemonnier and his friend Vacher, who was ten years his senior, had appeared at Saint-Mars-la-Futaie in Mayenne. Here they called on the local priest, Abbé Levêque, who was known to assist men on the run from the authorities. The two men seemed genuine and personable and he put them in touch with Josseaume, who was well connected with resistance groups. The three men travelled to Paris where Josseaume introduced them to José Dupuis and they handed her a letter of introduction from Levêque. The shortage of *agents de liaison* was acute and Lemonnier was taken on by Yeo-Thomas as a courier and Vacher became a member of Bingen's team of assistants. Grave doubts, however, soon arose about Lemonnier's character and commitment. He seemed more interested in chasing women and spending money than getting on with his job. Yeo-Thomas's concern about Lemonnier was not misplaced and Vacher proved just as unreliable. On 20 October, Vacher had been entrusted with 500,000 francs by Bingen and told to look after the cash for a few days. Instead, Vacher split the cash with Lemonnier and another associate, Écomar, and, with his 200,000 francs cut, headed home to Bordeaux. He had intended making for North Africa but this proved impossible and he remained in the south-west of France for the rest of the war.[7] Lemonnier also vanished from sight for a period, only to reappear in Paris claiming that he had been captured by the Gestapo. Initially, Yeo-Thomas felt that the safest option was to kill him, but José Dupuis persuaded him to adopt a less lethal solution. Nevertheless, when dismissing him, Yeo-Thomas informed Lemonnier that if he betrayed the organization he would be shot.

At the time, it seemed as if the significance of the Lemonnier and Vacher saga lay in their revealing that the resistance included individuals who proved too weak or lacking in commitment. However, their story was, in fact, much more sinister. Both men had been in the service of the Germans from their very first contact with Abbé Levêque.

The feckless and wasteful youths had first met in Paris at the Ministère de Jeunesse. They failed to find gainful employment in the capital and Lemonnier returned to his home town of Le Mans where he was recruited by the local Gestapo.[8] Max Stauch, the head of the Gestapo headquarters in the town, sent him to penetrate Levêque's network and, having met up with Vacher again, the two men undertook the mission together. It seems certain that they kept in touch with their German controllers but Yeo-Thomas's suspicions of them restricted the level of penetration that they were able to effect. It would also appear that both men were as frightened of Yeo-Thomas as they were of the Gestapo and feared his retribution if their treachery became known.[9] In contrast, Bernard Josseaume proved completely loyal, assisting José Dupuis until the Liberation.

It was not only a potential traitor in their midst that the network had to fear, but also surveillance from the Gestapo. Yeo-Thomas remained vigilant, and with good cause. He still frequented Madame Bosc's restaurant – perhaps a needlessly risky indulgence – even when he had no messages to transmit or collect. In his official reports, Yeo-Thomas acknowledged that he had been tailed on several occasions by enemy agents but it was only in his personal memoir, published here for the first time, that he admitted to his closest and most deadly encounter:

> As I left, at about 10.30, I noticed a man standing in the shadow of a door on the opposite side of the street. I immediately felt suspicious and, instead of walking straight to the Concorde, turned in the direction of the Madeleine; I had not walked far before I sensed that I was being followed. As I turned into the boulevard de la Madeleine, I caught sight of the man, quite obviously on my trail.
>
> I was feeling tired but the realization that danger threatened livened me up. It was essential that I should throw off my pursuer, so I descended the steps into the Madeleine métro station. Trains were not very frequent at this time of the night, so I had plenty of time to observe whoever was following me. I had to be back at the flat at Neuilly by midnight, owing to the curfew, consequently I had to catch the métro from the Madeleine to the place de la Concorde, and change to the Pont de Neuilly line. I sat down on one of the benches along the platform, and, sure enough, along came the man I felt was following me. He was about 5'11", clean-shaven, wearing a dark felt hat and a long, brownish overcoat. He sat down a little further down the platform. The train came in, I got up and stepped into the first-class compartment, my shadow got into the second-class

compartment in the next carriage. At the Concorde, I got down and briskly made my way to the Pont de Neuilly line, followed by my trailer. He was wearing shoes that made very little noise; I concluded that he must have rubber heels. I had to wait a little time for the Pont de Neuilly train to come along, so sat down again. The man walked up and down, even passing before me. This rather surprised me, because I expected him to try and avoid being seen too much. This action on his part led me to wonder if I was not mistaken, and if it was only pure coincidence. I thought to myself, I must make sure that he is following me. The train came in, I again got into the first-class carriage, whilst the man got into the neighbouring second-class one. In those days, owing to the need for economizing power, the métro did not stop at all stations; I knew that between the Concorde and the Étoile, the train would pass Champs Elysées-Clémenceau, stop at Rond Point des Champs Elysées-Marbeuf, pass George V (which strange to relate was never re-named by the Germans) and stop at the Étoile, before going on to the Porte-Maillot and the Pont de Neuilly. I therefore decided to get off the train at Étoile station, pretend to take another line and then return to the platform for the Pont de Neuilly. I duly did this, making as though to take the Porte Dauphine line. Sure enough, along came my shadow. Now I knew beyond the shadow of a doubt that I was being followed. The time was getting on for 11.30 and it seemed that, short of making a dash for it once I got out at Pont de Neuilly, I would not shed my embarrassing double. If I did run, the chances were that he would call for assistance from any passing German troops, so it would not be very advisable. The only other solution was to bump him off, but I could not do that in public, so I would have to get him somewhere where there would be no witnesses, and where the body would not be found too soon. One thing was certain, he was alone on my trail, which was a point in my favour, he would not expect me to chance killing him. What puzzled me was that I felt sure he knew that I knew he was following me, my manoeuvring had been obvious enough, so had his; my conclusion was that he had informed his chiefs that he had picked up my trail and intended reporting to them as soon as I had gone into a house. He knew I could not afford to be caught outside after curfew, therefore, once I had gone into a house, all that had to be done was surround the block, and search, thus getting me and any of my helpers. The train came in, I again hopped into the first-class compartment, he again got into the next carriage. I went and sat in a corner. I slipped my right hand inside my jacket and felt my .32 Colt nestling in its shoulder holster. There was one up the spout, the safety catch was on. I gently slid it off, made sure that the gun would slip out easily and quickly thought out my plan of campaign. I must fix this chap, but where? Suddenly I had a brainwave. Jeanne Helbling's flat was near the Pont de Neuilly, less than three minutes' walk from it. There was a ramp leading down to the river bank, passing under the bridge. It would be very dark there, if I could entice the man to follow me down by the river, I would be under the shadow of the bridge whilst he was coming up behind me. My eyes would have time to get used to the darkness, he would be visible to me and his eyes would not be attuned to the darkness. I could then shoot him at point-blank range and dump him in the river. It was a risky business, but I had no choice, and time was getting short, it was now 11.40, only 20 minutes to go! Pont de Neuilly, I got out, walked fast to the end of the platform, up the steps, into the avenue de Neuilly, my shadow close behind me. I deliberately accelerated my step and dodged into the rue du Général Lanrezac, leading towards the river, still followed. I could hear some German soldiers walking up the avenue, groups of them, in step, singing marching songs and laughing. As I walked, I pulled my gun out of its holster and slipped my hand into my overcoat pocket, holding it ready to pull out quickly once I got into the shadow of the bridge. As I came out of the rue du Général Lanrezac, I knew I must make sure that the man would follow me, so I broke into a sort of trot, and went down towards the river bank, making a last few yards' spurt to give me time to find the best position. I was quickly in the shadow thrown by the bridge, my gun was in my hand. I had pulled my hat down over my eyes and had my head bent forward so that my face should not show up. I heard the patter of the man's feet as he came dashing down. Then I saw him, clearly delineated against the moonlight. What a fool, I thought to myself, then before he realized anything, he was within a foot of me. I felt his chest against my gun as I pulled the trigger. He grunted, his knees sagged and I lifted my arm bringing the butt and trigger guard of my pistol down on his head with every ounce of my strength – it made a queer noise – the man crumpled up. Now I must act quickly and get away. I dragged him to the edge of the bank, God, but he was heavy, I was panting from the exertion, he was on the edge, one more effort. My heart was pumping away like a steam engine, sweat was pouring down my face, I felt all my clothes sticking to me. Heave, heave! Over he went, sliding into the river without any noise. I stuffed my gun back into my shoulder holster. Now I must come out from under the bridge without attracting attention. I kept well against the stonework, no one in sight. In a trice I was back at the end of the rue du Général Lanrezac. Instead of going straight to the flat, I walked back up the rue du Général Lanrezac, walked around the block, back to the rue Casimir Pinel, and was up the stairs and in the flat just about 11.55. I went into the kitchen, drank a glass of cold water, then helped myself to a stiff brandy. It had been a dirty job, but it had to be done. I wondered if he was dead when he hit the water. Maybe he wasn't quite dead . . . then he must have drowned. Well, it was no use thinking about it, the deed was done, I was still free. The best thing was to go to bed and sleep. I was so tired that no sooner had I put my head on my pillow than I fell fast asleep.

When I woke up in the morning, I suddenly remembered all that had happened the night before. It seemed impossible that a man could be so stupid as my follower. I took out my gun, cleaned it, replaced the used cartridge, then realized that there must be a spent cartridge case under the bridge. Well, that did not matter to me now. It might not be found for days, and even if it was, it could not be traced back to me.

Such a violent episode accentuated the need to maintain security, and Yeo-Thomas set about further improving his own. The Commissaire de Police du 17ème Arrondissement was a member of the resistance group Ceux de la Libération and provided Yeo-Thomas with an identity card in the name of 'Gaonach'. Registered at the Préfecture de Police, and with an accompanying birth certificate, the agent was able to fabricate a credible cover story to fit in with his 'genuine' documents. A consequence of his 'Gaonach' legitimacy was that he was entitled to acquire a residence of his own under this alias, to supplement the safe houses provided by his helpers. It was still his firm intention to stay most of the time as a guest of his supporters, but he could now obtain his own bolt-hole. Through the good offices of Monsieur Huret, a former colleague at Molyneux, Yeo-Thomas rented a large furnished apartment in the rue des Tourelles. It was served by several exits and, being on the first floor, also offered the chance of escape, should the need arise, by leaping through a window to the street below. 'Maud' Bauer was enlisted to provide a store of food and fuel, while Yeo-Thomas installed a small arsenal of pistols, hand-grenades and ammunition. Typically, he was 'rather amused' to learn that his next-door neighbour was a Wehrmacht colonel who was personal assistant to the Military Governor of France, General Karl-Heinrich von Stülpnagel. In spite of an exchange of pleasantries on the odd occasion when Yeo-Thomas used the apartment, the agent 'did think of knocking him off one night, but he always came back in a car with a bodyguard, so I had to give up the idea'.

Exploiting their contacts from their previous mission, Yeo-Thomas and Brossolette now resolved to meet with Roger Coquoin ('Lenormand') and Jacques Lecompte-Boinet ('Mathieu') of Ceux de la Libération (CDLR), Colonel Alfred Touny ('Lacroix') of the Organisation Civile et Militaire (OCM), Georges Beaufils ('Joseph') of the Communist Party, and Colonel Aymond of Libération, Zone Nord. This exhausting round of interviews served to confirm to them that the organization of the 'Secret Army' had deteriorated and that the responsibility for this state of affairs rested with Serreulles and Bingen.

Yeo-Thomas might have freed himself of his tail at the Pont de Neuilly, but it was clear that he and his network were under close observation by the German security services. Having perhaps moved in too soon on Serreulles's operation, they were now standing off and keeping a watching brief. It also soon became plain that Jeanne Helbling's apartment was no longer secure. Yeo-Thomas identified clear signs that the flat was under surveillance both from the building across the street and from the street corner. Although understandably concerned at leaving his hostess in the lurch, he nevertheless recognized that 'there was no alternative' and departed by a back door. Meeting Mademoiselle Helbling for dinner that evening, he learnt that the observation had been maintained, and that his move to Jacqueline Devaux's apartment at the rue Leverrier was therefore justified. Although not as compromised as Yeo-Thomas, Brossolette was also on the move, leaving Suni Sandöe's for Claire Davinroy's in the rue de la Faisanderie, and then going on to Yeo-Thomas's lair in the rue des Tourelles. Brossolette's second move was to prove most timely. Madame Davinroy was also working for one of SIS's intelligence-gathering networks, 'Parsifal', which was led by an agent codenamed 'Gulliver'. Following 'Gulliver's' arrest by the Germans, Claire Davinroy was at great risk, as she had found the SIS agent his apartment.

Yeo-Thomas and Brossolette knew nothing of Claire Davinroy's fate until she failed to attend a rendezvous. On telephoning her apartment, Yeo-Thomas heard the voice of a stranger who invited him to call round. An aide, Marcelle Virolle, was sent to investigate and reported back with depressing news. The Gestapo had raided the apartment at 6am the morning after Yeo-Thomas and Brossolette had visited for dinner. They had found some of Yeo-Thomas's kit that he had left there, along with 125,000 francs. Although the telephone bluff to inveigle her contacts into calling on her had failed, the

Germans tried to use Madame Davinroy's pet dog to incriminate her associates: 'Claire had a little, white dog that barked at strangers and made a fuss of friends. This dog was taken out by Gestapo men and promenaded through adjacent streets in an effort to identify possible friends of the owner.'

Claire Davinroy was not the last of the network to be swept up, and soon the 'Parsifal' *réseau* was all but wiped out in Gestapo actions, which included a raid on their 'Centrale' or main office. However, at least one member of the network was still at liberty. 'Berthe' (who, unlike most of Yeo-Thomas's assistants, has failed to achieve recognition under her real name) was in a similar position to Madame Davinroy and had also worked for Yeo-Thomas and Brossolette during their last mission. She now went to them for help. She had been away when the Centrale had been raided and, in spite of being warned of recent events, called there. Astonishingly, the office was unguarded and the network's files had not been removed. Showing remarkable nerve, 'Berthe' collected the most important documents and ferried them to a safe house. While she and the two agents pondered what to do next, another problem arose when one of 'Gulliver''s assistants arrived. This was Jean Guyot ('Périclès'), who was Marcelle Virolle's brother. It was known that the Germans had a photograph and a full description of him and he therefore had to be intercepted before he called on the Centrale. Fortunately he was found and installed in a safe house in the boulevard Montparnasse, while others turned their thoughts to the unfinished business of saving the 'Gulliver' documents. Typically, it was Yeo-Thomas who acted. He collected the suitcases of papers from 'Berthe's' safe house and took them to another apartment, where he and Guyot systematically examined them. The less vital papers were destroyed, while the most important, which included intelligence on German secret weapons, were taken to Guyot's apartment and left with him until a way could be found to get them to Britain.

These pressing matters could not, however, be allowed to detract from the overwhelming demands of the MARIE-CLAIRE mission. On 6 October, a meeting was at last convened to tackle the bad relations between the BOA and the various resistance movements. It was made practicable by the arrival of Louis Eugène Mangin ('Niel' or 'Grognard'). Mangin had originally been sent to France as Délégué Militaire of the Southern Zone but, with the arrest of Marchal, he had had to assume responsibility for both areas. In Yeo-Thomas's opinion, he 'was the only person wielding sufficient authority to be heeded by the groups'. Among those attending the meeting were Yeo-Thomas, Brossolette, Pichard, Chaumet and two representatives of the military organizations. Between them, they managed to make significant progress and, as Yeo-Thomas joyfully informed London, 'the atmosphere was cleared, and the conflict between the BOA and the groups quelled. I think this matter is now settled, and that there will be no further trouble.'

Though this specific problem might have been resolved, there were any number of difficulties in store. Having just proved his importance in Paris, Mangin, accompanied by his assistant Pierre Arrighi ('Charpentier'), left, in Yeo-Thomas's opinion, 'on some harebrained journey to Switzerland'. Once again the central direction of the resistance had been found wanting and the MARIE-CLAIRE team's general objective of establishing an effective overall command and liaison structure seemed further away than ever. The two agents persisted in their endeavours throughout the month of October, more in spite of, than as a result of, the assistance of Serreulles and Mangin. Contact was made with André Boulloche ('Marin'), the ODMR for Paris, and Valentin Abeille ('Fantassin'), the ODMR for the Western Region. (The latter was the refugee to whom Yeo-Thomas had loaned his trousers in London.) Although these two men were able to offer encouraging news of resistance activity in their areas, they reiterated the constant complaints of lack of cooperation and poor coordination within the resistance movement. Meanwhile, the threat from the German security forces showed no sign of abating and, shortly after concluding arrangements to inspect the state of affairs in northern France, Yeo-Thomas's contact Roland Farjon was arrested. Consequently, it is hardly surprising that, even in a brief telegram to London, the agent's anxiety and frustration, albeit laced with his customary sense of humour, should be clearly evident:

> Arrests continuing on increasing scale stop past week Lenoir of Tirf agent de liaison of Baudet [Bingen] Galile [Clouet des Pesruches] and secretary also Dupuis [Farjon] and several leaders OCM besides Poncarral [Dejussieu] and Dormoy [Degliame] of Zone Sud dot cinq du vingt cinq dash Sophie [Serreulles] and secretary appear followed and in danger have warned them repeatedly in vain stop energetic measures required to save situation consider Passy [Dewavrin] be requested to give Briand [Brossolette] means and authority to take matters in hand and avert disaster dot there is no time to waste dot great life if you dont weaken not arf Tom.

Before a decision was taken in London in response to Yeo-Thomas's recommendations, a positive step forward at last seemed to have been made in Paris with the calling together of a Comité Militaire. With the exception of Mangin, who was still in Switzerland, the meeting on

27 October was attended by virtually all of the disparate leaders whom the MARIE-CLAIRE team had been trying to pull together. It all promised so much, but ultimately delivered so little. Serreulles and the chairman of the meeting, Colonel Alfred Touny of OCM, forcefully advocated that military affairs should be maintained within a strict hierarchical structure, embodied in the Comité Militaire. In response, André Boulloche argued the case of the ODMRs who, having received their instructions from London, had no need of a committee in Paris providing them with another set of orders. Yeo-Thomas now joined the debate, yet again addressing the questions of security and efficiency. He felt it was both dangerous and illogical to maintain a nationwide system headed by a military chief acting through the Comité Militaire. It appeared to him that Marchal's fate provided an object lesson in the weakness of such a structure. On the other hand, the policy of decentralization that the MARIE-CLAIRE team had been encouraging offered direct control from London, in addition to the inherent security of self-contained operational groups. Serreulles and Touny strongly opposed Yeo-Thomas's proposal but he was backed by Georges Beaufils, representing the communist Franc-Tireurs et Partisans (FTP), and Roger Coquoin of Ceux de la Libération. After two and a half hours the meeting broke up. Whatever hopes Yeo-Thomas had entertained of a successful and conclusive outcome to the gathering, they were not to be realized. Even an agreed formal clarification of the role of the BOA was to remain uncirculated. In his subsequent official report to his superiors at SOE, Yeo-Thomas summarized his impressions of the Comité Militaire thus:

> The Comité Militaire presided by Col 'Langlois' [Touny] met at varying intervals, talked at length, produced minutes and, having done so, considered it had justified its existence and failed either to convert decisions into actions or to advise anyone of the conclusions arrived at. Under these conditions only an intervention of the holy spirit could possibly give any results.

On 1 November Yeo-Thomas had another and – for once – brief meeting with Serreulles, and 'gave him my candid opinion about his "Comité Militaire" and told him that all the evidence pointed to four whole months wasted, that I was most dissatisfied with the whole state of affairs, and that no doubt HQ would have quite a lot to say about it'. Having thus spoken face to face with Serreulles, Yeo-Thomas the next day sent a wireless message to London asking for the Frenchman's recall. From surviving records, it is clear that he had been more than patient, both in his meetings with Serreulles and in restraining his own forceful temperament, restricting himself to mere requests that London take a firmer hand. Now, however, he at last spoke his mind:

> Recommend immediate recalls of Sophie [Serreulles] and Secretary who are obstructive detrimental to improvement situation and security dot Bear heavy responsibility for recent arrests dash Will return with every justification of my request stop.

Yeo-Thomas's wireless message seems to have placed the question of Serreulles's future in London's hands and also indicated that the MARIE-CLAIRE mission had almost run its course. There still remained sufficient time to take a break from the complexities of resistance politics in Paris, and instead to investigate at first hand the state of the 'maquis' in the countryside. The organizer of this fact-finding mission was Michel Brault ('Jérome'), the Chef National du Maquis, whom Yeo-Thomas had met in Paris in the middle of October. Clearly both men had a mutual interest in the tour of inspection: Yeo-Thomas to assess the maquis's capabilities, Brault to convince the SOE man of the need for increased supplies.

On 2 November Yeo-Thomas took the train from Paris to Cahors in the south-west, where he was met by Brault. The two men spent the night discussing their respective plans for the future until, at dawn, they drove to inspect two maquis camps in the region. Yeo-Thomas, though impressed by the discipline and attitude of the groups, was particularly struck by their shortage of arms and ammunition. This meant that they would be unable to defend themselves adequately if attacked, and it precluded all target practice and hampered weapon training.

That night, Yeo-Thomas and Brault took a train from Cahors to Lyon where the agent was only permitted a brief moment to freshen up before being driven to visit a maquis group near Poncin, in the *département* of the Ain. This group comprised some sixty men and had close contacts with neighbouring camps, bringing a potential unified force of some 500 fighters. Like the men in the Cahors area, these maquisards were well trained and dedicated; furthermore, they had shown a willingness to carry out offensive operations, notably by the seizure of Vichy Government stores in Bourg. Yeo-Thomas was later moved to report: 'These organized maquis can, properly supported and armed, provide us with formidable and efficient support on D-Day.'

Thus far Yeo-Thomas's tour of inspection, although rapid and tiring, had gone like clockwork and, on leaving the maquis, he was driven to Bourg station with three hours to spare before he had to catch the 11.30pm train to Paris. However, an hour before the train was due to arrive, a packed platform was informed that saboteurs had cut three of the railway lines into Bourg and, consequently, the Paris train had been cancelled. Pleasure at the success of his fellow resisters was tempered by frustration that his return to Paris and a reunion with Brossolette had been delayed. It looked as if the main line was going to remain blocked for a considerable time and the best Yeo-Thomas could arrange was to catch a train to Lyon leaving at 6.30am. The train proved to be slow, cold and uncomfortably crowded, but it delivered Yeo-Thomas to Lyon by 8.30, in time for the 9am express to Paris. Even though he had purchased a first-class ticket, the train was full to overflowing and there was not a seat to be had in any of the compartments designated for civilian use. Exhausted by the exertions of the last few days and having effectively gone without sleep for three nights, Yeo-Thomas took a gamble and entered an empty carriage marked '*Nur für Wehrmacht*' ('Only for the German Armed Forces'). He did not have long to enjoy his comfort, for within twenty minutes he was awoken by a German railway police officer. Taking verbal (in this case) attack as the best form of defence, the agent exhibited such an air of offended rectitude at his plight that the two men spent the next two hours in conversation, before the German helped to find him another seat on the train. His next conversation with a member of the occupying forces was to prove far more intimidating. In the restaurant car he found himself sitting opposite SS-Obersturmführer Klaus Barbie, the head of the Lyon Gestapo. Fortunately, during his recent visit to that city, Yeo-Thomas had had the SS man pointed out to him and had received a warning that he was particularly dangerous. (At this time he had no inkling of the role played by Barbie in the arrest and murder of Moulin.) With customary understatement, Yeo-Thomas later recalled, 'I did not enjoy my tea very much,' but with the conversation remaining on the topic of the black market, Barbie's suspicions were in no way aroused.

Yeo-Thomas arrived back in Paris shortly before curfew on the night of Friday 5 November and spent the night at Jacqueline Devaux's apartment. Next day he renewed contact with Brossolette and, among other things, laid plans to carry out a further fact-finding tour in northern France. (It was probably during this meeting that Brossolette passed to Yeo-Thomas some Christmas presents he had bought for his wife and children. Yeo-Thomas promised to deliver them and, in return, asked his friend to pick up an engagement ring for Barbara that awaited collection at a shop in the place Vendôme.) The scheme came to nothing, however, for a message from London warned him to hold himself in readiness for a return to England. The likely pick-up ground was in the region of Tours so he was told not to venture out of Paris. As it transpired, on 10 November he was told that the operation had been switched to Arras, in the north. Collecting the 'Parsifal' documents from Guyot, he left Paris at noon that day, arriving at Arras in the late afternoon. There he met up with Madame Virolle and Pichard's sister, Cécile (but known to the resistance as 'Jacqueline'), both of whom were on the run from the Germans and who were to accompany him back to England. Following the instructions that had been issued to them, they walked down the rue Saint Auber and located a lingerie shop. On entering, Yeo-Thomas delivered the password: 'I would like a bra, size . . . please,' anticipating the response: 'Certainly, sir, would you like to come through to the back shop?' Instead, the assistant expressed her regret that she did not have one in stock, though perhaps she could interest him in something else? Immediately realizing that he had come to the wrong corset shop, Yeo-Thomas made his excuses and left. Sure enough, another shop was found nearby, the password and response were exchanged and Yeo-Thomas confirmed his identity by matching his half of a torn banknote to that held by the shop-owner.

Madame Virolle and Mademoiselle Pichard were taken to a safe house while Yeo-Thomas was conducted to the perfume shop of Madame Berthe Fraser, a Frenchwoman who had married an Anglo-Scot. At this time, Madame Fraser was actively involved in several aspects of resistance work, including helping on escape lines, gathering intelligence and assisting the BOA. One might question the wisdom of her pursuing all these various tasks given the security problems inherent in such overlaps, but she was a woman of great resource and bravery and had the distinction of being described by Yeo-Thomas as 'one of the most remarkable women in the history of French resistance'. She arranged for Yeo-Thomas to stay with another shopkeeper, Marcel Doutremépuich, while her own home became their temporary headquarters.

Next day, Yeo-Thomas met Jean-Pierre Deshayes, the BOA officer in charge of the flight arrangements, who explained that bad weather and confused instructions from London had forced the postponement of the operation. This gave Yeo-Thomas the opportunity of carrying out, at least in part, his scheme to inspect local resistance groups. Placed in the care of Édouard Paysant, known as 'Thierry', Deshayes's assistant, he visited groups in the Amiens and Lille areas. He was again most impressed by what he saw, but the spectre of capture was still ever present, and on the day after his visit to Amiens nearly fifty resisters were seized in a German round-up there.

Meanwhile, further arrests were still being made in Paris, and among those captured was an agent who had a longstanding arrangement to meet with Brossolette. A courier brought news of this arrest to Yeo-Thomas and, fearing that the man would talk and that Brossolette was unaware of his being compromised, he resolved to return to Paris to warn his friend. His decision was also influenced by news from London that his 'pick-up' might, after all, take place near Tours. Paris was, therefore, a sensible base from which to operate. However, the 'Parsifal' documents remained a problem. They could not be left in Arras, as it was becoming increasingly important that they be delivered to London at the earliest opportunity. It was also known, however, that strict searches of luggage took place on the Arras-Paris line. Yeo-Thomas realized that there was nothing for it but to trust to fate and his wits.

The train was due to leave Arras on the afternoon of Friday 12 November 1943, but Yeo-Thomas was only too aware that he had to find a way of secreting the suitcase containing the documents. Luckily, on the platform he spotted two German officers boarding the train while their orderly attended to their luggage. Once aboard, Yeo-Thomas placed his own suitcases near to those of the Germans and engaged the orderly in conversation. Over the course of the journey, using a judicious combination of drink, bribery and blandishment, he persuaded the German to hide his suitcase – containing 'black-market goods' – among the officers' effects. The plan worked to perfection; the railway police ignored the officers' belongings and, although they scrutinized Yeo-Thomas's papers and 'clean' suitcase, they did not examine the other case containing the vital documents.

Bidding his new 'friend' a fond farewell at the Gare du Nord, Yeo-Thomas made straight for Brossolette's safe house in the rue Claude-Chahu. Mercifully, his friend was there, for it emerged that he had been unaware of the arrest of the agent and had had every intention of keeping the rendezvous. Together they listened to the BBC and learnt from the encoded messages that Yeo-Thomas's flight would, after all, be from Arras. No sooner had the two friends been reunited than it seemed that they would have to part. In order that Yeo-Thomas should reach his safe house at Jeanne Helbling's before curfew,[10] he and Brossolette had only a few brief moments together, as the former was to write: 'I hated the idea of leaving him, he was my great friend, we had shared so many dangers that it seemed all wrong for me to go and leave him behind . . . I said "Goodbye" to him, it being agreed that I would relieve him in a couple of months' time. He wished me *"Bonne chance et bon voyage"* and I hurriedly departed.'

It was the last time the two friends were to meet.

The following day, 13 November, Yeo-Thomas returned to Arras (this time without any difficulties), but there was no news awaiting him there of the Lysander operation. However, he continued to make good use of his time, holding meetings with Raymond Fassin

('Piquier'), the ODMR for the north of France, and Jean-Pierre Deshayes. Deshayes was able to tell him that there was a good chance that the pick-up operation was on for the next night, 15/16 November. Matters now began to move with some rapidity. On the Monday afternoon, Deshayes called at Madame Fraser's accompanied by Monsieur Bisiaux, the local undertaker. This was not an act of extravagant pessimism, but part of the plan to convey Yeo-Thomas and his important documents in a hearse through the curfew to the landing ground. Yeo-Thomas found the plan most amusing, a sentiment not shared by his female companions, who became 'more silent than usual' while he burst out laughing. Everything now depended upon the coded messages to be broadcast by the BBC that would tell them that the pick-up would take place that night. Yeo-Thomas, 'Jacqueline' Pichard, Madame Virolle and Deshayes gathered at Madame Fraser's that evening anxiously to await their *message personel*. At last they heard it, and although they still had to receive a second, confirmatory broadcast later that evening, Madame Fraser opened a bottle of champagne to celebrate.

Deshayes and his men had laid their plans well. At 8pm the hearse was parked in a dark back street and the two women, followed by Yeo-Thomas, boarded it unobserved. Fortunately, they did not have to suffer concealment in a coffin, but the journey was still to prove uncomfortable enough with the three adults and their luggage bumping against each other during a jolting twenty-mile drive to the landing ground. Half an hour into their journey their worst fears seemed to be realized when the hearse was stopped at a German military police roadblock. If Deshayes's men failed to bluff their way through, Yeo-Thomas was more than prepared to defend himself, being armed not only with his Colt .32 pistol but also with a Sten sub-machine gun and a couple of hand grenades given to him by the driver. However, it proved to be a routine and superficial check and, with the German soldiers failing to look inside the hearse, the vehicle was soon on its way. Cold and bruised from their bumpy journey, they at last arrived at an isolated farmhouse at Canettemont, thirty kilometres from Arras. The hospitality of their hosts, the Boudy family, was almost overwhelming, but even more reassuring were the security precautions evident all around them. Twenty men guarded the farmhouse while a further eighteen protected the landing field. Deshayes soon arrived to take overall charge of the operation and, at midnight, they were taken out to the field to await the Lysander.

Bad weather had initially led the Lysander flight commander at Tangmere to cancel the operation, appropriately given the codename TOMMYGUN, but the pilot, Flying Officer Jimmy McCairns, convinced his superior that he should carry out a weather reconnaissance and, if the conditions looked favourable, proceed with the mission. In spite of the bad weather and the ever present threat of night-fighters and flak, the Lysander met no opposition. Miraculously, the weather even improved over the landing field, and McCairns had no difficulty in picking out a powerful torchlight flashing out the recognition signal 'X'.

It was only after touching down that McCairns noticed that the grassed area of the landing ground was perilously small and that he was fast approaching a ploughed field. Stopping just short of danger, he taxied back to the reception committee. As the incoming passengers disembarked, a brief and somewhat pithy exchange took place between the pilot and the agent. Interestingly, both men, while recording the occasion verbatim, differed in their recollections.

McCairns's version:

> Y-T: Nice work, it was pouring with rain here thirty minutes ago – you have about 300 yards in front of you for take-off. I am returning with you.
>
> McC: Yeo-Thomas?
>
> Y-T: That's me.
>
> ('My last briefing was that on no account was I to depart from the field with information only. Consciously or otherwise I was to return with Yeo-Thomas in the back.')

Yeo-Thomas's version:

> McC: Yeo, thank God you're here, I have orders to bring you back even if I have to club you on the head.
>
> Y-T: OK old chap, I'll come quietly.

It was a tight fit to accommodate Yeo-Thomas, 'Jacqueline' Pichard and Madame Virolle and some fourteen pieces of luggage in the cockpit, but at last it was done and McCairns took off. A violent attack of airsickness afflicting one of his fellow passengers did not make Yeo-Thomas any more comfortable. Although the open cockpit canopy had seemed a great inconvenience and a profound discomfort, the blast of fresh air must have been a great relief. At last the Lysander landed at Tangmere and the passengers and their baggage were driven off to the Cottage, the aircrew's mess on the edge of the airfield. The occasion certainly had all the makings of a most convivial celebration: food, drink, warmth and, above all, safety. In spite of the presence of McCairns and Yeo-Thomas's RF Section colleague, 'Johnny'

Johnson, the party never really got going. Mademoiselle Pichard and Madame Virolle were still queasy from their flight and could barely manage a drink before retiring. (They might have been feeling under the weather, but McCairns was able to extract a promise from one of them that she would have a date with him in London.) Yeo-Thomas was not at his most convivial either. He was suffering from a form of food poisoning, and, although a couple of stiff whiskies bucked him up a little, he could not forget the friend he had left behind in France. 'I was happy to be back in England, but I kept on thinking of Brossolette, alone and still in danger while I was safely home.'

CHAPTER SIX

• The Third Mission – Operation ASYMPTOTE •

The success of MARIE-CLAIRE gave Yeo-Thomas increased celebrity and recognition within both British and Free French circles in London. His reports did not pull any punches, but the candour and honesty of his descriptions of events in France were of immense help in gauging the strength and character of resistance, specifically when plans for an invasion of the Continent were growing ever more advanced. His vehement criticisms of Serreulles and Bingen in his messages from France and his post-operational reports were a source of much debate in Baker Street and Duke Street. The situation was especially acute because, with Brossolette still in France, Yeo-Thomas had to represent both their opinions. In fact, there were allegations that Yeo-Thomas was merely his friend's mouthpiece. In retaliation, Serreulles's and Bingen's admirers among the Free French in London sought to blacken Brossolette's reputation, for not everyone held the two men in as low esteem as did Yeo-Thomas and Brossolette. (Claude Bourdet of the group Combat wrote of Bingen: 'He brought me a letter from Frenay that heartily recommended him and our first meeting was excellent . . . He combined extremely keen political sense and exceptional diplomatic gifts with natural authority. Working with him was very easy.') In a memorandum dated 2 December 1943, Lieutenant-Colonel L H Dismore, the new head of RF Section,[1] warned Robin Brook of this feud and advised him that Yeo-Thomas 'is a most difficult person to influence and has considerable independence of character, with marked reluctance to have other persons' views imposed upon him.'

Never one to suffer fools gladly, Yeo-Thomas was destined to undergo a series of brushes with officialdom. The day after his return to England he was instructed to report to the Air Ministry where, instead of being congratulated on his achievements, he was upbraided by an air commodore for wearing his Volunteer Reserve insignia which, during his absence, had been deleted from Air Ministry orders. This was not the only unwarranted criticism he received at this time, for a few days later, this veteran of two missions into enemy-occupied France was sent an envelope containing a white feather and a note bearing the single word 'Coward'. Sensibly, Yeo-Thomas could see the funny side of this astonishingly misplaced accusation and looked upon it as a tribute to the success of his 'cover' as a deskbound military bureaucrat. Less amusing was the continuing saga of the award of decorations in recognition of his work. Although Air Ministry approval for his Croix de Guerre was given on 18 October 1943, they were still refusing to allow him to be awarded the Military Cross. The Air Ministry argued that his French decoration had been bestowed upon him for his SEAHORSE mission and 'the regulations oppose the grant of two decorations for the same services'. However, as SOE had advised him in July of the award of a Military Cross and his French friends had given him a celebratory party, the continued absence of a medal ribbon on his tunic was a source of great unease to him. Clearly Hutchison had been premature in making the announcement and his miscalculation had resulted in the embarrassment of a man before both his friends and his allies. Dismore tried to placate Yeo-Thomas by informing him that, while he pursued the question of the MC, he was putting him up for a Distinguished Service Order for the MARIE-CLAIRE mission. By now Yeo-Thomas was fed up with the whole business and told him that even if it were offered he would decline it.[2] Such pettifogging attitudes did little to improve Yeo-Thomas's humour and increasing preoccupation with events in France: 'But there were also others whose main interest was the acquisition of an additional pip or crown or ring. There were others who had an ingrained distrust of "foreigners" and who would not credit these "foreigners" with the slightest good intention; quite a number of these types deliberately obstructed anything calculated to aid "resistance" and belittled the efforts of devoted people who were daily risking the worst fate. There were also some officers, so hide-bound that they could not visualize the assistance that these underground allies could give us. The sort of war we and they were waging was unorthodox, and, as a result, valuable aid that could have been extended to us was refused.'

Yeo-Thomas had always tended to regard red tape with impatience, disdain and annoyance and was therefore most uneasy when asked to present a series of lectures to senior members of the armed forces. Although sceptical about the receptivity of his audiences he nevertheless still sought to raise their understanding of the importance of the resistance, and to emphasize the need for it to be given more support. He graphically described the current level of supply as 'like a man filling a swimming pool with a fountain pen filler'. In spite of the sincerity of his words, however, he could not sway the mandarins of Whitehall and in consequence 'just got more and more obstinate and aggressive. My temper became more and more uncertain, and in the numerous committees I attended to discuss various important problems, I made use of the most vitriolic sarcasm when certain senior officers poo pooed suggestions which they considered exaggerated.'

The sarcasm survived the years and after the war he wrote:

> It was my considered opinion at this time that our best weapon for winning the war would be to hand over the Air Ministry, the War Office and a considerable number of MPs to the Germans as assistants. They would so hamper Germany's war effort that it would collapse in a few weeks.

His ill humour appears to have extended into his daily work for SOE. He was back flying a desk and did not like it. One of his tasks was to interview candidates for the new JEDBURGH parties (three-man teams of especially trained officers and NCOs to be dropped to resistance groups in France at the time of D-Day) and he proved an unrelenting interrogator of candidates whose attitude he found unacceptable. His role within the JEDBURGH plan at one time looked as if it might have become even more substantial, for he was selected for full-time secondment. RF Section was reluctant to lose him, though, and appointed him second-in-command of the Section and its Liaison Officer with operations in the field. However, although these duties allowed him to be intimately involved with affairs in France, the daily wireless messages from 'the field' containing constant appeals for help both distressed and frustrated him. He suspected that other sections in SOE were getting preferential treatment in the allocation of supply drops. This was difficult to prove but it was evident that the source of most of the problems lay in the shortage of aircraft devoted by the RAF to clandestine parachute operations.

Meanwhile, he was becoming increasingly concerned over Brossolette's safety. Reports arrived daily describing increased Gestapo activity against resistance groups and he feared that his friend, exposed through being active too long and too prominently, was in increasing danger. 'It is at this time, I think, that I went through the most acute period of depression I have ever known. I had such a feeling of battling against overwhelming inertia, of banging my head against an immovable brick wall, that I began to think of packing up and getting transferred anywhere. It was a form of escapism I suppose. I got to dread coming to the office because I knew that I would only find there some messages from our hard-pressed agents, imploring us to do this or that or the other, which I would be unable to answer satisfactorily.'

The level of frustration reached such a point that Yeo-Thomas resolved that once Brossolette had been safely brought out of France, he would resign from SOE.

There was a small ray of light at the end of the tunnel when, in the middle of December, the Free French decided that Brossolette and

Émile Bollaert, Moulin's replacement as de Gaulle's Délégué Général in France, were to be brought back to London. Now Yeo-Thomas was able to *do* something and he set about arranging a pick-up operation that involved two Lysanders taking four agents to France and returning with his friends. After a delay occasioned by a period of bad weather, he was notified that the flights were on for the night of 10 December. Predictably, Yeo-Thomas was the Conducting Officer and drove with the French agents to Tangmere, breaking the journey for a drink at the Spread Eagle Hotel in Midhurst. At the airfield the usual checks of clothing and documents were carried out and they listened to the BBC coded message warning the reception committee of their imminent arrival. The aircraft took off on time and Yeo-Thomas settled down to the long wait at Tangmere with a feeling of apprehension, tempered by elation at the prospect of seeing Brossolette again. After five hours the aircraft, flown by Flying Officer J M McBride and carrying Gilbert Védy ('Médéric'), returned. The already poor weather had deteriorated to such an extent that McBride had been unable to make out the pinpoints to the landing ground near Vervins, close to the Belgian border. Anxiously they awaited news of the second Lysander, flown by Flying Officer J R G Bathgate. After seven hours' wait (far exceeding the Lysander's operational flying time), Yeo-Thomas reluctantly decided to take his party back to London, their worst fears being confirmed forty-eight hours later with the news that the aircraft had been shot down over France on its outward journey, killing the pilot and both passengers. The loss of these brave men was a tragedy, but for Yeo-Thomas it was compounded by the fact that Brossolette was in more danger than ever. It later emerged that he had barely escaped arrest when awaiting the arrival of the Lysanders. While at the landing ground, Brossolette received news that the Germans had raided the safe house that he had just left. With the failure of the aircraft to appear, there was nothing to do but return to Paris. As bad weather clamped down over all of southern England, making flying impossible, the prospect of quickly mounting another operation seemed increasingly remote.

Clearly Brossolette was as anxious to return as Yeo-Thomas was to receive him, and the Frenchman managed to send a message to London indicating that he was going to try and secure his exfiltration by one of SIS's cross-Channel naval operations. This was to be arranged by Michel Pichard, who had been with Brossolette at the landing field in Vervins and who was also to have been picked up and returned to England. These new arrangements were not to Yeo-Thomas's liking and he urged Brossolette to wait three weeks for the next moon period when another Lysander pick-up could be attempted, reminding him in a wireless message that *'Le Cheval*

[Yeo-Thomas] *n'oublie jamais ses amis'* ('Le Cheval never forgets his friends').

The crisis over Brossolette helped to change Yeo-Thomas's mind about leaving SOE. His frustration at Baker Street's and Whitehall's inactivity had not diminished and the 'drug danger' upon which Hutchison feared that he might overdose had gripped Yeo-Thomas more than ever. He resolved to return to France as a means of relieving his feelings of guilt at failing to do enough to help those he had left behind. If he could not adequately represent their interests in London, he determined once more to join them in their struggle. He therefore proposed to Dismore that he replace Brossolette when the latter returned to England and a submission was made to this effect to Robin Brook. Yeo-Thomas's account is matter-of-fact and fails to record Robin Brook's strong opposition to the scheme, although he does admit that Brook wanted to see Brossolette's report before making a decision as to whether to send Yeo-Thomas back to France. However, the latter was now a driven man and rapidly produced draft operation orders and timetables for his mission. He even began to lay plans for his future activities following his return from his mission: 'We all knew that invasion could not be far away, and I wanted to have my share of the excitement. I felt that having worked so hard for the liberation of France, the least I was entitled to was to be one of the first to land there when D-Day came. I had a plan already formed in my mind, to get out of the office after returning from my next mission, and getting transferred to an active unit where I would take part in the action.'

In the New Year he took a ten-day period of leave with Barbara in Torquay, but even this enjoyable break did not eradicate his frustration as 'my mind was constantly dwelling on the difficulties that had to be surmounted, and on the safety of Brossolette'. He returned to London to find that the number of parachute drops had still not increased and, in desperation, turned to the wise counsel of a family friend to help him decide his next course of action. This was Major-General Sir Ernest Swinton, a friend of Yeo-Thomas's mother and 'a sort of adopted father'. During the First World War, Swinton had been an early advocate of armoured tracked vehicles and found his revolutionary ideas readily accepted by the then First Lord of the Admiralty, Winston Churchill. After his plans had been adopted he had the distinction of giving the vehicles the generic title 'tank'. In 1934, he became Colonel-Commandant of the Royal Tanks Corps, and, although retired, in 1944 he was not a man without influence. The two men had met quite regularly during the war when Yeo-Thomas and Barbara had visited the General at his home near Oxford. As Yeo-Thomas poured his heart out regarding the lack of assistance offered to the resistance, the General sought to explain that, in spite of his position, Yeo-Thomas was not seeing the 'big picture'. The younger man remained obdurate and Swinton suggested: 'There is only one man who can decide on such an important point; that is the Prime Minister.' The General therefore proposed that he send a personal letter to Churchill asking that he grant an audience to Yeo-Thomas. Swinton was as good as his word and Yeo-Thomas and Barbara (who had the honour of posting the letter) left Oxford feeling a whole lot better, but not in the slightest way confident that they would hear any more of it.

Their lack of confidence was ill founded. A couple of days later Barbara answered the telephone at their flat in Guilford Street and a man's voice, sounding uncannily like their RF Section friend, George Whitehead, announced that he was speaking from 10 Downing Street. Immediately suspecting a practical joke being played by Whitehead, she replied, 'Come off it, George.' It took some time before she was convinced that the call really was from Downing Street and, now feeling very foolish, she took a message instructing Yeo-Thomas to make contact with the Prime Minister's office as soon as possible. Meanwhile, another call had been made to Dorset Square and Dismore informed Yeo-Thomas that Downing Street had telephoned summoning him to an audience with Churchill the following afternoon. Although the lack of time between this news and the appointment itself gave Yeo-Thomas little chance to prepare, it also prevented him fully succumbing to nerves at the prospect of meeting 'the man I admired above all, the man who had led us through the most critical crisis in our whole history, who had become the living symbol of the unconquerable spirit of Britain.'

On 1 February 1944, Yeo-Thomas was collected by a staff car and presented himself at 10 Downing Street where he was received by Major Desmond Morton, one of Churchill's closest aides. Morton was already aware of Yeo-Thomas, having been sent a copy of the latter's MARIE-CLAIRE report by Hambro. Yeo-Thomas refrained from mentioning that he 'was suffering from the worst attack of wind-up I have ever known' and was ushered into the Cabinet Room where the Prime Minister was waiting for him. Churchill's attitude was somewhat cool. He stated that he was receiving him out of respect for Swinton, that he questioned the latter's claim that Yeo-Thomas knew France better than any other Englishman and that he had a bare five minutes to spare. Yeo-Thomas wondered 'whether I was not being a bloody nuisance, but I was there and I had to justify my presence so I plunged in'. He outlined the frustrating lack of assistance from the service ministries, the need for more aircraft to be devoted to supplying the resistance and, perhaps most significantly, he explained just what the maquis represented to France and the Allied cause. Hoping to cover all the possible ground, his words came out in a torrent until Churchill interrupted him and asked him to take a seat. The Prime Minister then began to ask specific questions and, to Yeo-Thomas's delight, began to make promises. He proposed that 100 aircraft would make 250 sorties each moon period and instructed Morton to provide him with copies of Yeo-Thomas's SEAHORSE and MARIE-CLAIRE reports. He concluded by reassuring Yeo-Thomas that he would not allow this highly irregular approach to result in any censure or retribution from SOE or the Air Ministry. Churchill then dictated memoranda on their conversation before asking Yeo-Thomas to remain and attend his next meeting with Général Emmanuel d'Astier de la Vigerie, the one-time head of the Libération resistance group and now de Gaulle's Minister of the Interior. The two men had met many times in London and Occupied France and, it transpired, the Général had come on a similar mission to petition for more aircraft to be devoted to supplying the resistance. After the usual formalities, Churchill told d'Astier the results of his conversation with Yeo-Thomas and then dismissed the SOE man. As he left, Yeo-Thomas looked at his watch and noted that the five minutes allocated to him had been extended by half an hour.

Cynics might find the coincidence of d'Astier de la Vigerie's appointment with Churchill a little too much to swallow. Was there an intent to let him know that the British were addressing their requests independently of specific Free French demands? Churchill's war memoirs do not mention the meeting with Yeo-Thomas nor that with d'Astier de la Vigerie and, furthermore, he does not refer to the question of air supply to the resistance.

In the event, Swinton's observation that Yeo-Thomas was far from in command of all the facts was singularly apposite, for it is now clear that the whole question of air supply had been the subject of long, detailed and frequently acrimonious debate in Whitehall. While doubtless granting an audience partially out of courtesy to Swinton, Churchill appears to have found Yeo-Thomas a useful means of obtaining a colourful and personal insight into a policy question that had been under discussion for several months. Furthermore, both de Gaulle and d'Astier de la Vigerie had tackled Churchill in Marrakesh and 'succeeded in interesting him in the problem'.[3] A meeting had already been held at 10 Downing Street on 27 January to discuss matters. This was a decidedly high-powered gathering, including Churchill, Morton, d'Astier de la Vigerie, Sir Archibald Sinclair (Minister for Air), Sir Charles Portal (Chief of Air Staff), Lord Selborne (Minister for Economic Warfare), Major-General Sir Hastings Ismay (Cabinet Secretary) and Sporborg and Mockler-Ferryman of SOE. Churchill stated that he wanted south-east France to develop 'comparable to the situation in Yugoslavia'. On 31 January, a proposal was submitted by Selborne for the increased air effort but the haste with which it had had to be prepared resulted in his asking for more time to revise the details. While it is impossible at this remove to quantify categorically the impact of Yeo-Thomas's words, Churchill's minute to Selborne and the Chiefs of Staff written on 2 February, the day after their meeting, seems to show clear traces of Yeo-Thomas's advocacy:

> I approve the proposals in your minute of 31 January for arming the maquis, but if through bad weather or any other reason the number of sorties in February looks like dropping below your estimate, I want extra efforts made to improvise additional sorties to the maquis on nights when conditions are favourable. Even if fully successful the February programme is not enough. Pray start at once on a programme for the March moon. Let me see it in plenty of time. I want March deliveries to double those planned for February. *I am told that the stocks of ammunition in the maquis are far below what is reasonable, even for the few weapons they possess* [author's italics].[4]

A further source of encouragement came on 7 February when Michel Brault ('Jérome') arrived in London after a long and hazardous trip via Spain. Yeo-Thomas was looking forward to having the leader of the maquis corroborate his own entreaties regarding air supply. Furthermore, he wished to receive the most up-to-date information on the maquis's strength in order that a considered and effective policy be promoted in London. Yeo-Thomas was, as ever, at pains to help his visitor come to terms with the often strange and confusing world in which he now found himself. Having experienced the loneliness and uncertainty of being an agent abroad (albeit in his much-loved Paris), Yeo-Thomas invited Brault to his home, even providing him with spare clothes from his own wardrobe.

Then the bombshell dropped. One morning, Yeo-Thomas arrived for work at Dorset Square as usual only to receive the news from Major 'Johnny' Johnson that Brossolette had been arrested. 'The blow was stunning. For a few seconds I was numbed, then my brain began to function again, thoughts came rushing through my head, in a flash I relived all our adventures.' The first reports were sketchy, merely stating that Brossolette and Bollaert had been caught in Brittany while trying to escape from France using the SIS sea route. Now was not the time for Yeo-Thomas to reflect upon his unheeded warning to his friend not to use this method; instead he could draw comfort from the absence of any indication that the Germans were aware of the identity of their captive. However, Yeo-Thomas was also convinced that Brossolette's cover could not be maintained indefinitely. Like a time bomb ticking away, the dye disguising Brossolette's tell-tale streak of distinctive white hair would inevitably fade.

The strain on Yeo-Thomas and, as he admitted, on Barbara was immense. He reproached himself for leaving his friend behind and felt impotent to help him: 'I could not get him out of my mind. My temper did not improve as a result, and I was not easy to get on with. When I got home in the evenings, Barbara did her best to cheer me, thought up a thousand little ways of drawing my thoughts away from the obsessing subject, and, by her sweetness and patience, sometimes succeeded, but I would always come back to the same idea, and in the long silent nights lay awake wrestling with my imagination. The strain was intense and with the passing days became unbearable.'

At last, more detailed reports reached London outlining the circumstances of Brossolette's arrest. It emerged that Brossolette and Bollaert had finally secured a place on the sea escape route and embarked on the small cargo coasting vessel, *Jouet des Flots*, at Île Tudy in south-west Brittany on the night of 2/3 February. The plan, organized by Lieutenant Yves Le Hénaff, was for the small vessel to sail to Cornwall but, disastrously, the boat struck the bottom when coming in shore to pick up its thirty-one passengers and sprang a leak. Then, to make matters worse, in heavy seas the engine flooded and failed. The skipper, Le Bris, managed to beach the craft at Feunteunot Creek, near Plogoff, before it could sink. Here the local resistance took them in hand and hid Brossolette, Bollaert and Le Hénaff at the Bois-Charbon inn until they could be taken to the nearby town of Quimper. The next day, Le Hénaff set off on a bicycle while a car came for the other two in the afternoon. As they drove inland towards relative safety, they were halted at a roadblock near Audierne. The car's papers were perfectly in order, as were the identity cards of the driver, but the persistent questioning of the German soldiers uncovered one fatal flaw in the passengers' documents. Neither Brossolette nor Bollaert were carrying permits to be in the special coastal security zone and they were subsequently detained for further interrogation. However, there was still no major cause for concern. All Brossolette's other papers, in the name of 'Paul Boutet', were in order and there was nothing to indicate to his captors that he was one of the most wanted men in France.

The evidence suggested that, at least for the present, Brossolette and Bollaert were in no immediate danger of identification. This was a source of immense relief to Yeo-Thomas and he began to make plans for a return to France in order to rescue them. The situation appeared in many ways to replicate the decapitation of the resistance leadership that had occurred the previous summer with the arrests of Delestraint and Moulin. Although the resistance's organization was now on a much more secure footing, Yeo-Thomas could nevertheless claim that his unrivalled skills and experience as a troubleshooter were once more required. However, he was not blind to the risks: 'If I got caught, I knew all that there was to know about the underground but, even more dangerous, I knew a very great deal about our staff planning. Supposing I talked under torture, I could give away a tremendous lot of information.'

He used his considerable powers of persuasion on Dismore who 'did all he could to turn me from my idea, but ended by being won over to it and then backed me up'. On 15 February, Dismore submitted to Robin Brook a draft *ordre de mission* for Yeo-Thomas, codenamed ASYMPTOTE. The emphasis on security already present in the January draft was retained while, significantly, no reference was made to Brossolette and the scheme to rescue him. Yeo-Thomas held this to be the primary purpose of the operation but he clearly felt it politic not to emphasize this aspect of his plans.

Time was of the essence and Yeo-Thomas threw himself into a frantic series of briefings and preparations. 'During those days, I worked like a man inspired, every ounce of energy was directed to my task. Every bit of help and assistance was given to me by my comrades, the men who toiled, struggled, planned, worried, when time after time the Gestapo destroyed or crippled the organizations they were building up, supplying, nursing along. It was at this time that I appreciated to the utmost the friendship of such men as Colonel Brook, Colonel Dismore, Major Murray-Prain, Major Johnson, Captain Neverovski, Major Murray, Captain Hubble, Flt/Lt Whitehead and many others.'

His friends and colleagues in SOE may have lent Yeo-Thomas their support in this latest endeavour, but there was one person who could not endorse it. Barbara had immersed herself in Yeo-Thomas's world; she took French language classes, entertained his numerous French friends and even took a job with the BCRA in Duke Street. She had tried to share his passion for France and his determination to achieve its liberation and had agreed to his first mission there, recognizing Yeo-Thomas's need to experience the same dangers that faced the agents whom he was sending out. The agreement had been that this would be his only trip and therefore his decision to go on the MARIE-CLAIRE mission had been a breach of faith that it had taken her quite some time to forgive. However, the prospect of his undertaking a third operation threatened to destroy them. After the war and with the benefit of hindsight, Yeo-Thomas was to write with great sensitivity and understanding of the dilemma faced by Barbara:

Daisy Yeo-Thomas

John and Jean Yeo-Thomas (1945)

Yeo-Thomas with younger
brother Jack

Yeo-Thomas in his US Army
uniform (left) and an unidentified
British soldier

Eddie Thomas
12-2-1940

Sergeant Yeo-Thomas, a photograph published in the magazine, *Boxing*

Barbara Yeo-Thomas during her days in the Women's Auxiliary Air Force

No 7 anti-gas course, Salisbury Plain, winter 1940. Yeo-Thomas is in the second row from the back, fifth from the right

Flight Lieutenant Yeo-Thomas (right) with some of his BCRA colleagues

Colonel André
Dewavrin

Général de Gaulle, leader of the Free French Forces, in London

CARTE D'IDENTITÉ

Empreintes Digitales

Nom *Tirelli*

Prénoms *François Yves*

Profession *Courtier*

Nationalité *Française*

Né le *17 juin 1901*

à *Alger (Départ d'Alger)*

Domicile *28 rue Pasteur Vichy (Allier)*

SIGNALEMENT

Taille *1m 72* Cheveux *chât. foncés*

Bouche *moyenne* Yeux *bleus*

Visage *ovale* Teint *clair*

Signes particuliers *néant*

Signature du Titulaire,

Etabli à *Vichy* *Tirelli*

Le *26 février 1942*

Le Maire ou le Commissaire,

D.A 13 FRANCS

Enregistré sous le N° *983*

CHANGEMENTS SUCCESSIFS DE DOMICILE

22 Quai de Passy

1 Avril 42

Cachet Officiel

28 MARS 1943

LE PRÉFET DE

Cachet Officiel

REY, Editeur-Relieur
Réalmont (Tarn) - Téléph. 56
MODÈLE DÉPOSÉ

Two false identity papers of Yeo-Thomas and a selection of photographs used on other papers

Jeanne Helbling

Yeo-Thomas, after the war, returns to the scene of his arrest

Claude Bouchinet-Serreulles

Jacques Bingen

Michel Pichard

Desmond Hubble

George Whitehead

Paul Fourcaud

Paul Marchal

Raymond Fassin

Jean Ayral

Guy Chaumet

Gilbert Védy

Jean-François Clouet des Pesruches

Valentin Abeille

Armand Philippe

Drawing of Yeo-Thomas by a fellow
Buchenwald prisoner

Yeo-Thomas in June 1945
during his convalescence

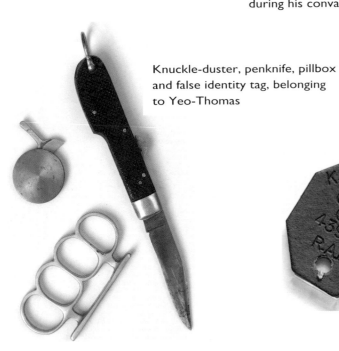

Knuckle-duster, penknife, pillbox
and false identity tag, belonging
to Yeo-Thomas

Yeo-Thomas, Jean Dulac and Jacques Foulquier at a reception in 1953

Pierre Brossolette shortly after his arrival in Britain, showing his trademark streak of white hair

Yeo-Thomas and Otto Skorzeny in Madrid in 1952

Barbara and Yeo-Thomas

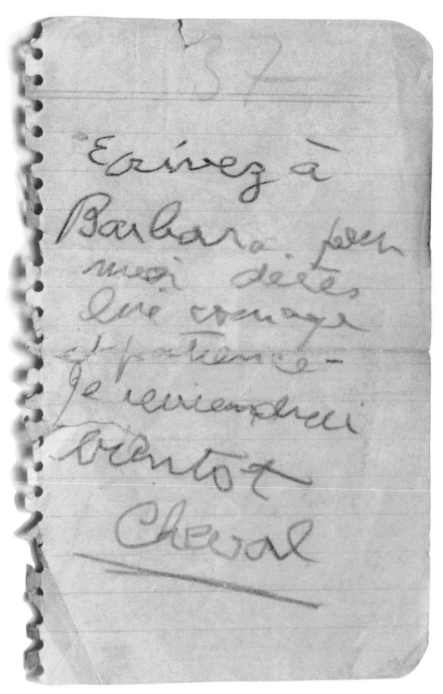

Yeo-Thomas's secretly scribbled note to Barbara, which he threw out of the truck taking him from Fresnes prison to Compèigne barracks

Chers amis
Tout va
bien je (vais) ...
...
rassurez
Barbara —
...
embrasse ...
et à bientôt
...
Barbara
Cheval

Shelley

Général Koenig presenting Yeo-Thomas with his insignia of an
Officier de la Légion d'Honneur, Paris, 1956

Yeo-Thomas giving evidence at a
war crimes' trial

Yeo-Thomas's medals, which are on permanent display
at the Imperial War Museum, London

Yeo-Thomas's headstone at Brooklands

She had a far harder time than I had. After all, the action would
be mine, there would be excitement, the thrill of pitting my wits
against the Gestapo; whereas she would be alone, with no means
of communicating with me, wondering, worrying, knowing
what my fate would be if I was caught. Unable to do the slightest thing. Until I fell into the hands of the enemy, I never
thought of this aspect of the problem; I believe that few men
ever do. They are so accustomed to having their womenfolk with
them, to taking them for granted, that they never realize the
silent agony that their life partners endure without the slightest
murmur, when the loved-one goes out to battle. How dreadful
the long nights must be, without news, with one's imagination
painting the most vividly disastrous pictures. The lot of a secret
agent's companion is worse than any other. In the fighting
forces, a man has his mates, his NCOs, his officers; if he is
wounded, or killed, in most cases his wife is notified, and at
the worst knows how it all happened, she can be told of her
husband's last moments, there is no uncertainty, it may be
shattering, but she is sure. But a secret agent's wife realizes what
she is up against; if her man is caught, it is just silence; he dis-
appears, no one knows where or how. All she can imagine is that
he has been tortured, probably executed, but she will never
know for certain, nor will she ever know where he rests.

Unfortunately, this understanding came too late to prevent this crisis
in their relationship. To make matters worse, Barbara had heard
the first news of his departure from a third party. Madame Prevost,
the wife of one of Dewavrin's officers, invited her to visit once Yeo-
Thomas had left for France. Armed with this information, Barbara
confronted him and was lamely told, 'I was going to tell you.' He had
broken his promise to her and she bluntly told him that, even if he
did return, she would not be waiting for him. With his supreme
self-confidence, Yeo-Thomas simply told her that he knew she would
still be there for him. Worse still, many of Yeo-Thomas's friends and
colleagues approached Barbara asking her to convince him not to go.
Even senior members of Dewavrin's staff, such as Robert and Duclos,
discussed the matter with her at Duke Street, pleading with her to
stop him from going into what they were convinced would be certain
death.

Yeo-Thomas was not unaware of the risks inherent in his third
mission to France and even experienced a sense of foreboding: 'For
the first time, I had a feeling of impending disaster. I had a premonition that this time, I would not get away with it, but I refused to give
in to these sombre thoughts . . . for the first time, I decided to make

a will and to give certain directives in the event of my being caught. I had never felt such an urge to take these precautions before.'

Perhaps this unease was reflected in his special request, not merely to be issued with his customary Colt .32 pistol (he had left his MARIE-CLAIRE weapon in France), but also with a 'sleeve gun'. Designed by SOE's research and development department, this weapon, resembling a short bicycle pump, could be hidden up the sleeve of a jacket. It could then be slipped into the palm of the hand and a .32 calibre bullet fired silently into an unsuspecting target.

The feeling that the mission was in some way blighted continued when, owing to bad weather, he was asked to parachute outside the moon period, at a time of particularly adverse conditions. From the night of 15/16 February 1944, the RAF's Special Duty squadrons were unable to fly any operations and it was not until the 24th that he learnt that his operation was 'on'. He had lunch with Barbara and then reported to Dorset Square. Unusually, many of his fellow officers had gathered to bid him farewell, increasing the feeling that this mission was somehow different from the others. It was a time when Yeo-Thomas's emotions and nerve ends were jangling together. 'As I got into the car, I saw Barbara standing at the top of the steps. I felt an overwhelming desire to go back and kiss her. I had a feeling that I might never see her again, and I wanted to look at her as long as I could. I mastered myself, but kept my eyes on her as long as I could until the car turned a corner. Then I was silent for a while, but pulled myself together and started talking to Dismore.[5] We chatted about all sorts of things, but I can't remember what I said, my thoughts were divided between the agony of leaving Barbara and the anxiety about Brossolette.'

They collected en route a BCRA agent who was to be parachuted on the same flight. This was Maurice Lostrie, codenamed 'Trieur', a saboteur who had only completed his training just before Christmas. Twenty years later, he recalled the journey with the two British officers – one of whom was *gros, fort, rougeaud et fumant un cigare impressionant* ('stocky, strong, ruddy-faced and smoking an impressive-looking cigar') – who spoke entirely in English. It would appear that Lostrie did not join them for supper at the SOE holding station near Tempsford, leaving Yeo-Thomas to spend some of the evening writing to Barbara and preparing a letter to be left with Dismore with instructions that it be opened in the event of his death. Later that evening when Yeo-Thomas and Dismore joined Lostrie at the airfield, the Frenchman was surprised to see the RAF officer now in civilian dress and speaking fluent French with a perfect Parisian accent.

Yeo-Thomas's spirits seem to have improved once the aircraft had taken off and he could devote his thoughts entirely to the weeks ahead. He had plenty to think about as the Halifax, piloted by Squadron Leader Len Ratcliff, headed for its drop zone near Clermont-Ferrand. Apart from some light flak over the coast, the flight was without incident and it scarcely seemed any time at all before the despatchers were telling Yeo-Thomas, Lostrie and a third passenger, codenamed 'Africain', to fasten their static lines and prepare to jump. The Halifax made a quick pass and then, with the lights of the reception committee reassuringly in sight, Yeo-Thomas pushed himself through the hole in the floor of the aircraft. Although he was now something of an experienced parachutist, he was taken completely by surprise when thirteen seconds later he hit the ground with stunning force. He should have been dropped at 500 feet, but clearly the aircraft was flying substantially lower. He was knocked out for two or three minutes and, on coming to, was convinced that he had either broken or sprained his ankle. The reception committee were soon with him and he was pleased to greet its leader, Yves Léger ('Évêque'), whom he had met during his training in England. Techniques and equipment had developed significantly since Yeo-Thomas's first mission and Léger was able to speak to the aircraft using an S-phone UHF radio telephone, informing the pilot that the agents had made a (relatively) safe landing.

There was no time to waste, and after a night's rest in a local farmhouse, Yeo-Thomas (whose injury was not as bad as at first suspected) and the other agents were taken by horse-drawn cart to Montluçon. Here 'Africain' parted company and Yeo-Thomas and Lostrie caught a bus to Clermont-Ferrand. En route, French gendarmes stopped the coach to make a security check, giving Lostrie, the novice, some uneasy moments as he feared that they would find a flaw in his false papers and discover his concealed revolver and sabotage plans. He noticed with more than a tinge of envy that Yeo-Thomas, the seasoned veteran of clandestine operations and who was sitting a couple of rows behind him, had fallen asleep and had to be woken up in order to produce his papers. At Clermont-Ferrand, they made contact with a friend of Léger's who was to help arrange the next part of their journey to Paris. As ever, there was time to satisfy the inner man and the two agents marked their return to the culinary delights of France with a dinner in a black-market restaurant, where oysters and a tournedos steak were washed down with bottles of Pouilly and Beaujolais. Yeo-Thomas and Lostrie then took the eleven-thirty train to Paris, arriving at seven o'clock the next morning.

Yeo-Thomas lost no time in contacting his network of devoted women helpers, telephoning Madame Peyronnet from a call box in a café near the station, using a simple coded phrase to ascertain that the coast was clear. He was not prepared to reveal the location of his

safe house to Lostrie and, leaving his colleague in another café, he
called on Madame Peyronnet in order to drop off his suitcase and get
the latest news. He next called Denise Martin who, together with her
sister, 'Maud' Bauer, arranged for another helper, Jacqueline Devaux,
to find Lostrie a small flat.[6] He also made contact with José Dupuis,
who had already been informed by a BBC *message personnel* that Yeo-
Thomas was on his way back. Finally, he notified Jeanne Helbling that
she would be having another house guest. At a council of war that
evening, Yeo-Thomas learnt that the news of Brossolette was encouraging. He was still deemed to be a low-category prisoner and was
being kept in Rennes prison with ordinary criminals. Furthermore,
one of his guards had been bribed to pass messages to and from his
friends on the outside. A note soon reached his contacts in Paris and
it was they who had notified London. Brossolette addressed himself
in particular to 'Maud' Bauer, who was able to send him messages
hidden in his laundry and who even visited him, passing herself
off as his mistress. In ignorance of Yeo-Thomas's arrival, Brossolette
began to plan his own escape, asking for equipment, such as saws,
chloroform, and a watch, as well as details of the prison layout and the
address of a safe house in Rennes. Yeo-Thomas judged that there
seemed no immediate purpose in dashing off to Brittany, deciding
instead to lay his plans carefully and carry out a full reconnaissance a
few days later.

He spent his time well in Paris, gathering information on the
developments that had taken place in the three months since his last
mission. Some of his earliest meetings were with Pichard and Clouet
des Pesruches, from whom he learnt that morale was low, owing to
the shortage of supply drops and increased activity by the German
security forces. He then made contact with Valentin Abeille and
Émile Kammerer, a former préfet who led the Breton resistance group
Commeurec, who were the obvious candidates to assist him in the
rescue of Brossolette. They, too, were to relate stories of problems
with supply drops with the result that any weapons and explosives
Yeo-Thomas needed for the jailbreak would have to brought into the
Rennes area from other regions, at great risk.

On 1 March Yeo-Thomas left for Rennes, accompanied by
Brossolette's 'mistress', 'Maud' Bauer. On arrival they visited a
trusted lawyer to discuss the possibility of having some trumped-up
charges laid against 'Paul Boutet', which would necessitate his
transfer to a prison in the South of France. This would offer an opportunity to snatch Brossolette en route or, failing that, to distance him
from possible identification and even secure his release on the basis of
his wrongful arrest. Although the scheme seemed a masterstroke, it
was rejected on the grounds that it would require too many people

to be initiated into the secret of Brossolette's true identity. M
importantly, it would simply take too long to put into effect.

An alternative plan was devised that consisted of a mixture of gui.
and force. A party of three German-speakers, wearing SD uniform,
would present themselves at the prison, bearing false papers for the
transfer of Brossolette and Bollaert. Having gained entry, they would
overpower the guard to prevent their making the routine telephone
call to Gestapo headquarters to check the visitors' credentials. They
would then force one of the guards to accompany them to the cells
where they would free the prisoners and drive them away in the
waiting SD car. An armed party of resistance men would be observing
their progress from houses across the street from the prison and
would intervene if more firepower was required. On the outskirts of
Rennes, the freed prisoners were to be transferred to another car and
brought back into the city where they would be hidden in a very
secure safe house. The original car was to be driven southwards for as
long as possible to lay a false trail.

As planning for the escape bid developed in Brittany, Yeo-Thomas
returned to Paris in order to fulfil the tasks laid out in his *ordre de
mission*. Appointments were made with the leading members of
the resistance groups, including Bingen, although the bad feelings
from the earlier mission remained and Yeo-Thomas felt that the
latter was 'dodging' him.[7] The daily round of tramping the streets
of Paris, moving on foot to avoid security checks on the métro, left
Yeo-Thomas extremely tired, but, at the same time, his spirits had
dramatically improved: 'My feeling of apprehension regarding the
outcome of my journey had by now vanished and I was full of energy
and confidence . . . I did not feel the nervous strain, yet I was
constantly on the alert to make sure that I was not followed, that the
contacts I met were also not followed and the thrill of getting things
going again was such that I felt quite happy.'

His thoughts also turned to home and, perhaps because of the
acrimony of his parting from Barbara, he had arranged for a weekly
coded message to be broadcast by the BBC informing her that he was
well and unaffected by the 'Baby Blitz' air raids that the Germans had
recently commenced against London.

The news from London was reassuring, but a personal tragedy was
about to unfold in Paris. Yeo-Thomas had asked José Dupuis to act as
an intermediary with his estranged wife, Lillian, to request that his
two daughters be standing at the window of their apartment at an
arranged time and date. He then hoped to pass by and gain a precious
glimpse of them. His request was denied with a warning that it was
not to be repeated. Then, on 19 March, José Dupuis visited Yeo-
Thomas's parents in the rue des Eaux to find them clutching a

telegram informing them that Evelyn, their son's eldest daughter, had died the day before of meningitis. They decided to keep the news from him and informed any mutual friends to do the same. Dupuis knew that Yeo-Thomas would criticize her when he eventually learnt the news but she felt that she had to defend him against his own emotions and impetuosity. She knew him well enough to know that he would try and go to the child's home or the hospital to pay his respects and that the risks were too great for this to be contemplated. The next day, Dupuis met Yeo-Thomas at the Muette métro station and was told, in the light of the certain knowledge that the Gestapo were closing in on her, that she must leave Paris. She followed his orders and the following day left to stay with friends near Gisors.

Yeo-Thomas remained highly conscious of his own security. He had already moved safe houses three times during his brief stay in Paris and was now living at the apartment of Suni Sandöe. He felt particularly secure there, knowing that only José Dupuis was aware of this bolt-hole. However, just at a time when his mission was reaching its culmination, events in Rennes took a disastrous turn. The Germans had at last discovered Brossolette's identity as a result of another piece of sloppy security by the resistance. A message had been sent to London by Serreulles and Bingen notifying them of Brossolette's arrest but the courier had been intercepted on the Spanish frontier. The German security services were not severely tested by a message that had not even been encoded. It made specific references to 'Brumaire's' and 'Baudoin's' difficulties in leaving the country by air, their shipwreck, arrest and incarceration in Rennes prison. On 17 March, an Abwehr officer interviewed Bollaert, addressing him by his real name and referring to Brossolette too. The German was accompanied by a colleague, SS-Oberscharführer Ernst Misselwitz, a member of the Paris SD, who had been attached to the German consulate in Lyon before the war and who recognized Bollaert as the former Préfet of the Rhône *département*. The two prisoners were transferred to the Rennes headquarters of the Gestapo, where Brossolette tried to maintain his 'Boutet' cover. However, it was clearly essential that prisoners of their calibre be transferred to Paris for interrogation as soon as possible and they were soon on the way under guard to the infamous SD headquarters in the avenue Foch.[8]

Yeo-Thomas remained ignorant of this tragedy and was preoccupied with concluding his arrangements to leave Paris for Rennes on the night of 21 March. That morning, he left his apartment at nine o'clock, planning to spend the day tying up a few loose ends before catching his train. One of these last duties was a meeting with his *agent de liaison*, Jean Alavoine, codename 'Antonin', a young man whose services had been lent to him by Pichard a week previously. They were to make a simple 'brush' contact at the Passy métro station and, if Alavoine gave the 'all clear' signal by having his hands in his pockets, the two men were to pretend to meet 'by chance' on the steps by the newspaper kiosk. In the course of their casual conversation, Yeo-Thomas was to pass on some fresh instructions, together with an encoded message he had prepared for transmission to London.[9] After making this contact, he was to meet 'Maud' Bauer and Jacqueline Rameil, Brossolette's secretary, for lunch and then take the train to Rennes.

At the agreed time of eleven o'clock, Yeo-Thomas ascended the steps to the métro station and passed the kiosk, but there was no sign of Alavoine. It was now that Yeo-Thomas, the stickler for security, broke the golden rule. Instead of aborting the contact he went down the steps on the other side of the station and decided to make another pass. He later conceded: 'I was therefore in two minds as to whether I would wait a few minutes, which was absolutely against my principles of security, or give up the contact, but as I was leaving for Rennes and might possibly be away for a few days, I decided that it was imperative to see "Antonin" in order to give him instructions to cover the possibility of a longer absence than I anticipated.'

Perhaps Yeo-Thomas's exhilaration and optimism had got the better of him. Perhaps he had begun to believe in his own invulnerability. Whatever the reason, he still did not abort the meeting when he looked up the staircase and there was still no sign of Alavoine. He continued up the steps and was reassured by the arrival of a train, which filled the staircase with passengers. Then, suddenly, from among the crowd of strangers, he was seized by five men. In an instant his hands were handcuffed behind his back and his pockets searched. Amid all the confusion, he caught sight of Alavoine passing him, escorted by two men.

As his captors searched his pockets, they shouted at the crowd to stand back and threatened to shoot anyone who intervened. Yeo-Thomas knew in an instant that this was no standard security check as he heard the Germans yelling exultantly that they had at last captured the elusive 'Shelley'.

CHAPTER SEVEN

· The Nightmare Begins ·

Yeo-Thomas knew enough about German interrogation techniques to realize that he was in for a tough time. He was bundled into the back of a waiting car and, as it drew away, two Gestapo men started yelling abuse at him and began to pummel his defenceless face. Whether as a result of his training or his own extraordinary sang-froid, Yeo-Thomas found that he 'was thinking in a completely impersonal manner just as though it was another person being beaten'.

By the time the car had reached the headquarters of the German security services at 11 rue des Saussaies, blood was pouring down the front of his suit and shirt. He was thrown out of the car and taken in a lift up to the fifth floor of the building that had once housed the French Sûreté Nationale. Here his captors continued to shout exultantly to anyone who would hear them that they had caught 'Shelley'. He was thrust into an office, occupied by three men who were waiting to join in the beating. Yeo-Thomas was then battered into a state of near insensibility. After three or four minutes, the assault stopped and he was stripped. The pistol that he had carried strapped to his thigh was immediately found along with the tear-gas pen in his pocket. The discovery of these weapons enraged his guards and encouraged them to subject him to further blows, now delivered with Yeo-Thomas, somewhat incongruously, standing nude upon a telephone directory. Their continued search of his clothes and effects also revealed a set of monocles that had been issued to him by SOE in order to help him change his appearance. These, too, became a source of annoyance and the offending lenses were flung on to the floor and ground under the heels of the guards. Even in his parlous state, the absurdity of the Germans' petulance was a source of amusement to Yeo-Thomas and he was rewarded for his laughter with yet another beating. Far more serious than the innocuous monocles were the four sets of keys that had been in Yeo-Thomas's possession. These were suspicious in the extreme and inevitably were going to invite scrutiny. In other circumstances, the set for his 'Goanach' flat, together with his perfect cover story and documents, should have been sufficient to withstand any interrogation. However, Alavoine's betrayal and identification of him, not to mention his weapons, left no doubt that the Germans had arrested a leading member of the resistance.

Yeo-Thomas was forced to remain standing on the telephone

directory for about an hour with his hands still manacled behind his back. Although beaten at regular intervals, he was able to take some consolation from the knowledge that, while the 'softening-up' process continued, his friends would have a chance to escape and he could mentally prepare himself for the inevitable, even more brutal interrogation that awaited him. He had missed his one o'clock appointment with 'Maud', who would even now be suspecting that something had gone wrong. This would, however, only be confirmed at six o'clock that evening when he also failed to turn up for his 'fall-back' meeting at the avenue Victor Hugo. Warnings would then go out to all his contacts, advising them to clear dead-letter boxes, change rendezvous and be on their guard. SOE training specified that captured agents were ideally to remain silent for forty-eight hours to enable security procedures to be put into effect. Thereafter agents might bargain with their captors in the knowledge that they had done their duty to their colleagues.

At last a new face appeared: 'Rudi', a tall, brutal-looking German who spoke in a mixture of his own tongue and French.[1] He greeted Yeo-Thomas by spitting in his face, slapping him to the floor and then kicking him as he made a stumbling attempt to rise. Yeo-Thomas deliberately feigned collapse and was helped up into a chair. Now, like two demented schoolboys in the playground, the prisoner and the captor tried to outstare each other. It was a brave or foolish act of bravado on Yeo-Thomas's part, for it merely encouraged the German to deliver yet another resounding punch in the face. Through the pain and dizziness Yeo-Thomas had the sinister comfort of knowing that his captors had not detected his 'L' tablet hidden in a signet ring. If only they would take the handcuffs off his wrists for a moment he 'would be beyond their power to hurt or question me'. 'Rudi' had other ideas. When the handcuffs were finally taken off, the ring was spotted and removed, but there was one consolation: 'I then suddenly realized that I had contemplated death without the slightest fear, without even thinking of it as the end of everything, and it gave me a great measure of comfort.'

The brutality continued. No specific questions were asked, just insults and demands that he cooperate. Silence brought about a renewed onslaught:

Then the big man ['Rudi'] started, 'You have played the game. You have lost. Now, if you are reasonable, everything will go well, or else!' I did not reply. 'So, are you going to talk?' I still remained silent.'Bastard!' shouted the big man. One of his acolytes slapped me across the face. 'So, are you going to talk . . . Yes or No!' I kept my mouth shut. The big man sprang up behind the desk – his fist landed smack on my mouth. I felt the blood welling up from my gums and the inside of my mouth; I swallowed it. I could feel that my face was all swollen, my eyes were peering at him through slits between my puffed eyelids. 'Bastard, scum, saboteur, spy, you will talk,' and he started beating me with the assistance of the two other men. It was painful, but I was gaining time, it was all to the good.

Now the real interrogation started, inevitably punctuated by violence. Another German, 'Ernst', entered the room with a typewriter and paper and prepared to transcribe the ensuing question-and-answer session. There was no point in persisting with the pretence of his 'Goanach' alias since Alavoine's identification of him, the scrap of paper with the details of the rendezvous and the Germans' knowledge of the existence of an agent codenamed 'Shelley' meant that he had to find another line of defence. It was for just such an eventuality that SOE had prepared yet another cover story for him. Yeo-Thomas now confessed to 'Rudi' that he was really Squadron Leader Kenneth Dodkin of the Royal Air Force. Dodkin really existed and appeared in the published RAF list of personnel, a copy of which was doubtless held by the Germans. Moreover, the real Dodkin had recently ceased to fly operationally and so there was no chance of him falling into enemy hands and complicating matters. During his preparation for ASYMPTOTE, Yeo-Thomas had met Dodkin at SOE's headquarters in Baker Street and learnt enough about his background and service history (he had also been provided with dog-tags in Dodkin's name) to pass himself off as a pilot who had been shot down. In this way he had hoped, in the event of capture, to be treated as a prisoner-of-war rather than a spy. However, Yeo-Thomas knew that this was now out of the question. The best that he could hope to achieve by maintaining his Dodkin alias was to protect his family and friends in France. In answer to 'Rudi's' questions, Yeo-Thomas gave Dodkin's name, rank and serial number. However, he refused to give an address in England and was rewarded with further blows, this time 'Rudi's' signet ring slicing open his cheek. Next came the 'nice-guy' approach. 'Rudi' gave him a cigarette and told him that Alavoine had told them everything that he had done since the beginning of the year. This gave Yeo-Thomas a great surge of optimism for, after all, he had only been back in France for less than a month and Alavoine had been working with him for barely a week. Now Yeo-Thomas began to play-act. He appeared shocked and depressed by the news of the Germans' omniscience. He asked if they knew of his various rendezvous and, specifically, the one in fifteen minutes' time at the Porte Maillot. He gave 'Rudi' a highly imaginative description of the female contact who would be waiting for him, carrying a bunch of flowers and a news-paper. Armed with this 'information', 'Rudi' dashed off, leaving him with the menacing comment, 'If you have lied, it will cost you dear.'

Yeo-Thomas had won some time in his joust with 'Rudi' but now 'Ernst' began to examine his personal effects and question him. The German was particularly methodical and was suspicious of a telephone number which, he spotted, had been written on one of Yeo-Thomas's bank notes. This had, in fact, been scribbled by an unknown previous owner of the note but, when Yeo-Thomas tried to explain that this was the case, 'Ernst' punched him in the face and announced his intention to send his men to the address where the telephone number was registered. This was going to be hard luck on the householder, but Yeo-Thomas soon had troubles of his own to worry about. 'Ernst' became intrigued by a keepsake that had been given to Yeo-Thomas before the war by one of Molyneux's man-nequins. The model, of Russian extraction, had given him a small leather pouch that he wore around his neck and which contained a tiny note written in her native language. 'Ernst' deduced that this was evidence of a sinister Soviet aspect to the case and consequently wasted more time in pursuing a line of enquiry that assumed Yeo-Thomas maintained connections with the communists and the Russian secret service.

To make matters worse, 'Rudi' now returned from his wild-goose chase: 'He was livid with rage and came straight at me. His fists pummelled my already puffed and swollen face. I was knocked to the floor, picked up, knocked down again, picked up, knocked down again. I ached all over, my head throbbed, all my teeth seemed loose, my nose felt like a squashed tomato, my lips were split, and I felt that my face was smeared with blood.'

Having vented his anger, 'Rudi' now rained down another torrent of questions:

> 'Where are the arms dumps?'
> 'I don't know of any.'
> 'Are you going to talk? Yes or no?'
> 'I know nothing.'

The dreadful litany continued until, at a sign from 'Rudi', two guards picked up Yeo-Thomas and dragged him out of the room. He was taken down a corridor and finally thrown into a freezing, tiled bath-room, where 'Rudi' wrapped a chain around his ankles and 'Ernst' filled the bath with cold water. The sinister reputation of the *baignoire* or bath treatment was legendary in resistance circles and, as he stood there, naked and helpless, Yeo-Thomas feared the worst. It was clear from 'Rudi's' evident excitement that he was building up to something. He gave orders to one of the guards, who left the room and soon returned with a gaggle of uniformed female German clerks. The audience seemed in no way uneasy at the prospect of the torture of a naked, helpless man, nor the sight of 'Rudi' punctuating his questions with slashes of a whip across Yeo-Thomas's chest. The humiliation and violence still failed to get a response from the prisoner, who was now sitting on the edge of the bath with his hands handcuffed behind his back and 'facing the girls, all of whom were either grinning widely or laughing'. Now the dreadful period of anticipation was ended. 'Rudi' smashed Yeo-Thomas in the face and pushed him backwards into the water:

> I was helpless, I panicked and tried to kick, but the vice-like grip was such that I could hardly move. My eyes were open, I could see shapes distorted by the water, wavering above me, my lungs were bursting, my mouth opened and I swallowed water. Now I was drowning. I put every ounce of my energy into a vain effort to kick myself out of the bath, but I was completely helpless and, swallowing water, I felt that I must burst. I was dying, this was the end, I was losing consciousness, but as I was doing so, I felt the strength going out of me and my limbs going limp. This must be the end . . .

This was to be far from the end. When Yeo-Thomas came to, he found himself out of the bath and lying on the floor. The women were still there, crowding in the doorway, laughing and chattering at the display. He closed his eyes to shut them out and tried to regain his breath and calm his beating heart. Then he felt himself lifted on to his feet and the questioning was resumed: 'Where are the arms dumps?' He had scarcely uttered his now familiar 'I do not know' when the chain was wrenched and he was propelled back into the bath. The routine was the same as before. As he was on the point of drowning and slipping into unconsciousness, he was pulled out, allowed a moment to regain his senses, and the questioning continued. It was only a temporary respite, for his uncooperative answers always resulted in another immersion and the painful and terrifying prospect of being drowned:

> Splash, I was kicking again and swallowing gallons of water, not much strength left to kick. My chest was about to burst. Oblivion. Distorted faces. 'Rudi', 'Ernst', others, girls laughing, mocking 'Where are the arms dumps?' Why reply at all, let me die. Water, gulps, bursting lungs, more faces above me, more

girls splitting their sides with laughter. Wish I was dead. How many times this went on, I don't know. I lay on the tiled floor, everything swaying around me, walls, bath, faces. I felt abominably sick, my tummy felt like an over-full barrel. Water kept on gushing out of my mouth, over my chest, I was numb with cold, I closed my eyes. I could hear voices, laughs, feminine laughter. What was so funny? Me, of course. I must look a fool, wilting like a doll that has lost its stuffing.

Then, as he was kicked into consciousness, Yeo-Thomas gradually realized that this ordeal was, if only temporarily, over. The women had left and he was dragged, swaying, to his feet. Hardly needing any further subjugation, he was nevertheless hit over the head with a rubber cosh and was hauled back into his original interrogation room. There he was dressed before the questioning and beating recommenced. This time he was beaten all over his body by two of the guards with rubber truncheons, leaving him to reflect: 'If they carry on in this way I shall soon be reduced to a pulp. The best thing is to pass out, but it is not so easy. Strange how much one can stand. How long are they going to keep this up. Won't they ever get tired? Every blow goes right through me and I can't get away from the bastards.'

Eventually, Yeo-Thomas did pass out but, as soon as he came round, the dreadfulness of his position was all too evident. He could barely see out of his swollen eyes and every bone in his body seemed broken. The only certainty was that it was not yet over. Incredibly, he even began to feel hungry, ironically recalling: 'At least I was not thirsty, having had more than enough in the bath.'

It was now well after six o'clock and, in spite of his pain and discomfort, Yeo-Thomas knew that 'Maud' would have deduced his fate and warned the others. He still had to hang on as long as he could so that the damage limitation could take effect, but at least he could console himself with the knowledge that he had passed the first milestone.

Now 'Rudi' continued the interrogation and returned to the question of the suspicious sets of keys. After what was now becoming the customary verbal exchange punctuated by beatings, Yeo-Thomas decided to continue to play for time. There was one apartment known only to himself, Brossolette and 'Maud'. As his friend was already in custody (although no longer in Rennes prison as he thought) and 'Maud' must by now have deduced that he had been arrested, it was safe to waste the Germans' time in searching the flat. He told 'Rudi' that the only key of any importance was the large one, belonging to 33 rue de la Tourelle, Porte de Saint Cloud.

Threatening more horrors if this proved to be another fool's errand, 'Rudi' handed over to 'Ernst' and left. They were soon interrupted by news that the unfortunate whose telephone number had appeared on the banknote had been arrested and was being held downstairs. A nondescript stranger was ushered into the room, and showed immediate and understandable shock and revulsion at the battered state of Yeo-Thomas's face and body. This was misinterpreted by the Germans as a sign of recognition between the two men and, no matter how strong the representation of the prisoners to the contrary, 'Ernst' refused to believe them. The two guards began to beat up the terrified newcomer and only broke off when Yeo-Thomas's shouted insults made them turn their attentions to him instead. Mercifully, he soon passed out again.

He came round to find himself being manhandled out of the room and dragged into a nearby tiny cell. For the first time since he was arrested he found himself alone and able to collect his thoughts: 'I was in complete darkness. There was not a ray of light from the aperture I had seen on coming in. I wondered how long I would be left alone. I was one mass of aches and pains. I could feel the clotted blood which had dried on my face drawing the skin. My head was buzzing, my nose felt as though it was the size of a pumpkin. My jaw pained me terribly and all my teeth felt loose. The salt taste of blood was in my mouth; my eyes burned, my wrists were tight in the handcuffs which I could feel cutting into the flesh of my wrists. I felt desperately sorry for myself. But at least I was enjoying a respite.'

His reveries were interrupted by the sounds of the stranger being beaten up once again. The sheer, mindless brutality of the victimization of this innocent man infuriated Yeo-Thomas and any self-pity that he had begun to feel was replaced by violent anger. At last, after about half an hour, the beating stopped and all was quiet. Now he could once again consider his own situation. Although desperately tired, he could not sleep, because, as his arms had been hooked over the back of the chair, every time he dropped off, his body leaned forward and the handcuffs bit further into his wrists. He was also desperate to urinate but his cries for assistance went unanswered.

Finally the door of his cell opened and he was dragged back into the interrogation room. Both 'Rudi' and 'Ernst' were present, along with the battered form of the stranger. They were now clearly satisfied that he had no connection with Yeo-Thomas but were demonstrably unconcerned at the bloody consequences of their mistake. The questioning of Yeo-Thomas now began again. 'Rudi' said that the apartment in the rue des Tourelles had not been slept in for weeks and wanted to know where he had stayed the previous night. Yeo-Thomas replied that he had been with a prostitute: 'It is what I always do – they keep their mouths shut.' Even the two Germans were now showing signs of fatigue and they ordered a late supper that was soon brought to them on a tray. For what seemed like hours, Yeo-Thomas had to watch his captors eat while all the time fighting to contain his straining bladder, determined not to let his tormentors have the pleasure of seeing him wet himself. Just as it seemed as if he could hang on no longer, 'Rudi' and 'Ernst' finished their meal and Yeo-Thomas was escorted back to his cell. As he was about to be locked in, he gave the guards an ultimatum. They could either take him to the lavatory or, very soon, his urine would flood underneath the door of his cell and into the corridor. He was led to the toilet and – 'What blessed relief' – was allowed to ease his aching bladder. The vast quantities of water that he had been forced to swallow resulted in an apparently unending torrent that tried the patience of his guards, who swore at him for keeping them waiting. At last he was taken back to his cell, where he determined to get some rest to give himself strength to face the next onslaught.

His manacled wrists and arms had been placed over the chairback and, with the handcuffs biting into his flesh, he found it impossible to get comfortable. Eventually, and after several attempts, he managed to tip the chair over, slip his arms free and slightly ease the pain. In spite of his discomfort, exhaustion soon got the better of him and he fell asleep. However, the respite was of short duration and he was awoken by the sound of the padlock being removed and then the cell was suddenly illuminated by a blinding light from the corridor. He was dragged back into the interrogation room where he was faced not by 'Rudi' and 'Ernst' but by two new inquisitors. The personnel were new but the methods remained the same. Questions were punctuated by punches, slaps and kicks and, after an hour, he was led back to the bathroom where he was undressed and plunged once again into the bath of icy water. Typically, Yeo-Thomas did not panic but tried to control his responses. At first he kicked frantically as if terrified and then feigned unconsciousness. He repeated this each time: 'In this way, I managed to get through the session without too much suffering. It meant swallowing a lot of water, and undergoing a lot of discomfort, but I was gaining time.'

This continued for about an hour, until he pretended to collapse completely. He was dragged back to the interrogation room where he had to endure the far more subtle torture of seeing his interrogators enjoying their breakfast. Fortified by their meal, the Germans resumed the beatings, knocking Yeo-Thomas into a semi-conscious state that came to him as something of a relief. As day dawned, 'Rudi' and 'Ernst' returned and resumed the relentless questioning and, for a stomach-churning third time, led Yeo-Thomas down the corridor to the horrors of the bathroom. Hardly surprisingly, he began to wonder just how much more of this constant torture he could take.

In the afternoon, the routine changed. Without warning, he was bundled downstairs and shoved into a waiting car. Escorted by two armed SD guards, he was driven up the Champs Elysées, past the Arc de Triomphe and into the avenue Foch. This attractive, tree-lined street belied its new-found sinister significance. Number 72 had been requisitioned as the headquarters of the Sicherheitsdienst. Subsequently three more houses, numbers 82, 84 and 86, were taken over and the street became the centre of many of the German counter-resistance operations.

It is not known precisely which of the houses Yeo-Thomas was delivered to but it was probably number 84. As he was rushed inside, his thoughts were doubtless filled with anxiety at what awaited him. However, there was another significance to his being brought to the avenue Foch, which, had he but known, would have filled him with despair.

Brossolette had been taken there from Rennes for interrogation and next door in number 86 had suffered the 'special treatment' that only too precisely replicated that experienced by Yeo-Thomas. He had been sent to Fresnes prison where he met Roger Lebon, a recently arrested associate of Pichard and Yeo-Thomas. That very morning, Brossolette had been brought back to the avenue Foch and, after several hours' 'treatment' at number 86, was dragged back to number 84 via a connecting passage. Semi-conscious, he was locked in a former maid's bedroom on the fifth floor, his guard being convinced that this battered, handcuffed man required little invigilation. He could not have been more wrong. Brossolette had gone on record to his wife, sister, Claire Davinroy and an old comrade-in-arms, stating that he would take his own life if captured: 'If I am arrested, I must, I want to die. I will not have a moment's hesitation. You never know how you might react under torture. You cannot accept the risk of talking.'[2]

Now was the moment of truth. Brossolette summoned up his remaining reserves of energy, climbed on to the window balcony and threw himself off. He was rushed to the Pitié Hospital where his injuries were diagnosed as fatal and, at midnight, having muttered the enigmatic '*Tout ira mieux mardi . . .*' ('Everything will be better on Tuesday'), he died. Rumours quickly circulated at the hospital as to the dead man's true identity. This was confirmed by a friend of Brossolette's who gained entry into the mortuary posing as a nurse.[3]

There was a terrible irony that the man Yeo-Thomas had risked his life to save had committed suicide barely an hour before his own arrival at the avenue Foch.

Yeo-Thomas was taken to the first floor of the building and thrown into yet another small, anonymous-looking office. Awaiting him was a two-man team: a massive, uniformed SS guard and a small, studious, bespectacled figure sitting at a desk behind a typewriter. They seemed an unlikely combination, but their respective roles were made clear when the seated man, christened 'Professor' by Yeo-Thomas, dismissed the guards and the giant shoved the Englishman into a chair. For some five minutes not a word was spoken as the prisoner was scrutinized until, in a precise, meticulous manner, the interrogator loaded paper and carbons into his typewriter. His words were measured and he was, in contrast to recent inquisitors, almost gentle. He stated that it was not his intention to hurt the prisoner, but the litany of name, rank and serial number that had so often been succeeded by a beating still filled Yeo-Thomas with fear. The question 'Where are the arms dumps?' that had been followed by so many punches was, as usual, answered by 'I don't know'. This time the interrogator merely typed up his words, but the next moment a new type of body blow was landed with the question: 'You know "Cadillac", don't you?' 'Cadillac' was one of Bingen's codenames and this specific enquiry was a departure from the norm. Yeo-Thomas answered: 'No, I don't know anybody of that name. I know it's the name of a type of American automobile.' Rather than hit him, the 'Professor' adopted a pained expression and asked, 'Where is "Cadillac"?' Now Yeo-Thomas was really uneasy: 'I found his calm way of examining me much more disturbing than the brutal methods of "Rudi". His very calmness and detachment seemed much more ominous. He was more subtle, maybe less brutal, but quite possibly more cruel. It was like being in the presence of a big spider, and feeling a web being coiled around me.'

The inquisitor continued to probe, now asking Yeo-Thomas if he knew 'Pic'. As Pichard, alias 'Pic', had provided him with Alavoine, there was no doubt that if, as seemed certain, the *agent de liaison* had talked, the Germans were already aware of the connection. He was next told to describe Pichard and, affecting cooperation, he painted a totally misleading portrait of his friend. The 'Professor' seemed happy enough with the response and, in turn, initiated his own bluff by stating that they had captured Pichard the day before. This was a comfort to Yeo-Thomas who realized that, if they really did hold his friend, his fictitious description would have been all too easily exposed.[4] The questioning now returned to 'Cadillac', but Yeo-Thomas resolutely denied all knowledge of him. The 'Professor' gave an exasperated sigh and spoke on the telephone. A moment later, the door opened and yet another of the Gestapo's seemingly unending supply of thugs walked in. He received his orders from the 'Professor', punched

Yeo-Thomas in the face and dragged him out of the office. The prisoner was manhandled to the fourth floor, where, in a small office, he was joined by the latest of his torturers. His handcuffs were attached to the end of a chain that passed through a hook suspended from the ceiling. The guards grabbed the chain and pulled, yanking Yeo-Thomas's arms up in the air, high behind his back: 'I felt the steel of the handcuffs sinking into my wrists as they were twisted upwards by the pull on the chain. Agonizing pain shot through my shoulders, I felt my heels leave the ground. A red film seemed to obscure everything, now only my toes were touching the ground. I was unable to restrain a groan . . . and I passed out. This was worse than anything I had endured so far. I had spasms of consciousness, when I suffered unbelievable pain, then I passed out again.'

It was dark when Yeo-Thomas was finally let down and he later reported that he had been suspended from the hook for eight long hours. The pain he had just suffered, together with the accumulation of horrors of the last day and a half, brought him to his lowest ebb: 'I felt that I had reached the limit of my endurance; I would not be able to stand any more. If I had to submit to this torture again, I would give in, I had reached breaking point.'

As had happened before, a brief respite followed. He was taken to another cell, allowed to go to the lavatory and even given a glass of water before being chained to an old settee. He managed to snatch a few moments' sleep while his guards dozed but, for most of the night, they woke him every time he dropped off. This sleep deprivation was calculated to add to the attritional assault on his strength and will. It was certainly beginning to have an effect. Yeo-Thomas grew ever more distressed, being cold, tired, hungry, in great pain and, most insidious of all, terrified at the prospect of what the new day held in store. ' . . . Inexorably, the morning light grew stronger, and every second brought me nearer to the moment when I would again writhe under the tortures of my captors. What was the use of denying it, I was at the end of my strength, my courage had oozed out of me, and I was terribly scared.'

It was therefore with grave foreboding that Yeo-Thomas found himself in a different office and confronted by yet another interrogator. Once again the questions concerned 'Cadillac', but now the German also referred to Bingen by his real name. This gave Yeo-Thomas the opportunity of admitting that he knew Bingen but had not recognized him under his alias. The questioning continued but, for once, without significant menace. The interrogator seemed obsessed by Bingen's Jewish ancestry and Yeo-Thomas was able to draw him into a wide-ranging discussion on anti-Semitism. At first, this had seemed like a good idea but the German became increasingly incensed and began to threaten him. It seemed to Yeo-Thomas to be a time for desperate measures and, uncannily, he decided to take the same course of action as Brossolette. The interrogation was being conducted on the fourth floor, with a window barely three feet away. Yeo-Thomas determined to throw himself out of it, calculating that, even if he did not die as a result of the fall, he would be hospitalized for some considerable time. He knew that he could not achieve much momentum because of his hands being tied behind his back. Nevertheless, he suddenly launched himself head-first at the window, smashing the lower pane. In an instant, he felt his ankles being gripped by one of his guards and he was dragged back into the room. The interrogator recognized his attempted suicide was born of desperation and played on this in his renewed questioning. Meanwhile Yeo-Thomas found himself unable to utter a word: 'I did not answer, I couldn't trust myself to. I did not want to beg for mercy and I knew I was on the verge of cracking.' Strangely, the interrogation was now concluded. He was taken downstairs and, with his interrogator, driven back to the rue des Saussaies.

His return to the scene of his first torment brought about a reunion with 'Rudi'. Clearly he had been told that Yeo-Thomas was at the limit, for he said: 'Now you are going to talk. You're scared – it's now or never.' The silence with which this was met led to the entry of five men who picked up the prisoner, placed him on top of a table and tied his ankles to its legs. While two held his shoulders, 'the others, armed with rubber coshes, proceeded to rain blows all over me. I felt the sickening thud on my face, my legs, my chest. Then they concentrated on the most vulnerable part of my anatomy. I could not restrain a scream, the agony was intense and they continued to slam away.'

Under this onslaught, Yeo-Thomas passed out, only to awaken several hours later in yet another strange cell. Every bone and muscle in his body ached, while his mental state had also begun to deteriorate: 'I was so exhausted in every way that I lost all idea of what I was going to do next or experience. I just did not care, and I have no very clear ideas about the next day. All I can remember is being questioned again and again, the questioners seemed far away, and I was in the clouds.'

In this befuddled state, Yeo-Thomas was taken back to the avenue Foch where, among his interrogators, was SS-Oberscharführer Ernst Misselwitz, who had accompanied Brossolette and Bollaert from Rennes to Paris. Misselwitz, a blond man in his middle twenties, seemed a cut above the other questioners, using guile rather than the cosh to prise information out of him. He continued to ask Yeo-Thomas where he stayed in Paris and eventually revealed that he knew of Suni Sandöe's apartment in the rue Claude Chahu. He further sought to appeal to Yeo-Thomas as a fellow officer and offered him his word as a German officer that if he cooperated no harm would befall him. In answer to Yeo-Thomas's scepticism, Misselwitz suggested he ask the opinion of another British officer in captivity. A short man with a small, toothbrush moustache was ushered in and the two agents were permitted a brief exchange. His fellow countryman was Captain John Starr of SOE's F Section who had been arrested near Dijon on 18 July 1943 on his second mission to France. He had been kept at 84 avenue Foch since September and was regularly introduced to new prisoners by the Gestapo in order to help undermine their resistance and enhance their feelings of helplessness. After a failed escape attempt in December, he had given his parole to the SD, and thereafter walked a thin line between self-preservation and collaboration. (After the war, Starr was investigated by the French military authorities but it was decided that he had no case to answer.) The two men only spoke a few sentences under the watchful gaze of their captors, but the look in Starr's eyes left Yeo-Thomas in no doubt that he was warning him of the Germans' perfidy.[5]

With the failure of the 'appeal to reason', Misselwitz sent Yeo-Thomas back to the rue des Saussaies and the tender mercies of 'Rudi'. After his customary outburst of violence, he handed Yeo-Thomas over to yet another interrogator who was particularly interested in the resistance's plans for sabotage action. A combination of genuine ignorance and overwhelming exhaustion resulted in Yeo-Thomas simply ignoring his questions. This resulted in another session in the bathroom and no less than six terrifying immersions in the freezing water.

The nightmare now seemed without end. Holding out for a couple of hours had given him a feeling of achievement, but now, with the passing of the seemingly unattainable target of forty-eight hours, 'nights had merged with days and I had not the remotest idea what day it was, or indeed whether it was night or day.'

While Yeo-Thomas languished in his semi-stupor, he was unaware that his arrest was not an isolated incident, but that it had been part of a major German security offensive.

In the early evening of 19 March, one of Pichard's aides, Pierre Manuel, and his secretary, Georgette Lancombe, were arrested at the métro Emile Zola. Manuel, the brother of Dewavrin's second-in-command, agreed to collaborate with the Germans in order to save himself and Lancombe. His betrayal soon bore fruit for the Gestapo. Later that night, two BCRA agents, Scriber and Valter, were arrested at the apartment of Lancombe's mother. The following morning, the Germans raided the central office of the BOA at 22 rue de Lourmel, arresting many of its leading members, including Anne-Marie Krug

Basse, Marthe and Roger Lebon (who was to be one of the last to see Brossolette in prison), Maria Polacek and François Delimal.[6] Pichard had left for Dijon the day before and consequently avoided arrest.

On the same day as Yeo-Thomas's arrest, Gilbert Védy ('Médéric') had been arrested in Paris by the French police, but any hopes that he nurtured of appealing to their patriotism (or even a cynical recognition of an ultimate Allied victory) were dashed. This brave patriot, who was described in the RF Section History as 'one of the most likeable figures in resistance, and universally respected', was handed over to the collaborationist Brigade Spéciale 'Anti-terroriste'. Faced with the certain prospect of torture and the inevitable risk of succumbing to interrogation, he took his suicide tablet.

Meanwhile, the ramifications of Manuel's treachery had continued. The Gestapo had learnt of another rendezvous. This time it concerned Brigitte Friang, the secretary of Clouet des Pesruches, and Alavoine, Yeo-Thomas's *agent de liaison*, who had been due to meet at the Trocadéro. Reports later made to SOE in London claimed that Friang and Alavoine had been approached by four German agents who shot the former in the stomach and arrested the latter. Friang was sent to the Pitié Hospital, while Alavoine was searched and interrogated. He was found to have in his possession a scrap of paper bearing the words 'Shelley Passy 11'. Yeo-Thomas's codename was by this time well known to the Germans and they had wasted no time in dashing to the Passy métro. There, the young and doubtless terrified Alavoine was forced to identify 'Shelley' from among the crowds of passersby.[7]

The course of events leading up to his arrest remained as yet unknown to Yeo-Thomas. He remained isolated from the outside world, his only contacts being yet another set of interrogators who tried a new approach. This team comprised a middle-aged man and a bespectacled younger companion. They asked Yeo-Thomas if he was hungry and, when he answered in the affirmative, ordered him some soup and sandwiches, and even made an attempt at joviality with the comment, 'It's not much, but at four in the morning Maxim's is closed.' The food was as manna from heaven and, to complete the treat, Yeo-Thomas was given a post-prandial cigarette. Even as he revelled in his new-found comfort, Yeo-Thomas recognized the need to be alert, and it was not long before he was shown a photograph of Jean Lapeyre-Mensignac and asked if he knew him. He admitted that he did but was able to feign surprise when the German told him that he was dead. This set the tone for the rest of the morning's questioning, with the two Germans feeding him scraps of information in the hope that this would so impress Yeo-Thomas that he would provide further details or at least confirm the known facts. The interrogators showed him a diagram of the BCRA organization which, while it contained much correct information, also contained many glaring inaccuracies. In an attempt to 'help', Yeo-Thomas supplied them with several false personalities and bogus departments.

At about noon, Yeo-Thomas was taken downstairs where, to his surprise and dismay, he was confronted with Suni Sandöe. Surprisingly, given Misselwitz's earlier admission that he knew of Yeo-Thomas's connection with her apartment in the rue Claude Chahu, the latter managed to exchange a few words with her, specifically warning her not to admit to having hidden or even seen any weapons. There was no time to learn how she had been caught, but it later emerged that after the affair at the Passy métro station, 'Poucette' Peyronnet had called at Suni Sandöe's to apprise her of events and remove weapons and codes left behind by Yeo-Thomas. In spite of the evident risk, Sandöe did not quit her apartment straightaway and on the 23rd was arrested. It has been alleged that the Gestapo were led to the rue Claude Chahu by a woman contact of Brossolette's, but the evidence to support this is sketchy.[8]

A further shock awaited Yeo-Thomas later in the day when, after an interrogation by 'Rudi', he was led into a large room in which he found several of his closest associates arrayed in handcuffs. Among the most important were Commandant Noel Palaud ('Artilleur'), who held an important role in the resistance's military organization in Paris, and Commandant Armand Philippe ('Chaland' or 'Khodja'), who had been sent to France as early as September 1943. Philippe was a saboteur and one of the resistance's most deadly 'enforcers'. Both men had been arrested on the Pont de l'Alma after Manuel had led the Germans to them. The other prisoners who instantly caught Yeo-Thomas's eye were Anne-Marie Krug Basse, Marthe and Roger Lebon and Manuel himself. With the exception of the traitor, all seemed as though they had been maltreated, with Palaud and Philippe appearing to have suffered extreme torture.[9]

The chairs upon which they were seated had been arranged specifically to prevent any communication between the prisoners and, when Yeo-Thomas turned his head to glance at Palaud, the guards bellowed at him and cuffed him around the head. Clearly he needed to find another means of communicating, and so began to hum the popular pre-war tune *'Tout va très bien, Madame la Marquise'*. He then started gently murmuring the lyrics and, when this did not result in any response from the guards, he began to substitute his own words. He quietly sang a warning to Palaud that he had not confessed to any knowledge of the other prisoners and described his own capture. In turn, while Yeo-Thomas hummed the tune, Palaud joined in with his own 'lyrics', sketching in details of his own arrest. Their dialogue was maintained for almost two hours until the door burst open and the guards yelled at them to stand up. The group were then led outside, across the courtyard and into a hallway where a prison van drew up. By this time, 'Rudi' and 'Ernst' had appeared and were ticking the prisoners off on a list as Yeo-Thomas was helped on to the vehicle. The interior comprised a narrow, central corridor in between two rows of tiny metal cells. A guard bearing a sub-machine gun stood at the end of the corridor and propelled Yeo-Thomas into one of the minuscule cubicles. The only light and ventilation consisted of narrow slats that gave the smallest of views of the ground outside. Soon they set off. Yeo-Thomas's intimate knowledge of Paris made him confident of gauging their destination just by sensing the turns of the vehicle. Soon he was certain that they were en route to the infamous Fresnes prison, in the southern outskirts of the city.

On arrival at Fresnes, he tried to keep with Palaud and Philippe, but the three were separated and Yeo-Thomas was locked in a small, cold, dark cell on the ground floor without even a blanket to keep him warm. The next days were uncomfortable, in large measure due to his hands still being handcuffed behind his back, making drinking and going to the lavatory difficult. However, although the guards were inclined to punctuate their instructions with slaps and kicks, he was in a far better situation than if he had stayed at the avenue Foch or the rue des Saussaies. He was even given some rudimentary medical treatment for a painful cut on his wrist that had been made by the handcuffs. The wound had turned septic and a German medical orderly grudgingly administered some first aid with the less than Hippocratic sentiment that there was not much point in treating him as he was going to die soon anyway.

Nevertheless, Yeo-Thomas's spirits gradually began to revive. The 'Professor' agreed that his handcuffs might be removed and he was given a small and grimy blanket that at least provided a little warmth at night and helped him to get some sleep. He also made contact with the prisoner in the adjoining cell by removing part of the tap and speaking to him through the plumbing system. It transpired that his neighbour, who used the alias 'Lecoq', had been an inmate of Fresnes for three months and had worked for Pichard. He bestowed the name 'Tartarin' upon Yeo-Thomas so that, if they were overheard, the guards would be uncertain of their identities. This friendship was short-lived. Yeo-Thomas was moved to a new, cleaner cell on the second floor and, to his relief, acquired a decent jailer named Korrel. Korrel maintained his kindness throughout the weeks, giving Yeo-Thomas a Bible, a toothbrush and some soap with which he was at last able to wash his dirty and blood-caked clothes. Denied the opportunity to talk to 'Lecoq', he began to analyse his situation and lay plans. He thought of Barbara and the need to let her know he was still alive, and inevitably he began to consider the possibility of escape: 'According to what "Lecoq" had told me, we were frequently taken up to Paris for interrogation. Hopes of escaping from Fresnes were pretty slender, so the best chances occurred either at the rue des Saussaies or avenue Foch, or else during transfers from Fresnes to Paris. I must study every movement, every habit of the guards, of all the Germans. I must not miss a single thing.'

In spite of being regularly scrutinized by his guards through the peephole in the cell door, Yeo-Thomas managed to remove one of the small panes of glass in his window. It was through this hole that he heard an English voice calling from outside. Yeo-Thomas lost no time in interrogating the speaker and learnt that he was 'Jim' (Sergeant E J Gillman), an RAF pilot who had been captured after being shot down and who was sharing a cell with another British airman, Joe Kenny, and an American airman, 'Tex'. An Australian pilot, Flying Officer Clifton Tucker, was also in one of the cells but, fearful of being discovered by the guards, their conversation had to be truncated. Later that day, he heard someone calling out a request from 'Lecoq' seeking news of 'Tartarin'. There was little the guards could do to silence these exchanges and Yeo-Thomas was greatly heartened by the feeling that he was not alone.

The next day he was sent both to the avenue Foch and rue des Saussaies, where he was interrogated with restraint by Misselwitz and brutally by 'Rudi'. Neither tactic secured any further information from Yeo-Thomas and he was intrigued to learn from Misselwitz that Lemonnier had resurfaced and had been giving the Germans 'information' about his activities. It was obvious to Yeo-Thomas that Lemonnier had lied to his Gestapo controllers regarding the extent of his knowledge and he informed Misselwitz that he would be more than happy to confront the traitor with his falsehoods. This encounter took place a week or so later at the avenue Foch. Lemonnier was an hour late in arriving and thereby hardly endeared himself to Misselwitz. His standing further deteriorated when he failed to recognize Yeo-Thomas, although it must be conceded that the physical deterioration the latter had undergone in the weeks since his capture had radically altered his appearance. Lemonnier began to list the frequency and importance of his meetings with Yeo-Thomas, but at virtually every point he was shown to be lying. The most notable falsehoods concerned bogus rendezvous that had allegedly taken place in Paris while Yeo-Thomas was back in London. It was easy to corroborate the refutation of Lemonnier's story by checking the BBC's *messages personnels*, which had announced the agent's departures and arrivals. Misselwitz had the Gestapo records of the broadcasts examined and soon realized that the 15,000-franc retainer he had been paying Lemonnier had been fraudulently 'earned'. He had Lemonnier taken to an interrogation room and, as Yeo-Thomas listened outside, Misselwitz extracted the full story of the betrayal both of his colleagues in the resistance and his Gestapo employers. Yeo-Thomas took great pleasure when he was subsequently informed that Lemonnier would be joining him as an inmate at Fresnes and made sure that the betrayals were broadcast across the courtyards of the prison.

Back in Fresnes, Yeo-Thomas began to develop a routine, both to maintain his morale and to try to reclaim some of his physical fitness. He began to do a rigorous series of exercises, in spite of being restricted by his damaged arm, and even set himself the unlikely task of polishing the wooden floor of the cell with the handle of a brush he had been given to clean his cell. Pointless as it might seem, he found this regime helped build up his strength and gave him a comforting daily routine, but, as usual, for every step forward, there was a reverse around the corner. One day, a Wehrmacht *feldwebel* entered the room and cynically beat him for no other reason than that Yeo-Thomas was a 'British officer'. By now it was less the pain that distressed Yeo-Thomas than the feeling of helplessness at this new assault. Amid his frustration, however, he had the consolation of knowing that there was a fellow countryman nearby, and he further improved his morale by calling out to Jim Gillman. He also dictated a message that he wished him to pass on to Barbara once the airman reached a prisoner-of-war camp and was able to send letters home.

During his stay at Fresnes, Yeo-Thomas made two escape attempts. The first was to take place from the prison van en route to the Gestapo headquarters in the avenue Foch. Security inside the vehicle consisted of only one guard armed with a sub-machine gun, but there were four others travelling behind in a car. He resolved to overpower the guard, snatch his gun and open fire on the following vehicle. He felt confident that, if he made his bid in the area of the rue d'Alésia, he would be able to reach one of his local safe houses where he had cached weapons, money and identity papers. Low-risk category prisoners were allowed to travel in the aisle of the van but, as a dangerous terrorist, Yeo-Thomas was locked in one of the cells. Fortunately the doors were not very secure and on one trip at the beginning of April, he prised his open and managed to creep into the aisle. The guard was conveniently looking the other way, but his fellow prisoners did not share his enterprise. When they saw what he intended, they tried to stop him and, although he managed to grab the machine gun, he was overpowered and thrown back in his cell. Frustrated at the cowardice of those around him, he also dreaded the reprisals that he felt sure would follow. However, his fears were not realized for the guard neglected to report the incident to his superiors, presumably to avoid a reprimand for himself.

The second attempt took place at the rue des Saussaies itself. It too lacked finesse and was the act of a desperate man. After another interrogation, Yeo-Thomas and the other prisoners waited for the arrival of the van to take them back to Fresnes. In the darkness he was able to slip into the shadows and made a dash for the archway leading into the street. It was a slim chance, but one worth taking. However, he was soon spotted by a guard who tripped him as he was in full flight and, with his hands manacled behind his back, he fell crashing to the ground. He was pulled to his feet, beaten and flung into the van. At Fresnes he was 'again given a thorough going over and, as an additional punishment, deprived of food one day out of every two for a fortnight. It was not much of a reduction by normal standards, but when one realizes that prisoners in my category only received one mug of so-called soup (mangel-wurzel and boiled water), one thick slice of soggy bread and one mugful of ersatz coffee a day, it was quite a privation.'

He settled into a routine of less brutal but persistent interrogations in Paris, followed by returns to Fresnes and the shouted conversations with his fellow inmates. His RAF colleagues had been transferred, but he had made contact with a variety of other inmates, including Brigitte Friang. She was later sent to Romainville prison and, shortly before being transferred to Germany, she smuggled out a message to her family in which she stated: *'J'ai de bonnes nouvelles du grand poète'* ('I have good news of the great poet'). Then, on 17 May, the door of his cell burst open and the *feldwebel* began to beat him up, accusing him of being the 'Tartarin' who shouted so many anti-German comments into the courtyard. Yeo-Thomas, who had not 'broadcast' that day, had been betrayed by his next-door neighbour in order to curry favour. After the beating he was hauled downstairs to one of the punishment cells: 'I was in complete darkness. As soon as the door clanged behind me, I felt dampness falling and closing around me. The floor felt peculiar and spongy. I bent down and felt it – it was covered with a layer of damp fungus.'

There was no bed and he had to try to sleep on a broken chair possessing only three legs. After a day and a half without light, food or water, the door opened and a jailer informed him that he had been sentenced to three weeks' detention with the special punishment of being fed once every three days. Yeo-Thomas tried to keep up his spirits with a 'campaign of annoyance', during which he bellowed out every British and French patriotic song that he could think of. Then, 'I shouted "To hell with Hitler" in French and English. I screamed that Germany was licked, I raised all hell, at the same time kicking the door lustily. I cursed my guards, Hitler, Germany with great gusto.'

His captors did not put up with this performance for long and, the next thing he knew, the door had been flung open and he was clubbed with a rifle butt. Not even this cowed him and, when he had recovered, he continued his singing until, exhausted, he fell asleep. When he awoke, he heard a voice coming from an air-duct in the ceiling. He precariously stood on his chair and managed to shout a message, hoping that he was addressing a fellow inmate. He was immensely relieved to learn from their response that he had made contact with two French prisoners who promised to keep in touch with him throughout his period of solitary confinement.

It was during his third week of punishment that he heard the news that ensured he no longer felt cold or hungry – the Allied invasion of France had begun. Even in his isolation on 6 June he heard the strains of the 'Marseillaise' being sung by the prisoners, followed by 'It's a Long Way to Tipperary'. Yeo-Thomas joined in and continued to celebrate, until, on 9 June, his special punishment was over and he returned to the relative luxury of his own cell. Anticipation of a more comfortable existence was dashed when he was transferred to a different cell on the ground floor. Although not as damp as the punishment cell, this room was covered in dried blood. This was disconcerting, but not so bad as the constant menace of the fleas that infested the room and mattress. Yeo-Thomas estimated that he killed 200 a day during the five weeks he spent in the cell, but he was nevertheless fighting a losing battle. During the first days he suffered terribly from them, but after a while he virtually developed a form of immunity and found that the worst aspect was the fleas' constant movement over his body.

Yeo-Thomas had now been in Fresnes for three and a half months. The Germans' failure to extract information from him and the inevitable ramifications of the Allied landings in Normandy had left him uncertain of his future. He may have felt isolated but, ever since the day of his capture, his friends and colleagues in Paris and London had been doing their best to find out news of him. Of all the people involved, Barbara was, of course, the most important. Her diary simply records that on 25 March she went to visit her family in Brighton and, on her return on the 27th, bleakly noted: 'Received bad news. Refuse to believe it.' There had been a telephone call to Duke Street that had been intercepted by a colleague. Hearing the admonition, 'You must be very brave,' she immediately went to Dorset Square where Dismore confirmed her worst fears.[10] As she came out of the building she felt totally stunned, unable to understand why the traffic was still moving and passersby were going about their business. She had managed to keep a hold on her emotions even when Dismore had told her the dreadful news, but it took a simple act of kindness to unlock her feelings. A neighbour gave her a bunch of violets to cheer her up and this reduced her to floods of tears. Her diary records the dreadful wait for news over the following weeks. When it did arrive, it was not encouraging. Her entry for Good Friday reads: 'Saw Dismore. Things look pretty black but Dizzy and I are confident.' The next day she wrote: 'This evening I feel that Tommy is very near and that he is telling me not to worry.'

Others were physically closer and they too were intent on getting the latest news. 'Poucette' Peyronnet had acted with great rapidity and foresight in clearing out Yeo-Thomas's safe house, but it really needed the return of the faithful José Dupuis to galvanize matters. She had returned to Paris on 30 March and soon learnt of his arrest. Thereafter, she pressed for any information of his whereabouts and wellbeing and, after a number of false trails, fragments of his story began to appear. Hélène Peyronnet received a note stating: *"Cheval" est à Fresnes, prévenir vos chefs.'* ('"Cheval" is at Fresnes, pass on the word.') A few days later this was confirmed by a message to Pichard from Anne-Marie Krug Basse in which she wrote: 'I have seen the great poet – he is in good health.' Further inquiries in Fresnes, however, drew a blank, not least because Yeo-Thomas's comrades were unaware of his 'Dodkin' alias.

Meanwhile, Yeo-Thomas remained uncertain of what lay in store for him. He gained an intimation that matters were soon to change when, in the second week of July, along with a dozen other prisoners, he was examined by a German doctor. He presumed that they were being selected for forced labour in Germany and resolved to escape before they left France. It was at this time that he was moved from his single cell and placed in one with a mixed group of resisters and black-marketeers. Among the former group were the brothers Paul and Raoul Simon, who had been part of the team he had been putting together to liberate Brossolette. They told him of the death of Valentin Abeille, who had been mortally wounded on 31 May when the Gestapo tried to arrest him, leaving Yeo-Thomas to reflect, not without reason: 'It seemed to me that all my friends were doomed.' In spite of the hardships that he had endured, Yeo-Thomas had lost none of his qualities of leadership and pugnaciousness. When the Simon brothers were bullied by some of the criminals in the cell, Yeo-Thomas confronted the ringleader and knocked him out: 'It was a great comfort to me to feel that I could still punch my weight.'

The next day the party was transferred to a prison camp at the former military barracks at Compiègne. Although he had planned to use this journey as an opportunity for escape, security was too tight. While travelling in a soft-topped truck, he took the opportunity of secretly scribbling a note to Barbara, addressing it to José Dupuis:

> Dear Friends. Everything is fine. I am leaving for Germany –
> reassure Barbara – see you soon, with love to you all, especially
> Barbara – Cheval – Shelley – Write to Barbara for me. Tell her to
> be brave and patient – I will return soon.
>
> Cheval

Yeo-Thomas dropped it out of the side of the truck as they passed a
group of workmen and he was delighted to see that one of the men
picked it up and waved.[11]

Compiègne was far from being a holiday camp, but in many ways
it was a great improvement on Fresnes. Yeo-Thomas, the Simon
brothers and two other resisters, Luquet and Deschamps, were able
to stay together in one of the barracks and, although the huts were
lousy and the ablutions disgraceful, the food was better and they had
much of the day to themselves. Inevitably their thoughts turned
to escape, but the camp perimeter was overlooked by watchtowers
containing machine-gun nests. As they could not get out through the
wire, they investigated the possibility of using the camp sewers, but
these proved too narrow for a man to pass through.

Never one to shirk a difficult undertaking, Yeo-Thomas worked on
an elaborate escape plan with Jacques Roberty, an inmate who had
been a member of the resistance and who now managed to exert a
surprising degree of influence over his German captors. He had
arranged for money to be smuggled into the camp and used it to
bribe some of his guards. This enabled him to maintain contact with
the outside world and Yeo-Thomas helped Roberty develop an escape
plan that had many similarities to the scheme he had devised to free
Brossolette. Accomplices were to enter the camp posing as Germans
with forged papers requiring that Roberty and Yeo-Thomas be
handed over to them. However, just at this time, orders came that
inmates were to be transferred to Germany. On 20 July, Yeo-Thomas
wrote a letter to José Dupuis that one of his contacts managed to have
smuggled out of the camp. It reflects the continued resilience of his
spirit and his undimmed love for Barbara.

> I am at Compiègne and about to leave for Germany. My morale
> is good, but I am very worried about Barbara. I beg you to do
> everything possible to reassure her and make her understand
> that the war will not last for ever and that we will be together
> again soon. It's Barbara that concerns me so do everything you
> can for her and remind her that if anything bad happens to her
> then life will have no purpose for me – she represents everything
> that I hold dear in this world – tell her that I love her more than
> ever and I think of her constantly – I embrace her with all my

heart, with all my love – it's the uncertainty about this that has caused me the greatest distress since my arrest.

Yeo-Thomas was a little premature in announcing his departure, for he engineered a scheme that would keep him at Compiègne a while longer. As prisoners suspected of having a contagious disease were not moved, as a precaution against spreading the illness, Yeo-Thomas had one of the camp doctors give him an injection that induced a high temperature. He was therefore taken off the roll of prisoners for deportation and, even when the fever had passed, he reported daily to the infirmary to receive 'medication'.[12] Even as he waited for his plan with Roberty to come to fruition, he also sought to bribe his way out. The camp dentist, Bernard Marty, was particularly useful to him and put him in touch with an inmate named Michel Nolde who, as something of an entrepreneur, tried to set up deals with members of the camp administration. However, the lack of mutual trust and the risks involved for prisoners and Germans alike led to the collapse of the project. Yeo-Thomas now had to hope that his scheme with Roberty would prove more successful.

He managed to avoid another clearance of the camp but then, after three weeks at Compiègne, he learnt that he was in serious trouble. The activities of his friends on the outside had resulted in his prisoner category being downgraded. His file should have borne three stars, indicating that he was a saboteur and terrorist; this would have marked him out for elimination within the concentration-camp system. Instead, they had managed to arrange for his papers to be altered, downgrading him to a one-star, minor offender. Now, he was informed that his three-star status had been restored. On 8 August he was ordered to report for immediate transfer to an unknown destination. Whatever his inner feelings, he made sure that he left his comrades with his motto 'Never give in'. Then, attended by no less than eight guards, he was driven out of the camp to the Gare de l'Est and a train for Germany.

CHAPTER EIGHT

· Buchenwald ·

At the Gare de l'Est, Yeo-Thomas was bundled on to a waiting train
and shoved into a carriage which contained two compartments with
doors of steel grilles. Both cells were crammed full of men and,
although there was already barely room for them all to stand, he
was nevertheless pushed in by his guards. Originally intended to
accommodate eight passengers, there were nineteen men in his
compartment alone. He quickly realized that it contained a veritable
Who's Who of the French resistance, including Lieutenant Stephane
Hessel, one of Dewavrin's agents, whom he had known quite well
in London. Hessel had been arrested while conducting a survey of
resistance groups in France. He spoke excellent German and was able
to inform Yeo-Thomas that the train was bound for Germany and,
probably, Buchenwald concentration camp. He also let him know
there were several other SOE officers among the party, including
Squadron Leader Maurice Southgate and two Canadians, Captain
Frank Pickersgill and Lieutenant John Macalister.

Southgate had first parachuted into France in January 1943 and
carried out excellent work in setting up a sabotage team. In October
1943, he returned to England but, after a debriefing and a well-
deserved rest, he was parachuted back in January 1944. He helped
develop maquis groups in his area until, in May, he was arrested by
the Gestapo at Montluçon. Southgate had neglected to observe the
agreed danger signals at his rendezvous and his capture showed yet
again that even the most diligent and experienced of agents could
make a mistake. It seemed at first that the Germans might remain
unaware of his true identity and his cover story held up well under
their questioning, but Southgate was transferred to Paris where, like
Yeo-Thomas, he was introduced to John Starr. The two men had
known each other well, even before their joining SOE, and Starr is
reported to have given the Germans confirmation of Southgate's
name and background.[1]

Pickersgill and Macalister had been dropped into France by
parachute in June 1943, but had been captured within days of their
arrival. The two agents resolutely resisted brutal interrogation but, in
spite of their unwillingness to assist their captors, the Germans were
able to 'play back' Macalister's wireless set using the crystals and
codes that had been captured with him. Pickersgill, and probably

Macalister, were sent to Ravitsch concentration camp in October
1943, while the 'radio game' was being played out in France. It was
not until March 1943 that London began to suspect that Pickersgill's
ARCHDEACON circuit was not all it seemed and instructed the
Canadian to make himself available for an S-phone dialogue with
Gerry Morel, a senior F Section staff officer. Pickersgill was brought
back from Poland and offered many inducements to collaborate in
the deception. He responded by attempting to escape, killing one
guard and wounding a second with a broken bottle before being
felled by four bullets. Starr was brought out of his 'sanctuary' in the
avenue Foch and was instructed to impersonate the recalcitrant and
incapacitated Canadian, but demurred at the last moment. The game
over, Pickersgill (now recovered from his wounds) and Macalister
were no longer of potential use in Paris and, with the Allied armies
bearing down upon the city, it was decided to remove them to
Germany. Yeo-Thomas learnt that, although other British officers
were in the second cell, the rest of his fellow passengers were Belgian
and French members of the resistance.

Although squashed and uncomfortable, Yeo-Thomas at least
initially had the unique privilege of remaining without handcuffs.
However, this situation soon changed when one of his guards
noticed Yeo-Thomas's comparative freedom and became incensed.
The German ranted and raved but, for a man who had just endured
months of torture and interrogation, the agent was far from cowed.
According to Hessel, Yeo-Thomas was clearly 'noticeable by a firm
and resolute attitude which he adopted towards German personnel'.
He doubtless expected worse than harsh words when he was
searched and a penknife was discovered sewn into the lining of his
waistcoat. Fortunately, the German's anger had already been spent
and he contented himself with handcuffing Yeo-Thomas to a fellow
prisoner.

As the train left Paris, Yeo-Thomas ascertained that he was the
most senior ranking officer among the party and therefore assumed
command. Southgate and another F Section agent, Major Henri
Frager, were enlisted as his assistants in organizing a rota that would
enable each of the crowded and tired prisoners to take a turn at sitting
on the compartment's benches. Frager was a Frenchman who had
joined SOE as a recruit in France and had then been withdrawn to
England, from where he made three missions back to his country. He
had only recently been captured and his evident strength of character
made a great impression on Yeo-Thomas. They also hoped to pool
the limited amount of food held by the prisoners, but some of the
more selfish among the group who were in possession of Red
Cross food parcels refused to share their good fortune with their

companions. It was both a depressing and annoying experience for Yeo-Thomas to witness such behaviour among men whom he felt should have been bound together by a common purpose. However, his endeavours did not go unnoticed and, as Hessel later reported: 'Throughout the journey, Yeo-Thomas paid great attention to the welfare of all in the party which is slightly exceptional for prisoners who are usually fully occupied in looking after themselves.'

It was soon apparent that the group needed to be further organized in order to answer calls of nature. Under Yeo-Thomas's instructions, Hessel spoke to the guards and negotiated an arrangement whereby each pair of prisoners would be escorted to the lavatory in turn. On his visit, Yeo-Thomas took the opportunity to look into the carriage's other compartments and noted that one contained women prisoners. Among them were two whom he subsequently discovered were F Section agents, Noor Inayat Khan and Violette Szabo.

Inayat Khan was a wireless operator who had been landed by Lysander in June the previous year. Exposed by a major German counter-espionage offensive, she bravely continued to operate, refusing suggestions from London that she be evacuated. Considering her lamentable sense of security, it was miraculous that she should have managed to survive as long as she did. However, she was eventually betrayed and captured in October 1943. She was yet another agent whose story crossed that of John Starr and, together with a French intelligence officer, Léon Faye, the three made an abortive attempt to escape from the avenue Foch. Inayat Khan's bravery is further emphasized by the fact that she had made an earlier unsuccessful attempt on her own. She was later sent to Dachau concentration camp, where she was killed on 13 September 1944. After the war she was awarded a posthumous George Cross. Violette Szabo, a courier, had parachuted into France on her second mission in June 1944. She had been captured after a shoot-out with German security forces a few days after her arrival and was taken to Paris for interrogation. Like Inayat Khan, Szabo was to die in captivity, being killed at Ravensbrück concentration camp early in 1945. She, too, was posthumously awarded the George Cross.

When it was the turn of the second cellful of men to go to the lavatory, they had to pass in front of Yeo-Thomas's compartment. Among the faces that went by were two that he immediately recognized. He had known Denis Barrett as a fellow translator at the RAF Interpretation Unit at Reims in 1939. Since that time, the two men had lost touch and, while Yeo-Thomas had joined RF Section, Barrett had been recruited into F. A wireless operator, he had been captured at a roadblock in July on his second mission to France. It was bad enough glimpsing a former colleague in such parlous circumstances, but Yeo-Thomas was particularly distressed to catch sight of his friend and fellow RF Section officer, Captain Desmond Hubble. In London, he had tried to persuade Hubble, a family man, not to accept an operational mission, but his words had fallen on deaf ears. As he later wrote to Hubble's mother: 'As a matter of fact I tried to dissuade him from carrying on in our somewhat insecure line of work, but he would not even consider changing his mind.' Hubble had parachuted into the Ardennes on Operation CITRONELLE, during which his group had been overrun by German forces. The fact that he had been operating in uniform (which he was still wearing) had not prevented him being treated by the Germans as a 'terrorist'.

Inevitably, it did not take long for Yeo-Thomas's thoughts to turn to escape and he found willing allies among most of his fellow prisoners. However, one of the faint-hearted members of the party proved to be the man to whom he was handcuffed: 'I had a rather heated conversation with him. I told him that as he was unfortunate enough to be attached to me, he would have to follow me whether or not he liked it, and that if he tried to hamper me, he would be behind and would therefore provide a splendid target if we were fired at. Our relations were, as a result, anything but cordial.'

Their best chance of escape appeared to lie in the hope that the train would be stopped by an Allied air raid or resistance action en route to Germany. In such an event, they anticipated that their guards might flee and, in the confusion, the prisoners could make a break for it. It was therefore with mixed feelings that afternoon that they realized that they were under attack. Aeroplanes roared overhead and, following an explosion, the train shuddered to a halt. It did not now seem quite so desirable to be under fire as cannon shells ripped into the carriages. At the outset of the attack, the guards had left them in order to set up machine guns at the side of the track to engage the aircraft, but the prisoners still had no means of escape and now felt dreadfully exposed. Furthermore, deprived of the cooling ventilation provided by the train's movement, they began to suffer badly from the heat. It was now that some of the women prisoners appeared with water, crawling along the floor of the carriage to try and gain some protection from the bullets. Yeo-Thomas marvelled at their bravery and selflessness and, noting that one of them was Violette Szabo, later wrote: 'They passed the water to us, went back and returned with some more for the other compartment. Through the din, they shouted words of encouragement to us, and seemed quite unperturbed. I can only express my unbounded admiration for them and words are so inadequate that I cannot hope to say what I felt then and feel now.'

Eventually the air raid ceased, but for several hours the train did

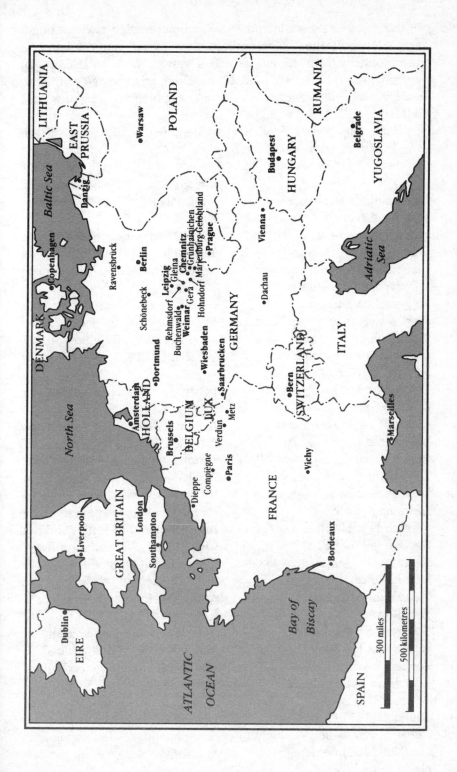

not move. At last, some lorries arrived alongside the track, but hopes of an escape during the transfer to them were dampened by the announcement from the guards that if anyone made an attempt, all the remaining prisoners would be shot out of hand. Nevertheless, Yeo-Thomas still intended to seize any opportunity that presented itself.

As they set off, Yeo-Thomas was able, at last, to examine the full complement of men. They were:

	Captured	*Organization*
Lieutenant E A L Allard	April 1944	F Section
Jean Avallard	?	?
Flight Lieutenant D J Barrett	July 1944	F Section
Captain R M C Benoist	July 1944	F Section
Lieutenant J Bougennec (served as 'F Garrel')	September 1943	F Section
Jacques Chaigneau	?	?
Marcel Corbusier	?	?
Pierre Culioli	June 1943	F Section
Lieutenant A Defendini	February 1944	F Section
Jean de Ségnier	?	?
Lieutenant J T J M Detal	February 1944	F Section
Jean Evesque	?	?
Major H J P Frager	August 1944	F Section
Lieutenant E A H Garry	August 1943	F Section
René Gerard	?	?
Lieutenant P A H Geelen	April 1944	F Section
Lieutenant Bernard Guillot	?	?
Lieutenant S Hessel	?	BCRA
Captain D E Hubble	June 1944	RF Section
Captain G P G Keun (known as 'Kane')	June 1944	SIS
Jean Lavallee	?	?
Lieutenant M Leccia	April 1944	F Section
Yves Loison	?	?
Captain J K Macalister	June 1943	F Section
Lieutenant J A Mayer	May 1944	F Section
Captain P L Mulsant	July 1944	F Section
Captain H L T Peulevé (known as 'Poole')	March 1944	F Section
Captain F H D Pickersgill	June 1943	F Section
Christian Rambaud	?	?
Captain C Rechenmann	May 1944	F Section
Henri Reusch	?	?

Lieutenant R Sabourin (known as 'Mackenzie')	March 1944	F Section
Squadron Leader M Southgate	May 1944	F Section
Captain A Steele	April 1944	F Section
Paul Vellaud	?	?
Captain G A Wilkinson and Yeo-Thomas.[2]	June 1944	F Section

The prisoners were driven to Châlons-sur-Marne and then on to Verdun, where they spent the night in the stables of a military barracks. Although the Germans tried to keep the men and women separated, snatched conversations were possible, and Violette Szabo and one of the other F Section agents, Harry Peulevé, were able to renew their friendship. They had met in London after he had returned from his first mission to France, having broken both legs on landing and subsequently escaped on crutches into Spain over the Pyrenees. The couple had hit it off and met on a few more occasions before Peulevé returned to France in September 1943. After a singularly successful period as a wireless operator and organizer of a large maquis group in the Corrèze *département*, he had been captured in March 1944. This meeting between Szabo and Peulevé, while comforting, was tragic. They were never to see each other again.

After a decent sleep and a rare opportunity for a wash, Yeo-Thomas's spirits improved immensely. They picked up even more when he managed to swap partners and was handcuffed to his friend, Hubble. He was even feeling distinctly bullish: 'I certainly was pleased to be rid of my former twin whose continual moaning was beginning to get me annoyed. I also knew that with Hubble as my partner, if there was an escape possible, he would join in it with might and main.'

At Verdun, the male prisoners parted company with the women and were driven across the border to the German city of Saarbrücken. Just before reaching it, they turned into a grim, hutted camp surrounded by barbed-wire fences and watchtowers. It seemed a distinctly menacing and a depressing place, an assumption immediately confirmed when Yeo-Thomas was beaten and kicked by a guard as he and Hubble jumped off the truck. A more systematic brutalization followed, with the guards lining up the prisoners and administering beatings at random, leaving Yeo-Thomas to recall: 'We had never expected to be particularly well treated but this was certainly far worse than we had bargained for, and we were only getting a foretaste of still worse things to come. I was boiling with rage, but could do nothing, none of us could, and that was the worst, the feeling of helplessness.'

They were next shackled together in five-man groups and locked in a tiny hut that had served as a camp kitchen. On a blazing hot day the thirty-seven men were confined in an area measuring less than ten feet square. As ever, Yeo-Thomas determined that the group should stick together. In addition to Hubble, Southgate and Frager, he had selected two other officers as suitable candidates to assist him. The first, Captain R C Benoist, another F Section operative, had been captured in July 1944 on his second mission to France. The second was, for once, not an F Section officer.

This was Captain 'Gerald Kane', who remained something of an enigma even among the group of secret agents. Even Yeo-Thomas seems not to have learnt much about him, only recording that 'Kane' spoke of his family. This shadowy individual was, with the exception of Yeo-Thomas, arguably the most important of the group. His real name was Gerald Philip George Keun, born at Tiverton, Devon, on 10 August 1911, the son of a Dutch Sephardic Jew who, it has been stated, travelled using a Danish passport, and who ran one of Europe's leading pharmaceutical opium companies. Although the family lived in great affluence at Cap d'Antibes in the South of France, Philip was sent to England for his education. One account[3] claims that he went to the Catholic public school, Downside, while one of Keun's official files states that it was Blundells. He then went on to the Collège Stanislaus in France, after which he appears to have flirted with communism 'and went to work as a labourer in Turkey, where, being a clever linguist, he began to translate Shakespeare into Turkish'.[4] During this time he also appears to have travelled in Rumania and Bulgaria and acquired a knowledge of those languages. Bearing in mind his cosmopolitan background, it is not surprising that, on the outbreak of war, Keun joined the French Foreign Legion. He served in the 2ème Compagnie, 12ème Régiment de l'Infanterie Étrangère, a unit that was so heavily engaged in the combat in northern France in 1940 that by 6 June it was reduced to 300 men. Along with many of his comrades-in-arms, Keun fell into German hands as a prisoner of war. After a year's captivity, he escaped from his prison camp at Cambrai and made his way south to the Unoccupied Zone, ending up in Marseille. Here he began to develop a variety of contacts and by June 1941 was working with French Naval Intelligence. The following spring, he was in touch with a Colonel 'Abel' of one of the British secret services and subsequently switched his allegiance from his French masters to him. The details of Keun's movements are, hardly surprisingly, far from precise. His file indicates that he was active in Paris, Bordeaux, Lyon, the Loire and northern France, as well as on the Mediterranean coast. It would also appear that he visited England to report to his British controllers. Keun was flown to England by Lysander on Operation POLYANTHUS on

20/21 June 1943, and again on 10/11 September on LARKSPUR. Later that year he returned to England by sea, and he seriously damaged his spine during his parachute drop back to France in February 1944. On one of these visits to England, he was appointed a Captain on the Army General List, Serial Number 282881, and, according to one document, had joined SOE on 1 June 1942.

It may be that his initial contacts were with this organization, but he certainly did not remain long under its auspices. In France he made contact with Father Claude Arnould, a Jesuit priest who was serving as an agent of the French Secret Service under cover of being a coal merchant, using the *nom de guerre* 'Claude Ollivier'. In 1943 the two men formed an intelligence network called 'Jade Amicol', the latter part of the name being formed from Keun's codename 'Amiral' and Arnould's 'Colonel'. Most of their informants and helpers were drawn from the Roman Catholic community and their headquarters was housed at the convent of the Sisters of St Agonie in the rue de la Santé in Paris. The organization reported directly to SIS and its controllers have been named as the ubiquitous Claude Dansey and Commander Wilfred 'Biffy' Dunderdale. The network proved to be an immense success. 'By mid-1944 Jade Amicol had become one of the largest and most secure networks in Europe, with some 1500 sub-agents, mainly former French officers and soldiers, railwaymen and clerics. Their chief success had been to secure the plans of the Atlantic Wall.'[5]

It has been reported that Keun and Arnould were in touch with members of the German resistance, notably Admiral Wilhelm Canaris, the former head of the Abwehr, in May and June 1944. There are even claims that Keun went to London for briefings on this matter with SIS and No 10 Downing Street, but substantiation of the episode remains far from convincing. By the late spring and early summer of 1944, Canaris had seen the Abwehr absorbed into the Nazi Party intelligence apparatus and found himself demoted to head of a special staff for economic warfare. Although there is always the possibility that Canaris managed to extricate himself from Gestapo surveillance, it must be assumed that it would have been most unlikely that he would have been able to conduct various clandestine activities in Paris undetected. Whatever the accuracy of some of the accounts of Keun's German connections in the summer of 1944, it is certain that he was not present to witness the joy of France's liberation. He was betrayed by one of his French contacts and, on 29 June 1944, was arrested by the Gestapo. It seems likely that his captors remained unaware of his real importance and, like Yeo-Thomas, he played up his status as an ordinary British officer. Thereafter his work in France remained secret and one trusted fellow prisoner later described him as 'tall, very dark, with marked brows and lashes, nose slightly turned up at the end, a very intelligent face. He spoke Bulgarian and was thus able to get into conversation with Russians in the camp. He had worked in Rumania and Bulgaria and had apparently done magnificent work.'

Opinions vary as to the length of time the group were kept at Saarbrücken, with Hessel stating it was two days, Yeo-Thomas three, and Peulevé four. Whatever the number, it seemed like an eternity with only the occasional release from the hut to swallow some foul-tasting soup, empty the oil drum that served as their latrine and bathe in a pond of green, slimy water. For men who had already experienced at first hand the brutality of Nazi Germany, the sights they witnessed in the Saarbrücken concentration camp made a great impression, as Peulevé later wrote: 'We stayed four days in Saarbrücken and I saw some of the effects that concentration camp life had on the long-term prisoners. Living out every moment of their lives like hunted animals, they had become like it in appearance; their features were animal, bestial. Some of them had been eminent men, leaders of European thought and art; their only thoughts now were how to scrounge more food or avoid a blow. I saw something too of the reactions of the SS. Handpicked sadists let loose to vent all their lowest instincts on helpless prisoners. My initiation into concentration camp life was beginning.' On witnessing the SS's violence against the inmates, Hubble commented to Yeo-Thomas: 'If this is an example of German Kultur, the sooner the bastards are wiped out the better.'

Even in the hell of the camp, hope still sprang eternal and they continued to speculate whether they would soon be transferred to a prisoner-of-war camp. Their hopes were raised when they were paraded and taken to Saarbrücken station, under guard by a detachment of army *Feldgendarmen*, not SS. Moreover, their travelling conditions were much improved. The journey began in a goods wagon in which there was sufficient room for them to lie down when they chose and which offered a limitless supply of fresh air. This respite allowed them to turn their thoughts once again to escape. The most obvious, if none too sophisticated, scheme was to overpower the three guards in the wagon and leap from the train. A dozen of the prisoners were willing to risk being shot by the other guards or killing themselves in the fall but, yet again, the weak-willed among them opposed their action. Convinced that they were being sent to a prisoner-of-war camp, they neither wanted to take the risk of escape themselves nor suffer the reprisals following an attempt made by the others. Yeo-Thomas overruled their complaints and approved the escape plan, but the malcontents were obdurate and threatened to inform the guards of their intentions. Yeo-Thomas considered having it out with them there and then but knew that the guards would intervene to separate the quarrelsome prisoners, and would increase their vigilance. There was nothing that he could do but accept the inevitable and call off the escape. Yeo-Thomas later reflected that, as none of the dissenters survived the war, 'they might just as well have followed us. Well, none of us could foresee at that moment what was in store for us. Had such been the case, I wonder what they would have decided to do?'

Eventually, the prisoners were transferred to an ordinary third-class railway carriage where they got into conversation with the officer in charge of the guard detachment. It was from this German that they received confirmation of Hessel's belief that they were destined for Buchenwald concentration camp, but according to the officer, the prospect did not seem too bad. According to Peulevé, 'He painted a glowing picture of the place. "But certainly," he said, "you will be much happier here than prison. There is a fine library with books in all languages, concerts on the square every night, a cinema, theatre and even a brothel. There is a finely equipped hospital and the food is very good; you get practically the same as the civilians." I don't think the captain was trying to fool us; probably, like many other Germans who had never been inside the camp, he believed Goebbels's story that it was a sort of prisoners' paradise.'

At about midnight on 16 August 1944, the train pulled into Weimar station and the prisoners' carriage was uncoupled and shunted into a siding within a barbed-wire compound. They had arrived at Buchenwald concentration camp.

The camp had been built on the side of the Ettersberg Mountain, some five miles north of the city of Weimar, the capital of the province of Thuringia. Construction had begun in July 1937 as part of the Nazis' programme of interning German society's 'anti-social' elements. The definition of anti-social was broad and encompassed virtually anyone whom the Nazis maintained constituted a political, moral or racial threat to their regime. Thus, inmates ranged from recidivist criminals to communists, from Jews to Jehovah's Witnesses. Even after the outbreak of war, the camp remained relatively small, rarely exceeding 10,000 inmates, but in 1943 its numbers began to increase until, in August 1944, when Yeo-Thomas and his party arrived, it housed over 82,000 people. Although not an extermination camp such as Auschwitz, the overcrowding and the SS's disregard for the prisoners' welfare had resulted in a radical deterioration of the already inadequate conditions. Yeo-Thomas sensed the pervading atmosphere as they entered: 'We marched past the ends of a lot of huts, all completely dark, standing ghost-like in the moonlight, still in complete silence, with only the occasional howl of dogs. The whole atmosphere was sinister. I felt as though some unseen danger stalked around us, chilling me to the bones in spite of the mildness of the air.'

When they disembarked from the train they were handed over by the *Feldgendarmen* to SS guards who, in turn, passed them to Lagerschutz or trusties, camp inmates who assisted the SS in camp administration. They were ushered into a disinfection centre where they stripped and showered before being shaved and disinfected like animals. Peulevé wrote: 'The delousing station impressed us: it was a modern, hygienic place. We passed through a hall where we were made to empty our pockets, the contents of which were put into little bags. We then stripped and our clothes were put on clothes hangers and enclosed in large paper bags; we were given a metal disc as a receipt. From here we went into a long room full of white-coated barbers, each of whom had electric clippers with which he shaved us completely from head to foot. After the clippers we were doused in disinfectant which burned horribly, each given a handful of soft soap and passed into an enormous white tiled room with hundreds of sprinklers in the ceiling. The hot water was turned on and we had a good shower.'

The prisoners were then issued with a pair of wooden clogs and an odd assortment of ill-fitting civilian clothes, in addition to the distinctive blue-and-white striped concentration camp uniform. It was while this was taking place that they were addressed by an inmate who spoke to them in English. It transpired that this was Lieutenant Maurice Pertschuk of F Section, who had been captured in April 1943. Known in the camp as 'Perkins', he gave them a warning that was far from corresponding with the glowing testimony from the German officer on the train: 'He warned us that we were in one of the worse concentration camps in Germany, that the life was dreadful, the death rate appalling, the treatment the worst, and that we must be very careful.'

Next, they were formally registered, given an identity number (in Yeo-Thomas's case 14.624) and issued with red cloth triangles to sew on their clothes, denoting that they were political prisoners.[6] They were then marched to one of the huts, Block 17, that was contained within its own barbed-wire fence. As ever, Hubble and Yeo-Thomas teamed up and, in the overcrowded sleeping area, with bunk beds stretching to the ceiling, they shared a bunk together.

Even in Buchenwald, where the extraordinary had become commonplace, the arrival of a party of secret agents created a stir. Although they were prevented from exploring the camp themselves, other inmates came to see them and questioned them through the barbed wire. The news was not good. Apart from the Kapos (head trusties) and Lagerschutz, most of the inmates seemed emaciated and totally apathetic. As the situation seemed worse than they had feared, Yeo-Thomas called together a meeting of the thirty-seven men. In spite of the usual grumblings of the few, they decided to form an escape committee and, as a first step, to carry out a full analysis of their position and a reconnaissance of the camp. They received immediate help from Pertschuk and another F Section prisoner, Christopher Burney, who had been captured in August 1942 and subsequently endured a year and a half's solitary confinement in Fresnes before being sent to Buchenwald. They explained that the camp had witnessed an internal power struggle between the criminal inmates (the 'Greens') and the communists (the 'Reds') that had left the latter in the ascendant. This struggle for supremacy was observed with some benevolence by the SS, who had exploited its divide-and-rule potential to the full and who used it to ensure that the camp was run in the most efficient and trouble-free manner. They had originally backed the 'Greens', 'for they saw in this reign of terror security for themselves and a simplification of their task of slave-driving, and only demanded of their creatures that they bow and scrape and click their heels before the sacred uniform'.[7]

However, as Buchenwald developed as an SS industrial complex, the brutality of the criminals became of less use than the communists' wealth of experience in the workshop and on the factory floor. Increased efficiency and productivity led the SS to see the communists in a new light: 'They began to look at the Reds from a new angle, and seeing all too clearly that the office administration of the camp under the Greens left much to be desired and was continually breaking down, they chose a few of the more important posts and handed them over to the Reds.'[8]

Burney and Pertschuk warned that not much assistance could be expected from the communists and predicted that the presence of British officers in the camp would be resented, especially if it were felt that the newcomers constituted a threat to their control.

As news of the agents' arrival spread throughout the camp, each day seemed to turn up an old friend or acquaintance. Among them was Commandant Pierre Julitte, a former member of Dewavrin's staff in London and a leading BCRA agent in France. There was also Colonel Frédéric Manhès, whom Yeo-Thomas knew well both from London and Paris, and Pierre Péry, who had been captured at Serreulles's office at the rue de la Pompe. Yeo-Thomas was at great pains to warn them of his 'Dodkin' alias, because he had already received warnings regarding stool pigeons among the inmates.

Slowly, Yeo-Thomas and the others began to acclimatize themselves to the camp routine. At the beginning and end of the day, prisoners were summoned to the *Appel* or roll call. They were lined up in their barracks groups on the square where they were counted by their block chiefs who then reported the numbers to the ss guards. If there were any discrepancies, the numbers were re-counted until the guards were satisfied. Therefore, in wind, rain or snow, and sometimes for as long as four hours, the prisoners had to brave the elements while the headcount continued. Block 17, as an isolation hut, was spared the general muster but the inmates still had to parade outside the hut while the roll call was made. After the evening *Appel*, details were sent to the camp kitchens to fetch the food that was brought back to the block for consumption. Hunger was a permanent feature of their lives and the meagre rations were barely enough to keep them alive.

The daily routine was ordered by the SS but was mostly adminis-tered by the Kapos and their staff. The rest of the camp began its day at 4am with yelled instructions of *'Aufstehen!'* ('Stand up!') to the inmates of the blocks which provided men for the work parties. Block 17 was excused this activity and therefore Yeo-Thomas and his companions did not have to rise until six o'clock. They made a point of maintaining personal hygiene as much as was possible and washed every day, in spite of the fact that most of the other inmates had long since ceased to bother. They were then ordered to leave the hut and had to remain outside for much of the day.

In addition to the schedule imposed by the camp authorities, Yeo-Thomas and his group began to develop their own regime. They were allowed to collect a selection of the few personal items that had not been looted by their German guards en route to the camp. These included articles of clothes, toiletries and, in Hubble's case, a small, wooden travelling chess set. The very possession of these items elevated their spirits and Yeo-Thomas determined to build on this by deciding, after consultation with his supporters, that the group should endeavour to maintain a rigorous group discipline. They were to march everywhere they went in the camp in a military formation of fours and engage in regular physical training to maintain their health and morale. Pickersgill was a keen supporter of this policy: 'When a ragged section went off to draw its rations Pickersgill would march at its head, chin up, shoulders back, singing. For a moment or two his followers would be too miserable to fall into step or take up the refrain. Then the poignant loneliness of Pickersgill's bearing and voice would shame them and they too would start marching and singing.'[9]

It was not all route marches and arduous callisthenics. During the brief periods when they were allowed in the hut they held a bridge competition with home-made cards (manufactured by Pickersgill) and played a chess tournament using Hubble's set. Yeo-Thomas was proudly to recall, with uncharacteristic immodesty: 'I was in an

BUCHENWALD   173

unassailable position, for I had won seven of my games and could not
be caught up.'

There was plenty of time for Yeo-Thomas and his associates to
develop their assessment of the camp's layout and organization.
Through Burney, Pertschuk and a Dutch naval officer, Lieutenant
Pieter Cool, they managed to obtain permission to move about the
camp. They were able to see that, in addition to the main camp in
which Block 17 was situated, there was a small camp of ramshackle
huts and tents in which thousands of inmates were incarcerated in the
most appalling of conditions.

> The population soon after opening stood at 7,000 to 8,000
> prisoners. Among them were numerous children of three years
> and up. These prisoners were poorly clothed and insufficiently
> nourished; most had no blankets and in scorching heat no water
> for drinking or washing. (At the beginning, after completion of
> the water pipes, water flowed only on Sunday mornings, later
> on, up to an hour every day.) In pouring rain that lasted for
> weeks, dressed in insufficient, worn-out clothing, barefoot
> prisoners sank into the softened clay soil.[10]

Another distinctly separate area was the compound in which Soviet
prisoners of war were kept. They made a profoundly favourable
impression upon Burney:

> There were the regular prisoners-of-war, recognized as such by
> the Germans, but treated as all other prisoners except that they
> lived in separate blocks, theoretically isolated, and that the
> senior officers did not work. They were about 800 in number,
> and included six brigade commanders (full colonels) and a
> large number of junior officers, of whom many preferred to pass
> as other ranks. They provided the best element in the camp.
> They were clean, honest, disciplined, cheerful and thoroughly
> deserved the respect which was accorded them. They kept
> themselves very much to themselves and had little to do with the
> non-Russians, but towards myself and the other Englishmen
> they never failed to show a spontaneous friendship, which was
> one of the warmest fires before which we could sit.[11]

There were various camp amenities that were either available solely
to the privileged or were amenities only in name. A brothel had
been constructed by the camp authorities in 1943, in preference to
expanding the infirmary. It was staffed by women brought from
Ravensbrück concentration camp and the SS had hoped to use it to

corrupt the Kapos and their associates. There was even a cinema in which German propaganda films were screened, although this also served as a place where punishments were exacted on inmates. Both the brothel and the cinema were a means of extracting money from those inmates who had either smuggled in cash or had managed to have funds sent to them from the outside. In terms of the revenue that was brought into the SS coffers, neither of these establishments could compare to the industrial and munitions plant that had developed alongside the camp, and from which it drew its workforce.

In addition to the camp hospital that ostensibly served the needs of the inmates, there were three other 'medical' establishments. The pathology department was a means by which the SS exploited the abundance of corpses in the camp for research and educative purposes. Even more sinister were Block 50, the laboratory, and Block 46, the hut housing inmates known as 'guinea pigs'. The former facility was devoted to the study of typhus and development of a vaccine, while the latter monitored the medical condition of those unfortunate prisoners who had been deliberately contaminated with the fever.

When Yeo-Thomas and his group completed their reconnaissance, they 'had a fairly good knowledge of the geography of the camp, and had learned a lot about the conditions reigning in it. The situation certainly did not seem promising; on the contrary it appeared far worse than we had thought possible. We had seen a large number of walking skeletons, shambling about aimlessly, with eyes that reflected utter despair; it was obvious that they were doomed and were on the verge of dropping dead in their tracks from starvation. We had seen the barbed-wire fences that ringed the camp and that they were electrified. We had noted the Miradors [watchtowers], all with machine guns trained on the camp, and also having searchlights. We had seen the patrols marching outside the wires and realized that the camp was very closely guarded. There seemed no chance of getting out through the wire, and it was evident that the only feasible solution to our problem was the use of some stratagem. In spite of this, we still kept in mind the possibility of getting some arms and trying to fight our way out if things got really desperate.'

Having concluded their survey, they continued to develop their contacts among the camp community. Two further F Section agents appeared, Alfred and Henry Newton. They had been parachuted into France in June 1942 and had been arrested in April the following year. Like Moulin, they had had to endure the tender mercies of Klaus Barbie during their interrogation in Lyon. The brothers had been placed in separate blocks and had both risen to the level of Stubdiensts (assistants to the block leaders) and therefore were well placed to provide information and even a few luxuries. At this time a further and ultimately crucial contact was made through Benoist. This was Dr Alfred Balachowsky of the typhus laboratory. Balachowsky had previously worked for the Ministère de l'Agriculture and had been about to join the prestigious Pasteur Institute in Paris when he was arrested for his membership of the SOE PROSPER network to which Culioli and Garry belonged.[12]

Yeo-Thomas, however, was concerned not to restrict his contacts merely to British officers and their French colleagues. If he was to realize his ambition of forming a potent resistance network within the camp, he needed to extend the range of connections. Together with Hubble and Keun, Yeo-Thomas met with the Lagerältesten (camp seniors) and the Kapo of the camp barbers. These men were the leaders of the communist faction within the camp and, as Yeo-Thomas had cooperated effectively with their French comrades, he had hoped that, in spite of Burney's warnings, he might manage to develop good relations with them. However, matters were not to be as harmonious as he would have wished: 'We exchanged views, but we very quickly realized that we could expect very little assistance from them, for we were obviously catalogued as "capitalists". We were extremely polite on both sides.'

Happily, contacts with other groups were far more amicable. The Poles, as usual, proved themselves the masters of intelligence and had developed an effective underground network in the camp that was able to feed important information to Yeo-Thomas. Clearly another significant group were the Russian prisoners and he called on the two colonels who were the senior ranking officers. During the course of several meetings, he 'discussed with them the possibilities of joining forces and forming a disciplined, efficient body of men, prepared to fight out the issue to the bitter end, if matters came to a showdown. We agreed on the principle, and went as far as dividing our combined forces into small groups of ten men each, each group placed under the orders of a competent NCO or officer, the whole to be commanded by a joint staff comprising the two senior Russian officers, myself, assisted by Kane [Keun], Hubble and Southgate.' However, events were to overtake them. Soon after their discussions the two Russian officers were executed.

While Yeo-Thomas's acclimatization continued, on 24 August the camp was subjected to an Allied air raid.[13] The target was not the camp itself but the factory outside it, in which the SS produced a variety of war matériel. The accuracy of the attack drew the praise of the inmates and they took great pleasure in witnessing the panic it induced among the guards and camp trusties. It was not without tragic consequences, however, and 384 prisoners were killed in the factories with a further 600 injured. Eighty SS were also killed in the attack. The camp itself was largely undamaged, apart from a few incendiary bombs that drifted into the compound, set alight a few administration huts and burned Goethe's oak. This tree at the centre of the camp, under which the German writer Johann Goethe had supposedly found his inspiration, had been lovingly tended. Its destruction was a source of further elation among the inmates, for there was a well-known superstition that, when it was felled, Germany would fall.

Ironically, it was shortly after the air raid that 168 Allied airmen were brought to the camp.[14] In total denial of the rules of war, they were stripped of their uniforms and dumped in the squalid conditions of the 'small camp'. They were blessed with a courageous and resolute senior officer, Squadron Leader Philip Lamason, who in Yeo-Thomas's opinion 'wielded a great moral and physical courage, a keen sense of humour and never admitted defeat'. Yeo-Thomas wasted no time in making contact with the group and enlisting them in his plans for a mass escape. The addition of such a body of men to his 'command' gave him far greater influence with his Soviet comrades-in-arms. Never one to shrink away from a grandiose scheme, Yeo-Thomas now began to develop another of his ambitious master plans, about which even he later commented: 'It was a harebrained scheme, but it was better than nothing.' This comprised a mass escape from the camp and, after seizing as many arms as possible, a raid on a nearby Luftwaffe airbase at Nohra, where they would steal aircraft to fly back to Britain. This plan seemed more like the storyline of an Errol Flynn film and, hardly surprisingly, the communists in the camp wanted to have nothing to do with it. Furthermore, they greatly feared the inevitable reprisals that would follow the attempt.

While their plans developed, the prisoners got to know each other better and sought to raise each other's spirits. Yeo-Thomas, Hubble, Barrett and a number of the others were sketched by a French inmate, Auguste Favier, and they spent much time talking about their back-grounds and their plans for their lives after the war.

> Hubble, Kane [Keun] and I became inseparable; we shared the same ideals, we were all three determined not to let the Huns get us down. We intended, in spite of being prisoners, to fight to the bitter end. We resolved to do everything in our power to boost the morale of all those around us, to remain cheerful and stick together. We were a truly happy trio, enjoying little jokes, reminiscing, sharing everything. Hubble would talk about his children, his family; Kane [Keun] talked of his school, his father, his friends; I did likewise. We discussed the relative merits of such and such a restaurant in London, discussed plays we had

seen, films, etc. It seemed as though we had formed a friendship that would hold us together, after the war was over, until we died. It certainly lasted unto death.

Then, on 9 September, they heard an announcement made over the camp loudspeaker system, ordering sixteen members of their group to report to the main gate. Among the names were those of Yeo-Thomas's two closest friends, Hubble and Keun, together with Allard, Benoist, Defendini, Detal, Garel, Garry, Geelen, Sabourin, Leccia, Macalister, Mayer, Pickersgill, Rechenmann and Steele. There seemed no reason for their being called and they came to the conclusion that it would simply be for a routine examination. After a few brief and, in hindsight, inconsequential words, the sixteen men marched off. Yeo-Thomas, Hessel and Peulevé went about their daily routine, but their minds were uneasy and, after a few minutes, they called on the block Älteste, to see if he could throw any light on the reasons behind the party's departure. At first the German seemed reluctant to answer Hessel's questions, then he pronounced the dreadful sentence: 'I do not think that you will ever see your comrades again.' When pressed for his reasons for coming to such a pessimistic conclusion, he simply told them that as condemned spies and terrorists, they would inevitably face execution. Aghast at the news, the trio confided in Southgate and Frager but resolved to keep the dreadful prediction from the other agents until they received confirmation.

That night Yeo-Thomas lay in his bunk, conscious of the space left by his bunk-mate Hubble: 'I was a long time getting to sleep, Hubble and Kane [Keun], my two bosom friends, where were they now? Were they alive or dead? I must find out in the morning, something must be done. I prayed for them and all the others; I still believed in God. I did not think He could forsake such fine men. My prayers gave me a certain amount of hope, and I slept.'

The morning brought no relief. A Polish informant told him that the sixteen were still alive but were destined for execution. During the day, there was no better news. One report stated that they had been seen outside the bunker but the block Älteste remained certain that they were soon to die. Another whole day was to pass before the Pole and Balachowsky came to confirm that the sixteen had been killed and their bodies had been cremated the previous night. In a postwar report, Balachowsky stated that they had been hanged at 5.30pm on 11 September, having first been beaten. The means of execution was particularly brutal, the nooses being hung from hooks let into in the wall a few metres from the ground. Thus they were killed by strangulation, taking an estimated five to ten minutes to die.

The news could not be hidden from the other members for long and, as senior officer, it was Yeo-Thomas's duty to tell the remaining men of their friends' fate. He did not pull his punches and informed them that a similar end probably awaited them: '. . . on the whole, they all took it well, but two or three were shaken and their morale dropped very low.'

The victims' effects were divided up among the survivors. Hubble's death had hit Yeo-Thomas particularly hard and he later described the depth of their friendship to the mother of his dead comrade:

> It is impossible to put in a letter the thousand little memories that constitute the story of our friendship, but if some day I have the pleasure of meeting you, I will tell you the whole story. I can only say this now: Desmond was one of the finest men I have ever met, one of the bravest. He never faltered, never weakened, and no man ever could have a better friend than he turned out to be. I feel proud to have been his comrade and to have been trusted by him. As long as I live, I will never forget him. He did his duty quietly and without fuss. His family can be very, very proud of him.

Inevitably, Yeo-Thomas acquired something of Hubble's, and he chose the chess set that had miraculously survived so many ordeals: 'I decreed that I would look after it, for I had made up my mind that if I managed to escape I would take the set back to Hubble's children.'

Yeo-Thomas had not forgotten his 'Never say die' adage and, even in this dark moment, he still strove for a means of escape. Hessel later wrote that Hubble's death gave extra inspiration to his friend's determination to save the remaining men. One scheme was proposed by Julitte, who suggested that the communist Kapo of the canteen might be able to assist them in an escape bid, but nothing came of it. The Russians were not able to help either and could only offer their condolences. Since he found himself unable to do anything to affect his destiny, Yeo-Thomas decided to leave a final testimony. Balachowsky provided paper and a quiet environment in Block 50 in which, aided by Peulevé, Yeo-Thomas encoded letters to Barbara and Dismore using his old SEAHORSE code. He wrote:

> Invaluable documents concerning latest research and discoveries bacteriological warfare also plans secret underground dumps and factories kept here at Buchenwald stop all prepared to secure them but can succeed only providing rapid assistance arrives just before or immediately upon German capitulation as camp officials will try destroy all valuable documents warrants every

effort stop speedy arrival airborne or paratroops essential will find organized assistance within camp but I have no arms stop bearer this message trustworthy and knows everything awaits reply and instructions stop acknowledge by Idoform du moineau au lapin stop have everything under control and hope for early victory stop vingt-cinq septembre stop all my love Barbara Tommy stop Cheerio Dizzy Asymptote.

A less upbeat letter was written for Dismore and was, demonstrably, the last testament of a condemned man:

14 September 1944

My dear Dizzy

These are 'famous last words' I am afraid, but one has to face death one day or another so I will not moan and get down to brass tacks.

I will not attempt to make a report on my journey except to say that up to the very moment of my arrest it had been a success and I had got things cracking and woken up a number of slumberers. I was quite pleased with things – I took every precaution and neglected nothing – my capture was due to one of those incidents one cannot provide for – I had so much work that I was overwhelmed so I asked PIC [Pichard] to provide me with a sure, dependable *agent de liaison*, and he gave me a young chap called Guy, whom I renamed Antonin. He worked for me for a week, and then got caught; how I do not know, but in any case, he had an appointment with me at 11am on Tuesday 21st March by the métro Passy and brought the Gestapo with him. He was obviously unable to withstand bullying and very quickly gave in to questioning. I was caught coming around a corner and had not an earthly chance, being collared and handcuffed before I could say 'knife'. I was badly beaten up in the car on the way to Gestapo HQ, arriving there with a twisted nose and a head about twice its normal size. I was then subjected to four days' continuous grilling, being beaten up and also being put into a bath of icy cold water, legs and arms chained, and held head downwards under water until almost drowned, then pulled out and asked if I had anything to say. This I underwent six times but I managed to hold out and gave nothing away. Not a single arrest was made as a sequel to my capture. The only trouble was that the party who was lodging me got arrested and will have to be compensated for losing liberty and home. The name is Mlle Sandöe, 11 rue Claude Chahu, Paris, 16ème. Further information you can get from Mlle José Dupuis, 39 rue de la Felicité, Paris, also Mme Peyronnet, 102 avenue des Ternes, Paris. They will be able to clear up much, in addition Paul and Raoul Simon, 32 rue Pierre Demours, Paris, can help a lot.

I was interrogated for about 2 months, but dodged everything. I was offered freedom if I would hand over Bingen – some hopes – I nearly lost my left arm as a result of the tortures, as I got blood poisoning through my wrist being cut to the bone by chains and remaining unattended with handcuffs biting into them for about 6 days. Apart from that I was kept in solitary confinement for about 4 months at Fresnes. I was very unpopular as a Britisher and one of the German NCOs, a feldwebel, was particularly glad at every opportunity of punching me or slapping my face. He gave me 3 weeks of glasshouse in a darkened cell, without a mattress, blankets, deprived of all means of washing, and with ½ a pound of bread per day as sole food. I was pretty weak when I came out, had lost about 2½ stone in weight. I was sent to Compiègne on July 17th, whilst there recuperated a bit and had arranged an escape with a chap well known to 'Passy' [Dewavrin] and the BCRA, whose name is Roberty, and got sent to Weimar on the eve of escaping. Roberty succeeded. Bad luck for me.

The journey here was an eventful one, it took 8 days. The first man I ran into when being entrained was Hessel of the BCRA and the second was Hubble. We had various adventures, all were handcuffed the whole time, 19 men in one compartment and 18 in another. We could not move being packed in like sardines. The gates of the compartments were padlocked and we had very little air, no food had been provided for. We were given 1 day's rations which had to last 5 days, luckily some had Red Cross parcels or we would have starved. The train was bombed and machine-gunned on the way and we had a very narrow shave. Our escorts ran and left us helpless, had the train caught fire we would have burned like trapped rats. We had to stop at Saarbrücken for 3 days in a punishment and reprisals camp, and were beaten up on arrival. As usual, I seemed to attract particular attention and got well and truly slapped and cuffed. We were confined for three days and nights, 37 of us in a hut 9 feet by 7 feet by 7 feet. It was Hell. We then came on to this place Buchenwald. On the way our escorts plundered and stole practically all our effects. Never believe about German honesty, they are the biggest thieves, liars, bullies and cowards I have ever met. In addition, they delight in torturing people and gloat over it. Upon arrival which took place about midnight, we were locked up in the disinfection quarters and next morning we were nearly hanged summarily, but temporarily reprieved. We were stripped, completely shorn and dressed in prison rags, losing our few remaining belongings, and 16 of us, including Hubble, were told to report to a certain place. We never saw them again and found out that they were being hung without trial on the night of 11/12 September. They have been cremated so no trace remains of them. We are now awaiting our turn. There are 170 airmen (British and American) brought down and captured in France, but they are being treated as Terror Fliers and sleeping in the open, living under appalling conditions in violation of all conventions. They ought to be treated as POW. Men die like fleas here. I sent a message to you through Geneva.[15] I hope you received it, but have no means of telling. The bearer of this letter will give you all details so I will not say more – whatever he tells you is Gospel truth. He is no romancer, and he will never be able to really do justice to the horrors perpetrated here. For God's sake, Dizzy, see to it that our people never let ourselves be softened to the German people, or there will be another war in 15 years' time and all our lives will have been sacrificed in vain. I leave it to you and others to see that retribution is fierce. It will never be fierce enough.

A further note, written and signed by Yeo-Thomas and Hessel, was also prepared:

> Bearer is trusted messenger. We have some important and vital documents of considerable value to Allies. Please transmit urgently to London the attached coded message and convey the reply to bearer for onward transmission to me. The matter is of considerable importance and delay may mean disaster to all of us as well as documents.

The documents were given to Balachowsky and passed to Heinz Baumeister, a German inmate who had retained connections with the outside. He bound them in a book and had them smuggled out of the camp. It was not until December that they reached Wilhelm Duding, a political associate of Baumeister who lived in Dortmund, and it was on 10 April 1945 that Duding passed the letters to the American forces when they occupied the city. It was a desperate throw, but as Yeo-Thomas later conceded: 'Looking back I realize that I was drawing a long bow, but though I was a prisoner under sentence of death, I always regarded myself as an active member of HM Forces, and as such it was my duty to carry on the fight no matter how hopeless it might seem.

While there is life there is hope, and even if I was killed, I would still have left something behind that might be of assistance to our forces, that would guide them in their investigations. I considered that I was to blame for my arrest, and that having been entrusted with a mission which I had failed to complete, it was up to me to try and atone for my failure. Therefore, on no account was I going to admit defeat.'

The writing of the messages may have improved Yeo-Thomas's frame of mind temporarily, but there was still the imminent prospect of his name being called out for execution. 'We all realized that it was only a matter of time before we were called, and outwardly, in the presence of the other prisoners, none of us showed any signs of worry. I do not know how my comrades felt inwardly and I cannot pretend to guess. I can only speak for myself, and when the news of the execution of Hubble and Kane [Keun] reached me, as I said before, I lost all feeling save that of a steely determination to avenge them if I could. I seemed to have lost all sense of feeling and to have become a machine. I had no fear of death in any shape or form, and I felt absolutely no apprehension. Never during those days did I worry for myself; it was not a matter of courage, I just cannot explain it.'

In spite of this neutering of his emotions, he continued to meet with his friends in the camp to discuss any possible avenue for escape. It was during one of his daily conversations with Balachowsky that the Frenchman proposed a scheme in which members of Yeo-Thomas's group would switch identities with inmates who had died in the 'Guinea Pig' block. Yeo-Thomas must truly have been touched by despair, for this inveterate optimist considered the plan to be a 'very difficult if not an impossible one to execute'.

Balachowsky fully recognized the difficulties and therefore deemed it essential that, if the plan was to have any hope of success, they should enlist the support of the SS. This meant engineering an approach to SS-Sturmbannführer Dr Erwin Ding, the commander of the laboratory and the 'Guinea Pig' block. Obviously, the approach had to be timed and phrased to perfection and it was decided to gain access to him via Eugen Kogon, an Austrian inmate of Buchenwald for the last seven years, who acted as Ding's secretary. At a meeting with Balachowsky, Kogon agreed to intercede, but wished to meet Yeo-Thomas first. The two men met in secret in the laboratory and Kogon almost immediately offered to help. Thus far, Balachowsky had focused his plan on saving Yeo-Thomas, 'for whom, apart from friendship, he had the highest admiration', but, as the plan began to build up momentum, Yeo-Thomas reaffirmed that 'any measures taken for safeguarding members of our group should apply to all my comrades and that I should be the last . . . being the senior officer it was my duty to be the last to be saved.'

While Balachowsky began to set about making the arrangements, Yeo-Thomas considered the order of priority in which the men should be saved. He simply decided upon reverse seniority, placing the most junior first and himself last. Then Balachowsky came back with some dreadful and heartrending news. Ding had set the limit of inmates to be rescued at only three men and demanded that Yeo-Thomas be one of them. The latter, predictably, vigorously argued against this decision but Ding, who wished to ensure that the senior officer would be representing his case after the war, stated that if Yeo-Thomas declined to be one of the three, then no one would be saved. It put Yeo-Thomas in a terrible situation, but he had no alternative other than to accept. Meanwhile Balachowsky's work was far from over; it was all very well that Ding had clandestinely agreed to the scheme but it could not be implemented without the assistance of Arthur Dietzsch, the Kapo in charge of the 'Guinea Pig' block. Balachowsky was far from impressed, describing him as 'a former regular policeman, now entirely devoted to the SS cause and most brutal towards the inmates of the block'. Understandably, Yeo-Thomas's appreciation was a little more mellow and, although he later testified at a war crimes trial that Dietzsch had administered typhus injections, he commended Dietzsch's courage in taking the risk of helping them. Hessel had a different opinion and described Dietszch as a 'very obstinate and despotic man and very difficult to approach'. However, using Dietzsch's assistant, Baumeister, as an intermediary, they were able to represent a similar deal to the one they had concluded with Ding, namely that, after the war, the Kapo might expect favourable treatment from the Allied victors.

The next dilemma was for Yeo-Thomas to decide who, of the remaining twenty men, he should choose to save. The strain on him was immense. He was helped by Balachowsky's recommendation that one should be French and the other British and, after hours of agonizing, he chose Hessel and Peulevé. Having made his decision, Yeo-Thomas now offered himself as a genuine 'guinea pig', but he still retained understandable suspicions that all the various agreements and assurances of help would prove to be false. Nothing was said to Hessel, Peulevé or any of the others regarding the scheme in case word got out. He made an arrangement with Kogon that only if he sent a message that all was well were the other two men to be allowed to follow him. Yeo-Thomas was secretly smuggled into the 'Guinea Pig' block, where Dietzsch injected him with a serum that, he was assured, would induce a high temperature. This would allow him to report sick, have typhus diagnosed and then be sent to the 'Guinea Pig' block for quarantine with the other, genuine, sufferers. The plan went like clockwork, albeit with Yeo-Thomas harbouring doubts about just what it was that Dietzsch was injecting him with, and he duly returned to Block 17, where a raging temperature set in during the night. In the morning, he reported sick to the Block Älteste who had him examined by a Czech doctor. Yeo-Thomas was duly sent to the hospital where they suspected that he had typhus (he had been briefed to feign the necessary symptoms) and sent for Dietzsch. The Kapo's examination confirmed the diagnosis and he was taken to the 'Guinea Pig' block. The pretence had to be maintained here too and he was admitted as a bona fide patient and given treatment by the orderlies to reduce his temperature. At the same time, Dietzsch continued to give him injections so that his high temperature might be maintained. After two nights, by which time he was convinced that Dietzsch was not double-crossing him, he received a note from Kogon, asking if everything was going to plan. He replied, 'OK. The others can come,' and handed it to Dietzsch for delivery.

The next day Hessel and Peulevé arrived and Yeo-Thomas initiated them into the plan. As long as their names were not called for execution, they were now in comparative safety, especially after Dietzsch had the original orderlies transferred, thereby allowing the three agents to be moved to relatively comfortable quarters above the ward. Here they passed the days, waiting for Dietzsch to give them the macabre news that he had found them their alter egos. At last they were informed that likely candidates had arrived in the hospital. These were members of a group of French and Belgian prisoners who had recently contracted typhus while working on German fortifications. It was essential that, if each of the three agents were to stand any chance of convincingly assuming the identity of a dead man, they had at the very least to share a common language. Dietzsch was able to inform them that three of the group, Maurice Chouquet, Michel Boitel and Marcel Seigneur, were all of suitable age and stature. He reassured them that the genuine patients were unlikely to recover, but Yeo-Thomas and the others refused to allow the deaths of the Frenchmen to be hastened in any way: 'We impressed upon him that he must do all he could to save them, for we did not wish to owe our lives to the sacrifice of other men's.'

As they waited for the death of three strangers, Yeo-Thomas, Hessel and Peulevé heard the dreaded news of another summons broadcast on the camp's loudspeakers. On 4 October Barrett, Corbusier, Chaigneau, Frager, Gerard, Loison, Mulsant, de Ségnier, Vellaud, Wilkinson and 'Pool' were selected for execution. There was nothing they could do for the others but Peulevé had to be saved, not only for his own sake but so that Yeo-Thomas's and Hessel's situation should not be compromised. Dietzsch gave Peulevé an injection that brought on another temperature that would, at the very least, convince any guards who came to collect him that he was genuinely ill. When Peulevé did not report along with the rest of the group from Block 17, he was traced by the SS guards to the sickbay. The Camp Commandant, SS-Oberführer Hermann Pister, when informed that Peulevé was in the hospital, replied that he did not care about the man's condition and that he was to be executed along with the others. When it transpired that the 'patient' was in fact in the 'Guinea Pig' block, the process radically slowed down. The SS were unwilling to enter the building and Dietzsch was conveniently absent when they called. When he returned, Dietzsch informed them that he could not release into the compound a patient suffering from typhus without Ding's express permission. Meanwhile a message was sent to Ding, who genuinely was away from the camp, to return post-haste. It now became a contest of will and guile between Ding and the hospital doctor, SS-Hauptsturmführer Dr Gerhard Schiedlausky. Pister was adamant that the execution be carried out, for he had even received confirmation of his orders from Gestapo headquarters in Berlin. It was agreed to give Peulevé a lethal injection, but Ding refused to carry it out himself. Knowing that Schiedlausky would also be loath to do the job and would hand it over to a corruptible underling, he suggested to Pister that the former undertake it. As expected, the task was given to SS-Hauptscharführer Friedrich Wilhelm, a man notorious for administering lethal injections to inmates. Fortunately, Wilhelm was known to be a drunkard and, when he arrived at the 'Guinea Pig' block to carry out the killing, Dietzsch plied him with alcohol. When so inebriated that he was physically incapable of carrying out the injection, Wilhelm was shown one of the dying men in the ward and was told that it was a waste of time bothering with someone who was anyway going to die within a couple of hours. Wilhelm was convinced and eventually reported back to Schiedlausky that he had carried out his order.[16]

This was by no means the end of their problems, for they still needed to produce Peulevé's corpse and Marcel Seigneur, his alter ego, was hanging on to life with a remarkable resilience. Throughout the night, Yeo-Thomas and Hessel could hear Seigneur's groans. On the one hand, they were trying not to wish for the death of another human being, but they were also aware that the prolongation of the doomed man's existence might mean the death of their friend. At last, after a night of uncertainty and acute moral dilemma, they were informed at 7.30am that Seigneur had died. The switch was made: Peulevé's number was painted on Seigneur's thigh and the body was transferred to the crematorium.

If Peulevé was out of immediate danger, Yeo-Thomas and Hessel remained in no man's land. They could be called for execution at any time and the chances of repeating the delaying tactics and subterfuge were slim. The second group of Block 17 victims had been shot at the SS rifle range and, to increase their unease, the executions continued, with Avallard and Evesque being shot on 7 October and Rambaud following them two days later. 'It was a gamble with time, and the dice were loaded against us. It seemed that the orders for execution arrived as a rule towards the end of the week, and that Friday was the worst day. If by Friday no execution order had arrived, one could be considered safe until the following Thursday or Friday. So we went from day to day.'

Then, on Friday the 13th of all days, Maurice Chouquet died and with him went 'Kenneth Dodkin'. Now Yeo-Thomas was in the same position as Peulevé, safe but having to endure the uncertainty of his friend Hessel's fate. However, some five days later, the final patient, Michel Boitel, died and the three agents were, to all intents and purposes, safe from the execution squad.

Safety in a concentration camp was relative. They would not share the fate of their friends in the crematorium or on the firing range, but they remained prisoners within Buchenwald and could not stay on in the 'Guinea Pig' block indefinitely. Kogon once again proved of great help and provided them with whatever details he could find on the backgrounds of their new identities, in preparation for their being posted from the camp to an outside work Kommando. This course of action was deemed to be much safer than remaining in Buchenwald and ultimately offered a much better opportunity for escape. Hessel and Peulevé were the first to go, being sent to a Kommando at an aircraft factory near Schönebeck, where Kogon was in touch with the manager. Hessel, with his knowledge of German, was to work as a clerk while Peulevé was to use his pre-war skills to act as an electrician. It was a sad day for Yeo-Thomas when they went, 'for it left me alone, and we had become such good friends. I wished them the best of luck, we arranged to meet after the war, if we managed to live that long. We agreed to do all we could to make the enemy pay for the execution of our pals, and we also promised one another that we would give news to the families of those of us who failed to get through.'[17]

Yeo-Thomas had barely a week on his own in the block, preparing yet another false identity as Maurice Chouquet, born in 1909 at Elbeuf, south of Rouen, and a carpenter by trade. Then he was told that he was being sent to a Kommando at Gleina, near the town of Zeitz, where he would stand little chance of being recognized and where Kogon had a friend who was awaiting his arrival. He bade his friends a truly heartfelt thanks and left Dietzsch a note, outlining the services he had rendered:

The bearer, at the risk of his own, has saved the lives of several Allied officers and rendered valuable service to three agents of the Allied secret services. I request that all Allied authorities he may come in contact with afford him assistance and protection. The bona fides and standing of the undersigned can be verified by communicating with SOE London.

F. Yeo-Thomas, MC, Squadron Leader, RAF

On 9 November, he left the 'Guinea Pig' block in a driving snow-storm. His friends had pulled together as good a collection of food and clothes as they could manage and, huddled up against the wind and snow, he was able to disguise these and Hubble's chess set as he boarded the truck.

CHAPTER NINE

· The Nightmare Continues ·

As the lorry left Buchenwald and headed north towards Zeitz, Yeo-Thomas struck up a conversation with a young Jewish boy, Andreas Weiss. He was joining his father who had already been sent to the concentration camp at Gleina. It was soon clear that, although he was keen to see his father, the youth had no confidence in either of them surviving for long. Such fatalism was complete anathema to the profoundly optimistic Yeo-Thomas and he spent the rest of the journey trying to instil some hope into Weiss. It was during the course of this conversation that he discovered a new purpose in his life, namely 'that I would do everything I could to sustain those who weakened, to give hope to those who had abandoned it. The fact that so many of the men around me had more or less given up the Ghost, gave me inspiration and strength. I would never admit defeat, never give up as long as I could draw breath.'[1]

The camp at Gleina, also known as Kommando Wille, was very unlike the imposing hutted city of Buchenwald that had been carved out of a wooded mountainside. His latest place of imprisonment was situated virtually in the centre of the village and its main gate gave on to the street. Its accommodation was limited in the extreme and most of it consisted of little more than farm buildings. The prisoners were ordered off the truck and formed up for a roll call taken by the camp Rapportführer, SS-Unterscharführer Otto Möller. They were then handed over to the Kapo, Hans Gentkow, a Dutch inmate who led them into one of the buildings. After Gentkow had taken another roll call, Walter Hummelsheim, Kogon's friend, made himself known and told Yeo-Thomas that he would help him find a decent job the next day. Another man then offered his services in finding him a bunk for the night. It transpired that this was Dr Jean Dulac, the head of the camp hospital, who soon disabused Yeo-Thomas of his expectations by explaining that the establishment was a hospital only in name. This was soon made evident when Yeo-Thomas was led through the 'ward': 'It was dimly lit by widely spaced weak electric bulbs. I stopped whilst my eyes became accustomed to the semi-darkness, and I saw a vision which seemed to come straight out of Dante's *Inferno*. In the bunks lay human beings in a state of emaciation I did not imagine could ever be reached, many of them wearing paper bandages, stained with blood, pus and filth. Every now and then, low moans could be heard, mutterings, mumbled prayers. As I stood there, appalled by both the sight and the awful smell, I could see countless eyes turned towards me, eyes full of misery, despair, eyes that had seen into the uttermost depths of hopelessness.'

Yeo-Thomas was escorted into a small room in the corner of the ward where he met a group of 'fellow' Frenchmen. Once again, he accorded himself a rapid promotion and introduced himself as Colonel Maurice Chouquet, of the Armée de l'Air. Most of the other men present were captured members of the resistance and Yeo-Thomas was delighted to be among his own, and felt: 'I had struck lucky, for there had been only one spare bunk in the little room and I had got it.'

As they were finishing their meal, a rare treat of potatoes and onions, Hummelsheim entered and, after a brief chat with those present, asked Yeo-Thomas to follow him. Once they were alone in his cubicle, Hummelsheim confirmed that Kogon had asked him to help and that he would do all that he could. He briefed Yeo-Thomas on the various intrigues and rivalries within the camp, warning him, in particular, to beware of three notorious bullies. Hummelsheim's whole demeanour convinced the newcomer that here was a decent and intelligent ally. However, when he returned to his French bunk-mates, Yeo-Thomas detected a distinct 'atmosphere', doubtless brought about by his unexplained and apparently suspicious rendezvous with the German.

The next morning, Dulac told Yeo-Thomas that he was going to have him listed as an orderly in the hospital and instructed him to wait with a fellow inmate while he arranged matters. This man, who had been introduced the previous night as Pierre Kaan, looked disconcertingly familiar to Yeo-Thomas. As they chatted, it transpired that Kaan had also been arrested in Paris. Then he suddenly asked the disconcerting question: *'Vous êtes "Shelley"?'* Yeo-Thomas replied enigmatically that 'Shelley' was dead but 'Chouquet' lived. Kaan took the hint and told him that he had been using the name 'Biran' when they had last met. Now all became clear and he remembered Kaan as the efficient and hardworking secretary of the Comité Militaire. Yeo-Thomas impressed upon the Frenchman the need to keep 'Chouquet's' true identity and nationality a secret but conceded that he could tell the other inmates that he was a prominent member of the resistance. Then Dulac returned and informed Yeo-Thomas that, as well as serving as a hospital ward orderly, he was also, when required, to act as a *Totenträger* or corpse shifter.

Yeo-Thomas was now placed in the care of two of the Frenchmen he had met the previous night. These were Jacques Foulquier, a young member of Dewavrin's organization, and Pierre Fauvage.

From these men he learnt that Gleina was not itself a camp but rather the medical centre for a larger establishment at Rehmsdorf. However, the treatment available for the inmates was lamentable and Yeo-Thomas soon discovered that his duties consisted less of care for the sick than collecting the bodies of dead patients. It was a dreadful task, having to remove the bodies from the infirmary for, although they were light enough, their filthy state made them extremely difficult to handle. Furthermore, the SS had ordered that the bodies should be stripped of the few rags that they were wearing. As Yeo-Thomas recalled: 'I eventually got used to it, but I admit that at first I was violently sick and that it took me a few days to get used to the job. With every body I carried out, my hatred of the Nazis grew.'

Linked with this macabre task was a perverse exercise in SS capitalism that shocked even the hardened agent. Yeo-Thomas was stunned to learn from Foulquier that the bodies were to be put in coffins. Having been treated with such scant consideration during life, he could not understand why the formality of interment in a coffin was extended to them. It emerged that the funeral arrangements of the dead inmates who had worked at the nearby Brabag factory in Zeitz were the responsibility of their 'employers'. Sixty marks were allotted for each funeral and it just so happened that the camp commandant's mistress owned a funeral undertaker's that produced thirteen coffins a day at a cost of fifteen marks each. The Commandant, SS-Obersturmführer Kenn, and his paramour split the grisly profit of forty-five marks a corpse. A potentially deadly postscript to this deal occurred when, with the death rate soaring, Yeo-Thomas and Foulquier had to double up the corpses. It so happened that, as they were carrying a coffin across the camp square, the poorly made box collapsed and two bodies fell to the ground in front of Kenn. He became incensed at this abuse of his arrangements and demanded that the doctors restrict the fatalities to the thirteen-corpse level that could be accommodated by the undertaker's output of coffins. Not even the express orders of Kenn, however, could cheat death and the numbers that Yeo-Thomas and the others had to handle rose inexorably:

> When I look back and remember that at times, Foulquier and I
> had to climb on piles of bodies in order to place the latest dead
> men on top, it seems incredible, yet it is true. We even had long
> discussions on the best way of laying the bodies so that they
> should take the least possible space, rather like packing sardines
> in a tin. Yet I don't want readers to think that we were indifferent
> or callous; we lived in the shadow of death, we knew that we
> might at any time ourselves be laid out in this same hut, naked
> and stiff. Though we could not render the last rites, we always

did our best to treat the remnants of our fellow prisoners with all the reverence we could. The only thing we could do was uncover ourselves as we laid each body down and stand for a few moments in silence, for we were constantly watched, and if we were too long SS men would curse us and aim blows at us.

Yeo-Thomas and Foulquier shared another duty, that of collecting the bread ration for the hospital. At first this was not too onerous a task, offering the chance of stealing additional rations that they were able to pass on to the weakest of the patients, and initially Yeo-Thomas was able to carry a sackload of fifty loaves without too much trouble. With the onset of dysentery, however, he became increasingly weak and could carry fewer and fewer. Consequently, this necessitated more trips to the stores, and the latrines, and even greater fatigue and weight loss.

When not pursuing his corpse-removal and bread-fetching tasks, Yeo-Thomas assisted in the handing out of rations and the nursing of the sick. This latter task was soul-destroying and often physically revolting. In spite of the work of Dulac and the other doctors among the inmates, the plight of the patients was terrible to behold. What medicines were issued were sold by the camp doctor, SS-Oberscharführer Grosser, to local civilians. Therefore, the patients had to suffer malnutrition, sores and sickness, without any real hope of improvement. Nevertheless, other inmates such as Kaan, Dulac, Gentkow and Hummelsheim did their best to alleviate the lot of their fellow prisoners, and Yeo-Thomas also recognized the decency of some (albeit all too few) of the camp guards, such as Möller and his colleagues, Sauerbier and Hebestreit. Sadly, these men were very much in the minority. Kenn was a violent and unpredictable man who had Sauerbier sent to jail in Buchenwald for being too lenient with the prisoners. Furthermore, for every kindness offered by the civilized few, there was brutality meted out by other SS men, such as Rudolf, Kraus and Schmidt.

Amid this torment, Yeo-Thomas was to enjoy one brief moment of respite and hope. Hummelsheim's privileged position allowed him occasionally to visit Leipzig, to negotiate the acquisition of supplies for Gleina. He arranged on one occasion for Yeo-Thomas to accompany him, especially as he knew that there were British prisoners of war in the area and Yeo-Thomas hoped to pass a message to them. It would have been relatively easy for Yeo-Thomas to escape his guards, but, as this would have resulted in Hummelsheim's certain execution, he had to content himself just with trying to make contact with his fellow countrymen. He got his wish when the truck stopped at a factory where British prisoners of war were working. He whispered to

one of them that he was a British officer and then whispered fragments of his report to each of the soldiers in turn, asking them to
collate the pieces and send them to London: 'The fact that I had been
able to speak to some of my countrymen gave me renewed courage.
I knew that they would do their best to get the message through and
that Barbara would know that I was still alive and have an idea of my
whereabouts.'

His optimism was short-lived and, as Christmas 1944 approached,
the death toll continued to rise. Yeo-Thomas was moved to ask himself some fundamental questions: ' . . . we were hardened, we did not
display our feelings but still, deep down inside us, there was pity and
loathing. Pity for the unfortunate victims of an inhuman system,
loathing for the creatures who enforced it. In those strenuous days,
I frequently asked myself, "Can there be a God? If there is, how can
He allow such revolting things to happen?" I came to the conclusion
that there was no God.'

With such feelings in his heart, the prisoners' pathetic celebrations
had an even greater pathos. A Christmas tree was acquired, carols and
festive songs were sung and even little presents made and offered.
Kaan, perhaps recognizing Yeo-Thomas's loneliness and feeling
of isolation, considerately whispered 'Merry Christmas' to him in
English.

Towards the end of December, the prisoners learnt that Gleina was
being handed over as accommodation for British prisoners of war
and that the present inmates were being transferred to Rehmsdorf
camp. It was at this time that they also lost the support of
Hummelsheim, who was caught trying to smuggle a written message
out of the camp. He was sent to Buchenwald for punishment where
he was sentenced to death. Fortunately Kogon and other inmates
helped to save him from execution. Meanwhile at Gleina, the move
was rushed through and just after the New Year the evacuation was
completed.

Conditions at Rehmsdorf were even worse than at Gleina. The
hospital was in a separate compound in the middle of the camp, with
the patients and staff crowded into two huts that had been intended
to accommodate 300, but now had to house 1250. There was no
internal sanitation and patients suffering from pneumonia, dysentery,
tuberculosis and any number of other diseases had to use the outside
latrines. The best that Yeo-Thomas and the others could arrange
for the very sick were oil drums that quickly proved to be inadequate
to the hospital's needs. Within a week, overcrowding was such
that patients were lying three to a bunk, and it became increasingly
difficult to differentiate between the dead and the dying:

Day after day, I lugged corpses out of bunks, some of them lying
between two still living prisoners who could hardly move, which
gave me considerable trouble, for with only a foot and a half of
head space to move in, pulling a dead body over a helpless man
was no picnic. Sometimes, in order to get the dead man's rations,
sick men would not advise us that one of their companions had
died, and would keep the corpse between them deliberately,
so as to get the rations, and when I came to take temperatures
would take the thermometer, pretend to put it under the dead
man's arm. When my back was turned, they would rub the
thermometer to make it register, and hand it back to me.

The horror was unrelenting and Yeo-Thomas was later to write: 'Each
day, I thought to myself, "Now I have seen the worst that can possibly
happen," but each day I saw something worse than the previous day.'

Then the good news arrived that the British prisoners of war were
now installed in Gleina, renamed Arbeitskommando G123. Here
was another opportunity to make contact, especially as Gentkow
was responsible for organizing the work parties that were still sent
there from Rehmsdorf. As an opening gambit, Yeo-Thomas wrote a
message to the senior NCO and had this smuggled in by Gentkow.
An understandably cautious reply was returned by Corporal John
Stevenson of the Leicestershire Regiment, who asked for some proof
of Yeo-Thomas's bona fides. Luckily, the agent had a distant relative
in the regiment and was able to send this name to Stevenson as proof
that he was a genuine British officer. The corporal was satisfied and
wrote back offering to do what he could, so Gentkow arranged for
Yeo-Thomas to join one of the parties sent to Gleina to dig vegeta-
bles. On arrival, he was pulled off the regular detail and introduced
to Stevenson who took him to the cookhouse for a meal. For Yeo-
Thomas, after months of imprisonment, torture and maltreatment, it
was incongruous to have British soldiers standing to attention before
him. He also struck a pretty strange figure to the soldiers. Desmond
Bennett, a paratrooper captured at Arnhem, was in the sickbay when
word spread that there was an RAF officer in the washroom. He went
to look for himself: '. . . and to my surprise I saw a rather small type,
smoking a pipe I believe, dressed in striped pyjamas with a small red
square and a black F on it. This queer type said that he lived in Russell
Square and that he had flown into France just before D-Day in a
Lysander. He and I also spoke of Ringway and Tatton Park and
of a queer device called the Fan, and of an experience known as
"jumping through the hole".'

His fellow countrymen gave him the first decent meal that he had
had in months and finished it off with mugs of tea with milk and

sugar. After lunch, they arranged for messages to be sent reporting Yeo-Thomas's whereabouts, together with information on the camp. They also agreed that if the Allied armies advanced close to Leipzig, Stevenson and his men would try and take over at Gleina and march on Rehmsdorf to help Yeo-Thomas and a small band of would-be resisters who, Bennett recalled, 'were prepared to make a fight for it – if the worst happened – rather than be shot down like dogs'. The soldiers pressed a variety of food and cigarettes on him and he rejoined the work detail before returning to Rehmsdorf feeling 'greatly comforted'.

His living conditions were as bad and overcrowded as those of the other inmates and he and the doctors and orderlies had no cubicle of their own such as they had enjoyed at Gleina. However, he had obtained a pencil and on the boards of the bunk above him had inscribed Barbara's name: 'I was able to lie back in my bunk with my eyes on her name, which did a lot to keep my spirits up.' As ever, the elation was only temporary and conditions in the hospital continued to deteriorate.

Starting in January, 'Death Transports' began to take place, in which inmates deemed to be incapable of work or physical improvement were sent to extermination camps. SS officers visited the hospital and briefly inspected the patients, judging those who could not rise from their bunks or who were unable to walk as being hopeless cases. On two occasions, the hospital was completely emptied, but filled up again with new patients within a matter of days. Often the best that the hospital had to offer inmates was a brief respite from work details and this allowed those fortunate enough to be admitted a little time to regain their strength. But, in spite of the endeavours of Dulac and the other doctors, there was little that could be done to ease the plight of the sick. The hospital was scandalously deprived of resources and boasted one bedpan, a thermometer, a pair of scissors, some paper bandages, a little iodine substitute and a small supply of Clorethyl to cater for some 1250 patients whose suppurating sores required daily dressing. The absence of anaesthetic made every operation a torment for patient and medical staff alike, and it was little wonder that Yeo-Thomas should describe it in heartrending terms: 'Every passing day just increased the misery, suffering and horror that surrounded us. At times, I wondered if I was still alive, or even if I was dead and in Hell. How we managed to remain sane, I don't know. Death was all around us, in every shape and form; we were at the mercy of the whims of several hundred SS of the worst type. We lived in a perpetual nightmare.'

Caught up in their own nightmare, the inmates of Rehmsdorf were unaware of the continuing Allied drive towards Germany. By the

end of January 1945, the Red Army had liberated most of central
and southern Poland and reached the River Oder. In the west, the
Anglo-American forces had repelled the German offensive in the
Ardennes and, in February, pushed towards the River Rhine, but these
encouraging developments did not alter the fact that the prisoners'
daily lives were preoccupied with the freezing cold weather, the
scarcity of food and the violence of the SS guards. Allied air raids
were a manifestation of the deterioration of Germany's strength and
engendered contrasting feelings of elation and danger among the
inmates. On one occasion in March bombs landed on the camp,
destroying one of the huts. Dulac and Yeo-Thomas did what they
could to assist the few survivors of the carnage and the two men
amputated the leg of one of the wounded, having to use, in the absence
of proper equipment, a surgical knife with a one-and-a-half-inch blade.
The patient survived for a few days but the shock and total absence
of medication resulted in his death. Following another raid, this time
on the nearby town of Gera, orders were sent for the camp doctors
to help. As they tended to the wounded, Allied aircraft continued to
strafe the town and one of the inmates, a Jewish Hungarian doctor
named Imre Klein, was mortally wounded. He was taken back to the
camp where he died several hours later. The feeling of remorse at his
death was such that Yeo-Thomas and the others decided that the
body would not be stripped of its clothes before being cremated. The
SS officer in charge of the hospital was incensed, but the prisoners
remained obdurate. The situation could have turned even more
serious but for the arrival of Möller, who gave his permission that, on
this occasion, the corpse would be left clothed. It was a pathetically
small moral victory.

By the beginning of April the weather had begun to improve, but
rumours had started to circulate that the Nazis were beginning
to massacre the inmates of the concentration camps. Yeo-Thomas
got permission from the camp authorities to have trenches dug as
protection against the air raids but he intended these also to serve a
double function should they need to protect themselves against the
guards. To this end the inmates had secretly gathered a small arsenal
of weapons, including rifles, pistols and hand-grenades, which they
were prepared to use in the event of the guards turning on them. The
threat of violence came not solely from the guards and the already
volatile factional infrastructure within the camp began to deteriorate
into anarchy. Fights broke out among the inmates, especially over the
supply of food that grew ever scarcer, and Yeo-Thomas in his own
weakened state had a difficult time trying to protect the meagre
rations of the patients.

Then, at about midnight on 13 April 1945, the order came for the

immediate evacuation of the camp. No one was to be left behind and
even the hospital patients had to carried on to the train. Yeo-Thomas
found himself in one of the open trucks with Dulac, Kaan, Foulquier
and other close associates. They had no idea where they were bound
and the train made numerous halts throughout the day, even stopping
at a siding next to a women's concentration camp, before returning
through Rehmsdorf. They continued onwards and Yeo-Thomas
predicted as they passed through wooded and rugged countryside that
they were heading for Czechoslovakia. He warned Dulac that their
best opportunity for escape would soon be upon them and told him
to ready himself. After a further two days' travel, they passed through
the small station of Marienburg-Gelobtland and then halted in a small
clearing in the woods that bordered each side of the track. The SS
guards had amused themselves by throwing dead inmates from the
train but they had now tired of this macabre sport. The SS commander
gave the order for a mass grave to be dug near to the engine and the
inmates started placing the corpses of more than a hundred of their
number on to the track prior to their being carried towards the pit.
Yeo-Thomas decided that now was their best chance for escape. He
told Dulac and the others that they must carry the bodies and, when
they were all together at the grave, they were to turn as if they were
going back to the train to collect others. At a sign from him they were
to make a dash for the relative safety of the woods. As most of the
guards would be facing the inmates on the train, he hoped that they
would have a half-decent chance of success.

To improve the odds, Yeo-Thomas decided to risk speaking to
Möller. Through an interpreter, he told the SS man that he was really
a British officer of the Secret Service who had passed details to his
superiors of all that he had encountered. He recognized that Möller
had not ill treated the inmates but, unless he helped their escape
attempt, there would be nothing he could do to help prevent his
prosecution by the vengeful Allies. Either Yeo-Thomas managed to
be even more convincing than ever, or Möller recognized that
Germany was about to lose the war. Whatever the grounds for cooperation, the SS man agreed to assist them. Yeo-Thomas went back
to the other members of his group and told them of his plan. He had
a personal choice to make: whether he should take two pieces of bread
to sustain him in his flight or settle for one piece, thereby leaving
room for Hubble's chess set. He chose to honour his promise to
return the set to his friend's family.

In all, twenty of his group decided to make the attempt. In pairs
they picked up corpses, arrived at the grave, threw in the bodies
and the pretented to take a momentary rest. They turned as if to
return to the train, and then Yeo-Thomas yelled 'Go!' (This was how

he described his shout but one must presume that he shouted in French.) As they ran for the treeline they heard shouting, followed by shots, but they all carried on into the undergrowth. None of them was in any condition to run a marathon and even Yeo-Thomas felt himself slowing down to a trot and then a gasping walk. He could make out the sound of voices speaking German behind him and, flinging himself into a clump of bushes, landed on Jacques Foulquier. One of the voices could clearly be distinguished as Möller's and the tension must have been intense as they wondered whether he would keep his word. Suddenly he fired a shot, yelled an order and led his men off in pursuit in completely the opposite direction.

In spite of this attempt to divert the chase, only ten of the escapees made a clean break. Nine were recaptured and executed, while Pierre Kaan was discovered by the loyal Möller and returned to the train without anyone else having realized that he was one of the fugitives. Tragically, this deliverance did not have a happy ending. Kaan died in hospital a few weeks later, shortly after his eventual liberation by the Allies. Meanwhile, the ten men still at liberty set about destroying their concentration-camp uniforms and arranging the dishevelled civilian clothes that they had collected. Yeo-Thomas sported a corduroy jacket and grey trousers and a pair of decent boots that Dietzsch had given him before he left Buchenwald. Neither he nor any of the others cut a particularly impressive figure but, at this stage of the war, Germany was awash with refugees and the flotsam and jetsam of the collapsing Third Reich and they anticipated that they would be able to lose themselves among the many. Nevertheless, they recognized that it would attract too much attention were they to travel as a party. After waiting for a few hours in case Möller appeared to join them in their flight, they split into three parties. Yeo-Thomas teamed up with Dulac and a Belgian named Georges Piot. They took off at half-hour intervals with Yeo-Thomas's group leaving last in mid-afternoon.

They kept to the woods and walked in silence to husband their strength for the uncertain journey ahead, only stopping well after midnight to snatch a few cold hours' sleep. The next day they headed northwards, still in the dense forest until, at midday, they came to a large clearing where they were challenged by woodcutters, but managed to escape. All the rest of the day they walked and when night fell they guided themselves by the stars. At last they reached a river but, finding the nearest bridge guarded, they decided to wade across, with Yeo-Thomas in the lead, followed by Dulac. Halfway across, the former stepped into a hole and would have been carried away by the current were it not for Dulac grabbing him. Recovering themselves, they managed to get across and continue their plodding march, except that now they were wet as well as cold, hungry and tired.

Eventually they halted and huddled together for warmth, but Yeo-Thomas could find little comfort. To add to his other problems, his dysentery had started up, probably from drinking freezing cold water from a stream. Although the next day dawned fine, they soon found difficulties crossing a road that was meticulously guarded by a group of heavily armed Volksturm soldiers, members of the German Home Guard created to supplement regular armed forces. To make matters worse, they heard noises of men approaching behind them in the trees. Assuming themselves to be trapped between two groups of armed and hostile forces, they were delighted, and not a little relieved, to discover that the men emerging were Foulquier and his companions, Paul Jacquin and a young Dutchman known only as Pete. After resting for a while, they decided to make individual dashes across the road while the soldiers briefly had their backs turned. Although this took quite some time to achieve, they all reached the safety of the other side and split up again with Yeo-Thomas, Dulac and Piot remaining together.

Their next obstacle was a mile-wide stretch of open country with only the sanctuary of a clump of trees halfway across to offer them a haven. Nevertheless they had to press on, but, well before they had reached the trees, three men began approaching from their left. The fugitives broke into a run, but for Yeo-Thomas this could not long be sustained with his body racked with the pain of his dysentery:

> I saw Dulac and Georges disappear in the trees, well ahead of me, and I realized that I could not make the shelter of the clump before the men saw me. My mind worked at top speed. Now it was a question of luck: there was a solitary large tree within feet of me; I flung myself down at its base, hoping that the men might pass me by without seeing me, but deciding that, if they did, I would feign sleep and trust to luck. I could not have run another step. I lay huddled up on my belly, my head resting in my arms in such a way that I could just peep through one eye and see the men. They almost missed me, but one of them saw me and shouted something in German. I pretended to be fast asleep. They came quite close, and one of them shouted at me again. Getting no reply, he turned to the others and made some remark, at which they all laughed loudly. I gathered something to the effect that I was a lazy hound. My heart was in my mouth, supposing they came and shook me. I did not know enough German to put them off, and I would be handed over to the authorities. To my great relief, after standing some seconds looking at me, they moved on.

When the coast was clear, Yeo-Thomas headed for the clump of trees, but was unable to locate his companions either there or in the nearby wood. He had to face the fact that he was now on his own. As he reflected on his situation, the future did not look too rosy. He was suffering from acute dysentery, had run out of food and did not know where he was. His sole plan was to make for Chemnitz and from there head for the Allied lines, but if he thought that he was in a bad way already, things soon started to get worse. A steady drizzle began which developed into an unrelenting downpour, saturating his clothes and making them 'as heavy as a coat of mail'. Cold and bedraggled, he managed to cross a river at an unguarded bridge and made once more for the relative safety of the woods. He badly needed to rest but there seemed to be no refuge until he suddenly found himself falling and realized that he had tumbled into a pit full of sapling branches. Not only did the foliage cushion his fall, it also offered a soft and welcoming bed. With no more ado, he pulled the branches over him and fell asleep.

It was still raining when he awoke, but the respite had done him some good and he was soon on his way. The benefits of his rest were, however, rapidly dissipated by the unrelenting torment of dysentery, cold, hunger and fatigue. He was reduced to scavenging fruitlessly in a potato field in order to find some sustenance and finally collapsed behind a pile of logs and once again slept. When he awoke it was dawn, but nothing else had changed and the rain came down as persistently as ever. As he came upon a small road he was spotted by a group of armed men who challenged him. Instinct and desperation gave him sufficient energy to dive back into the woods and run for his life. He heard shots but kept running until he finally collapsed in complete exhaustion: 'I was spent, I tried to rise, but my legs would not carry me, they were trembling all over. My head was throbbing and I had shooting pains in my eyes. Then I felt violently sick but could not bring anything up. I was as empty as a drum. I then realized that, whilst I had been running, so my dysentery had been active, and my legs were wet with my own excreta which had trickled down them. I was a sorry mess.'

In spite of this, he managed to find the energy to stumble on. He frequently collapsed and once again tumbled into another pit. This time there was no soft carpet of branches and he began to panic when he thought that he did not have the strength to climb up the steep and slimy walls, but he managed to retrieve his equilibrium, and even fell asleep. When he awoke, the rain had stopped and the sun was shining. This improved his spirits a little, but there was no disguising the fact that he could not carry on much further. At last he passed out, and came around to find himself propped against a tree with a

man standing over him. The stranger's clothes and smiling face
marked him out as far from hostile and, although at first he spoke in
a language unknown to Yeo-Thomas, when he continued in French
he explained that he was a Yugoslav prisoner of war. Yeo-Thomas told
him that he was an escaped French prisoner of war and that he must
be on his way. When he tried to rise, however, he found it impossible.
The Yugoslav then picked him up and carried him to the shelter of the
wood and left him. Yeo-Thomas soon passed out again and only
awoke when the Yugoslav tapped his shoulder. He had brought bread
and a small bottle of wine, the first of which made Yeo-Thomas ill
when he tried to eat a morsel, but the second gift acted as a tonic and
revived him. The 'Good Samaritan' pressed him to accept the food
as a gift, placing it in a small bag he had brought with him. He then
kept watch for patrols while Yeo-Thomas rested for a little, before he
continued his journey: 'As I reached the woods on the other side of
the field, I turned back to look at him, and waved, he waved back. I
did not know his name, he did not know mine. We shall probably
never meet again, and in any case I would not be able to recognize
him but he was a damn good bloke and he probably saved my life.'

Fortified by the bread and wine, he plodded on and, although his
legs and feet were now also giving him trouble, he felt much more
optimistic. He decided to take the risk of carrying on along a wide,
main road in the hope that he would encounter a signpost that would
give him his bearings. He was consequently overjoyed when he came
upon a crossroads with the thrilling sign indicating that he was just
two kilometres from Chemnitz. He continued to ride his luck and
walked through the town centre, observing the heavy bomb damage
and the citizens busying themselves in fetching and carrying water.
He also heard French being spoken by prisoners of war and civilian
workers and took great consolation in the knowledge that, if
challenged, he could pass himself off as one of them. To crown this
upturn in his fortunes, he managed to hitch a lift with a French prisoner of war driving a horse and cart and, as well as enjoying a blissful
rest, made the most rapid twenty-five-kilometre advance of his escape.
Then it was back to the seemingly unending footslogging and, with
the rain beginning once more and his food exhausted, his situation
deteriorated once again.

The following morning, after another miserable night spent in the
open, he heard the distinct noise of artillery ahead of him that was
soon supplemented by rifle and machine-gun fire. He encountered
refugees streaming away from the front line and, to make himself less
conspicuous, he gathered a bundle of firewood and moved into
the woods. He spent quite some time spotting the location of the
German machine-gun nests and tried to assess the safest means of

crossing no man's land to the Allied lines. As night fell, he made his final bid for freedom. He stealthily edged his way forward out of the woods and had moved some twenty-five yards on to the field when a voice from behind him shouted to him to 'Halt!' He tried to run, but he was now far too exhausted even to break into a trot and as bullets began to hit the ground around him he collapsed. He was sufficiently conscious to realize that he was being kicked and at any moment anticipated a bullet in the head or a bayonet thrust in the stomach, but neither came. Two German soldiers hauled him to his feet and dragged him back into the woods and he reflected on how near but yet how far had been the success his attempt:

> It is impossible to describe my feelings at that moment, for it would mean trying to express the surge of bitterness against fate, that after letting me go to the utmost limit of my strength and will, failed me at the last minute. It was as though a few hundred tons of wreckage had landed on my head. All those days and nights of acute, painful progress, wasted, thrown away. Yet, there was no feeling of despair, but more a feeling of baffled rage. Though I was exhausted both in mind and in body, I was inwardly seething with temper. It all appeared so unfair.

In spite of the unfairness of the situation, at least he was not maltreated. His captors took him back behind the lines where he was interrogated by an army officer. Yeo-Thomas explained that he was Adjutant-Chef 'Maurice Thomas', an escaped French prisoner of war, who had been living off the land for quite a while. His captors seemed to accept his story and he was fed a substantial amount of potato soup and accorded the blissful luxury of bedspace in a warm hut. Apart from the inevitable onset of his dysentery, Yeo-Thomas enjoyed a remarkably comfortable night.

Matters were not so pleasant the next day. He was escorted under guard to a nearby village where orders came through to send him to Chemnitz for interrogation. He was now handed over to an escort of Hitler Youth, who took great pleasure in abusing him as he struggled to keep up with them. They slapped him, spat at him and beat him with their rifle butts for the duration of a long, ten-mile walk to the next town. There he was incarcerated in the local jail and obliged to share a cell with a singularly disreputable thief who tried to rob him while he slept. The German did not try it again after Yeo-Thomas had hit him.

Later that day, he was taken to Chemnitz, handed over to the German Army and allowed to strip and wash himself. His feet remained untouched, however, for they were so swollen that he was convinced that if he took off his boots he would never manage to get them on again. The next day he helped take food to the other prisoners and was able to speak to some of his fellow countrymen. Things improved two days later, when he was sent to a transit camp on the edge of town, where he made contact with some more British prisoners, including Norman Wood, a Scots Guardsman. He confided in Wood and another serviceman, William Birchall, and wrote his real name and address on a photograph held by the latter,[2] but to all others he remained a French airman.

The next day, Yeo-Thomas and the other prisoners were marched out of Chemnitz and, the following day, he and the other French prisoners were separated from their British allies. Following a further march, he was admitted to the French prisoner-of-war camp at Grünhainichen. After being interrogated by the camp authorities, he underwent another questioning by his fellow inmates. There was no problem in his passing himself off as a Frenchman, but he found it very difficult to offer a convincing explanation of his recent background as a prisoner of war. As soon as he told them that he had been held at the Stalag IVD camp, he immediately noticed one of the inmates examining him with suspicion. He was later interrogated by the man, who stated that he himself had been in the camp and wanted to know why Yeo-Thomas was unknown to him. There seemed little point in trying to maintain the bluff and he asked for an audience with the senior NCO. This was granted and Yeo-Thomas told them much of his real story, managing to convince them of its veracity by telling them about Hubble and showing them the chess set with its prominent British trademark. This clinched it.

Typically, in spite of his lamentable physical state, Yeo-Thomas had no intentions of staying at the camp and waiting out the war. He told the senior NCO of his plans and, after initial disbelief, the Frenchman agreed to help him. It was decided that a number of prisoners would join him in his escape and a selection of passes, travel documents and money was prepared to enable them to catch a local train that would take them towards the front and the Allied lines. At ten o'clock in the evening, a mere two days after his arrival, Yeo-Thomas and ten others climbed out of their hut window and escaped from the camp. At the station, Yeo-Thomas booked tickets for Chemnitz and they all safely boarded the train. They arrived early the following morning and, splitting up into pairs, headed westwards. Yeo-Thomas was accompanied by an NCO named Albaret who soon had to help him along: 'I had presumed too much on my strength and feet. I had not recuperated long enough, and I was soon in difficulties. All my old pains came back even more acutely than before. My feet felt like open stumps, my legs were stiff and appeared to be receding into my guts.

Dysentery kept wringing my innards, I could hardly place one foot in front of the other.'

In spite of his problems, it was clear that the escapers, now reunited, were very close to the front line. Gunfire sounded all around them and they could make out the shapes of camouflaged tanks hidden among the trees. It was now that Yeo-Thomas's last resources of strength ran out. He collapsed and was incapable of getting up. He urged the other escapers to leave him and he promised to move on when he had regained some strength. Commendably, they refused to leave him and, when he tried to order them, they refuted any obligation on their part to accept the instructions of a British officer. Ignoring his remonstrations, they picked him up and carried him towards the firing and the Allied lines. Reaching the edge of no man's land, their next decision was whether to wait until nightfall. They eventually decided to make their attempt straightaway, hoping that, in daylight, it would be clear that they were not wearing uniform, and that both the Allied and German units would assume them to be civilians. Supported by Albaret and another comrade, Yeo-Thomas led the file of escapers as they crossed the field (a mine-field, as he later found out) and had the distinction of being the first to make contact with American troops. Although understandably mistrustful, the Americans soon accepted Yeo-Thomas's explanation that they were escaped prisoners of war and the party was taken to the rear: 'I was thrilled and happy. We had made it, at last I was free. I might be able to take part in the end of the war and get the chance of avenging my comrades who had been murdered at Buchenwald.'

They were escorted to a nearby village, Hohndorf, where they were questioned by an army lieutenant. Yeo-Thomas was now an experienced interrogatee and enjoyed the novelty of having enquiries conducted in such a civilized manner, accompanied by apparently limitless luxuries, such as food, real coffee and oranges. His story appeared so extraordinary that each American officer in turn who interviewed him still harboured doubts over his bona fides. It was only when the French Army liaison officer attached to the American unit arrived and spoke to Yeo-Thomas that his story was fully accepted. This officer, Lieutenant Javal, was sufficiently well informed that he was able to tell Yeo-Thomas of the personal investigation that Robin Brook had conducted into his disappearance. A formerly sceptical American major then shook Yeo-Thomas warmly by the hand and offered him the use of his own quarters. Such an opportunity was not to be missed and, after a hot bath, he was issued with clean socks and underwear and a civilian suit formerly belonging to the Nazi Bürgermeister of Hohndorf. The rest of the evening was like a dream come true: Yeo-Thomas dined with the major, was given a bottle of

Napoleon brandy and sat in the unit's command post as an attack was launched against the German lines.

The next day, Yeo-Thomas was told that he was being sent to Divisional HQ and his thoughts turned to the prospect of a rapid return to London. However, he had underestimated the extent of his physical weakness and he remained with the Americans for another three days. He was then driven to Weimar, where he bumped into Colonel Pierre Fourcaud, one of the leading BCRA agents and a good friend. At first, Fourcaud did not recognize him (understandably, because several days later, after many meals, Yeo-Thomas still only weighed 6 stone 5 pounds), but as soon as he did so, the Frenchman's joy was unconfined. He determined to drive Yeo-Thomas back to Paris as there were no aircraft available to fly him.

The details of Yeo-Thomas's and Fourcaud's trip to Paris are a little sketchy, but an account by an RAF officer whom he met en route has survived:

> I was commanding an RAF Intelligence unit attached to the Headquarters of the American 9th Air Force in Weizbaden [*sic*], and one evening in the spring of 'forty-five, I was just going to sit down to dinner when I was asked by an American officer to see a 'strange guy who claims to belong to your outfit'. A moment later, I met for the first time Wing Commander Yeo-Thomas, thin and weak from his deprivations, and dressed in ill-fitting civilian clothes which he told me he had obtained from a German burgomaster. Although he had no credentials, he soon persuaded me that he was the person he claimed to be, and I took him in to dinner . . . As his tale unfolded, I could not help but wonder if such things were possible and whether he was suffering from delusions caused by his sufferings in Buchenwald, but the sincerity of his voice finally convinced me that it was all true.
>
> No doubt he can still remember that meal, and my anxiety for his wellbeing when he drank a whole bottle of wine and ate two huge steaks, for I feared that his digestive powers would not be equal to such fare after his starvation diet in the hands of the Germans.

Yeo-Thomas's arrival in Paris on 8 May, appropriately VE Day – the formal date marking the end of the war in Europe – became something of a blur, not because he was drunk (although the celebrations were prodigious, the alcohol had no apparent effect on him), but because of the constant stream of old friends overjoyed to see him safely returned. The remaining staff of SOE's RF and F Sections were now based at the Hotel Cecil in the rue Lauriston. It was ironic that the first news of his reaching safety had been received here by Joan Morrison, a FANY cipher clerk and, more importantly, the sister of Denis Barrett. When the news was announced, the whole office burst into spontaneous cheering.[3] Their elation was not merely because of Yeo-Thomas's reputation, but also because SOE had been searching for him and monitoring reports of his movements for more than a year. Yeo-Thomas's friends and associates in the resistance had immediately sought to discover news of him with a view towards securing his release, and SOE had not stood idly by.

Major Thackthwaite of the RF Section had been sent to Paris soon after Yeo-Thomas's arrest and operated there from 20 to 23 April 1944. The report that he submitted to Dismore on 18 May 1944 was based on his conversations with José Dupuis, Jeanne Helbling and Abeille. He was able to lay to rest rumours that Yeo-Thomas had taken his suicide pill and confirm that he was held in Fresnes. Further interviews continued to be conducted with all personnel possessing any knowledge of recent events, including Michel Pichard who, on 22 June, was able to submit his own summary of the circumstances surrounding Yeo-Thomas's arrest. Significantly, Pichard's interpretation of the string of betrayals in his and Yeo-Thomas's networks was far from accurate. However, he was able to describe attempts to bribe German officials in order to secure lenient treatment for Yeo-Thomas and, perhaps, his release. Furthermore, he was able to report that the prisoner was still alive.

In September, after the liberation of Paris, Thackthwaite was sent back to France on Mission HOUND, 'with the object of trying to trace "Shelley"'. This was in response to three telegrams that SOE had received that erroneously indicated 'that Yeo-Thomas was in a POW camp in Germany in early June'. Understandably, Dismore was worried about 'the important information which he [Yeo-Thomas] possesses and which the Germans would not scruple to use any means to extract'. Thackthwaite was instructed to prevent any ill-considered attempt by any other military agency to confirm his identity as this might arouse German suspicions. Together with José Dupuis, he carried out investigations into Yeo-Thomas's imprisonment in Fresnes and Compiègne, located inscriptions left by Yeo-Thomas on cell walls and traced fellow inmates with whom he had come into contact. They were able to ascertain that he had adopted his 'Dodkin' alias although, initially, they were unable to find evidence to confirm that he had been taken to Germany. At the beginning of October 1944, shortly before his return to England, Thackthwaite spotted an article about Pierre Brossolette in the Paris newspaper, *Carrefour*. This made two specific references to 'Shelley':

On one of his [Brossolette's] trips, he took with him to Paris this Captain Shelley, who was to explain to Mr Churchill what he had seen in France. Mr Churchill believed in the French resistance immediately and began to supply the newborn underground movement with arms. . .

At the same time, Captain Shelley, a friend, landed in France determined to save him [Brossolette]. He was arrested almost immediately.

SOE were aghast at this leakage of information and quickly raised the matter with the BCRA: 'As you know, we have been trying to close down all mention of "Shelley" in the hope that he has been able to lead the Gestapo off the scent and assume another identity.'

Dismore acknowledged that the harm has probably already been done, but strongly suggested that no further references to 'Shelley' should be allowed to appear. The BCRA replied the next day, promising that the appropriate action would be taken and that Dewavrin and Manuel expressed their personal distress at the prospect of this error having any deleterious consequences for Yeo-Thomas.

Meanwhile Yeo-Thomas's own endeavours to get messages back to London started to bear fruit. Sergeant Gillman, with whom he had made contact in Fresnes, had been transferred to the prisoner-of-war camp Stalag Luft III. From here (propitiously on D-Day), he sent a card to Barbara, saying that he had seen 'Tommy' who was alive and well. Although by the time this communication reached London it was old news, it nevertheless was one more piece in the jigsaw of Yeo-Thomas's disappearance. Gillman also took the trouble to write again on 24 November from Stalag 357, advising: 'Sorry but I can't give you any news of "Tommy" as we are no longer together, but the last time I saw him "our hearts were warm and gay".' Another message from a British prisoner followed in December. It was written by Flight Sergeant David Slack on 18 October 1944, and was sent to Barbara at her home address. By this time she was in Paris, serving with the Free French and, at the same time trying to find out what she could about Yeo-Thomas. The letter read:

Dear Barbara,
How are you keeping yourself. I'm an old friend of Tommy's who always called me Bobby, although my name is David and my home address is DAVID SLACK, DALTON MAGNA, ROTHER-HAM. I've seen Tommy and he's OK and sends his love and says keep your chin up. Hopes to see you soon. I'm OK myself. Well I'll say cheerio for now.

All the best,
David

In her absence, Dismore intercepted the note, and on 7 December 1944 sent her a telegram asking if she knew of Slack.

Barbara had no recollection of having either met or heard Yeo-Thomas mention him and, to add to the mystery, the Air Ministry had trouble locating him in their files. MI5 and the West Riding Constabulary were called into action and, on 3 January 1945, rather tetchily reported that Slack was who he said he was and suggested that the Air Ministry's problems had stemmed from their failure to realize that Slack had been granted a commission at about the time that he was shot down.

In February 1945 even more concrete information arrived in the form of Flight Lieutenant L F Gregory. Gregory had been repatriated from Stalag Luft III where, before his departure, he had been briefed by Squadron Leader Lamason, the commanding officer of the party of airmen who had been briefly imprisoned in Buchenwald. He was therefore able to report, albeit at second hand, on fairly recent events in the camp. Not only did he confirm Yeo-Thomas's switch to 'Dodkin', but also the murder of the group from Block 17 as well as the switch of the three agents' identities in the 'Guinea Pig' block.

As the Allied armies overran Germany, information hardly flooded in, but snippets of news continued to be collated. These were enhanced when several of Yeo-Thomas's fellow prisoners began to reach the safety of the Allied lines. They were able to provide news that, even if it was out of date, gave cause for hope. Stephane Hessel, Henry Peulevé, Christopher Burney and Corporal Stevenson from Gleina all gave information in their debriefings of their last sightings of Yeo-Thomas. The trail was therefore still warm enough for Robin Brook to undertake a mission to Buchenwald on Gubbins's instructions: 'To follow up the various rumours on the "Shelley" case, including tracing him if possible.' He spent two days at the camp, on 20 and 21 April, but apart from being impressed by Kogon ('the most trustworthy and the only man of intelligence to engineer the plot for "Shelley's" and others' escapes') and unimpressed by Dietzsch ('a very dubious German communist'), he found few witnesses who could throw much light on Yeo-Thomas's story. Brook's conclusion was none too optimistic, but he was not prepared to give up: 'I myself have no hope other than that he may be overrun on the railway leading southwards through Hof and Weiden. I certainly feel a mobile team should stand by to search for him.'

Brook's faith in Yeo-Thomas was not misplaced, although the latter did not require the assistance of an SOE team to rescue him.

The return of Yeo-Thomas was such a memorable occasion that at least two SOE staff officers included their none too accurate versions of the event in their memoirs. Douglas Dodds-Parker, the former head of SOE's MASSINGHAM mission in North Africa, gave the impression that Yeo-Thomas had just walked out of Rehmsdorf, rather than spent more than a week in Allied care:

> Suddenly the door flew open and a figure appeared, of such a dishevelled appearance that, used though I had become to such apparitions, I began to protest at the interruption. Then, through the shock, the face . . . I think, contrary to my nature, I kissed him . . . made him bath and clean up, found clothes and drove him to the Club.[4]

A rather more touching and heartfelt comment on Yeo-Thomas's release was written by O'Bryan Tear, one of his closest associates in RF Section, who had been posted to Brussels and was unable to welcome his friend home. He clearly recognized his friend's impending elevation to celebrity status:

> I'd hate to say all the obvious things, since presumably you've had your fill of congratulations and expressions of joy & relief, etc. but, Jesus, I am glad you made it . . . You've probably discovered a lot of other friends you never even knew you had! I often came across people who talked about S/L Y-T who'd never as far as I knew even seen you. As somebody once remarked after an official supper to celebrate the liberation of France, 'I never knew so many people in London & America had been the leaders of the French Resistance.'

On his arrival in Paris, as Dodds-Parker mentions, Yeo-Thomas was taken to dinner at the Officers' Club in the rue Faubourg St Honoré, where he was overjoyed to meet the faithful José Dupuis. The next day he went to see his father who 'was just the same as usual, shook hands with me as though I had only been away for a holiday, and asked a few questions. I heard later, however, that when he saw me for the first time, he had quite a shock and told a friend of his: "My son has returned, but he looks like an old man of seventy."'

After his visit to the rue des Eaux, he was taken to the airport and flown to England. He was, understandably, exultant: 'I felt like a million dollars. I had surmounted the most incredible difficulties, faced death in a hundred horrible forms. I had fooled the Germans and succeeded in escaping. I had not admitted defeat and I had not been defeated. I was going to rejoin the one person in all the world that mattered. My cup of happiness was full.'

The aircraft landed at Croydon airport where a reception committee of Dismore, Alex Murray and, of course, Barbara awaited him. His feelings at this reunion can barely be guessed, and he himself later found it impossible to describe them adequately: ' . . . and then I saw her . . . and I was speechless. It was too much happiness for words.'

CHAPTER TEN

• Freedom •

Yeo-Thomas's first evening back in London was spent in a celebratory dinner at Alex Murray's apartment. The next day, he did the rounds at Baker Street, then he and Barbara went away for a long weekend at Henley followed, after a brief return to London, by a week's touring holiday in the Cotswolds and Wales: 'I was given leave and had to follow treatment. It was only after my return that I really began to feel how much vitality I had expended. Until I had seen Barbara, I had not relaxed, I had still remained under pressure, but after, I just flopped.'

In spite of his poor medical condition and SOE's desire to give him an extended debriefing, Yeo-Thomas was determined to return to Germany as soon as possible to trace and arrest Buchenwald and Rehmsdorf concentration-camp guards. As early as 22 May, senior staff officers at Baker Street were discussing proposals that he investigate the whereabouts of these alleged war criminals. On 31 May, less than three weeks after his return to England, a draft proposal for the mission was submitted and, the next day, with the backing of Robin Brook, it was approved. It was no longer an RF Section affair, but had to be undertaken under the aegis of SOE's German Section, at that time supervised by Lieutenant-Colonel R H Thornley. With the area around Weimar under American control, Thornley did his best to secure cooperation with the Office of Strategic Services (OSS, the American equivalent to SOE and SIS) in the region of Buchenwald in order to facilitate Yeo-Thomas's mission. On 5 June, the project was accorded the codename OUTHAUL. Surviving documents certainly give the impression that SOE was, in part, indulging Yeo-Thomas's desire for retribution, but, in spite of this, he and officialdom once again failed to see eye to eye. To give him more authority when dealing with Allied personnel, SOE sought to obtain a temporary promotion for him. On 13 June, Baker Street received notification that the Air Ministry declined to bestow the local rank of Wing Commander on Yeo-Thomas as it 'never gives local rank'.[1] Furthermore, Yeo-Thomas had incurred the displeasure of Air Commodore A R Boyle, variously SOE's Assistant Chief, President of the Personnel Board, Director of Personnel Services, Intelligence, Security and Liaison, who minuted that he had 'received several complaints about the fact that Squadron Leader Yeo-Thomas is almost invariably improperly dressed'. This preoccupation was not allowed to rest and Boyle minuted Thornley a fortnight later: 'I saw him [Yeo-Thomas] this morning and told him that in no circumstances must he wear a parachute badge or any of the other exotic decorations which he has been sporting. He said he fully understood, but it may be advisable to repeat the warning if you see him before departure.'

The object of operation OUTHAUL was succinctly given as: 'To trace certain SS concentration-camp guards known to members of the mission believed to be in hiding in the American occupied area of Germany,' and was to be undertaken by a small team of three men with Yeo-Thomas in command, supported by his old RF Section friend George Whitehead[2] and Lance-Corporal Stevenson, whom he had met at Gleina. The operational instructions were intended to hem Yeo-Thomas in with a variety of protocols, needed to secure effective liaison with the French and American authorities. However, the team had only just set off for France, when, on 29 June 1945, the head of SOE's German Directorate at last introduced a questioning note regarding the underlying motivation behind OUTHAUL. As had so often occurred in the past, Yeo-Thomas's strength of character and enthusiasm imparted a momentum to his scheme that took even the most sober of staff officers along with him. Now, a note of caution was finally being expressed:

Memorandum from AD/X to VC/D 29.6.1945

Operation OUTHAUL

Confirming our telephone conversation, this operation, which has been sponsored on a high level and which we have been instructed to carry out, is causing me considerable alarm.

I cannot help feeling that, in view of the present unbalanced state of mind of the leader of the Mission (a state of mind which can well be understood in the light of his experiences), the Mission is unlikely to achieve any positive results and may possibly degenerate into a romp which may have unpleasant repercussions. Without any reference to this Directorate, the leader of the Mission has put in through RF Section an indent for stores which has only just been shown to me. This totals 799lbs of material, mostly foodstuffs, intended presumably for bribery or distribution to old friends. It also includes several pistols, welrods [a silenced pistol developed by SOE], carbines, silent stens etc with ammunition.[3]

For any normal operation, I would not pass the quantity of foodstuffs but, in view of the peculiar circumstances of this mission, I have agreed to pass them with your approval. Also,

> with your approval, I have given instructions that the weapons
> and ammunition should not be included and should be removed
> before the stores are shipped to Paris.
>
> In my operation order for OUTHAUL, I have laid down very
> carefully how this mission should operate both in France and
> Germany and, if these orders are not carried out to the letter,
> I consider there may be trouble and unpleasant repercussions.

It does not take a mastermind to recognize the nature of the 'unpleasant repercussions' likely to arise from the combination of a large arsenal of weapons and Yeo-Thomas's proximity to his Nazi tormentors.

Yeo-Thomas and his small team stopped off in Paris to renew
contacts and, on 5 July, reached Frankfurt. Then, with Baker Street
exercising understandable misgivings about OUTHAUL, and with the
recent occupation of the Weimar area by the Red Army, Sporborg
made the decision to cancel the operation and recall Yeo-Thomas to
London. All was not lost, however, and out of the ashes of OUTHAUL
came OUTHAUL II, an operation that wisely kept Yeo-Thomas away
from the temptation to exact revenge in Germany. The brief for
this mission was to tidy up his affairs in France and, in particular, to
investigate some of the outstanding questions over the circumstances
leading to the arrests of Brossolette, Hubble and some of his other
comrades. The faithful George Whitehead was to accompany him and
assist in the compilation of a report. For Yeo-Thomas, the trip lasted
barely a week, leaving London on 22 July and returning on the
28th. The brevity of the operation may in part have been due to a
deterioration in his health, which was hardly surprising, given his
demanding schedule since his return. At the beginning of August, he
underwent a series of medical tests that were primarily concerned with
investigating the cause of constant headaches and nasal difficulties.
X-rays did not reveal any fracture of the skull, but showed a broken
nose or 'deviation of the septum probably of a traumatic nature'.

The answer seemed to be another spell of leave and, on 13 August,
Yeo-Thomas and Barbara went on holiday to the West Country. The
break seemed to do the trick for, on the 26th, he wrote to Gubbins
saying that he was 'already feeling the benefit of my rest, and am in far
better condition than I was a fortnight ago. I am getting plenty of
exercise, riding, etc and spend most of my time in the open – even
though the weather has not been too good. I think that after my nose
has been put right, all will be OK and I will regain my former fitness
very rapidly.'

However, SOE's doctors were not quite so sure. Following an
examination after Yeo-Thomas's return from leave, the doctor
reported: '. . . although he has made fairly good progress and his

physical condition has improved, his mental make-up is still unstable and he has not adjusted himself to his new mode of life.'

Evidence of this was provided when Barbara and Yeo-Thomas, perhaps unwisely, went to see a screening of a documentary film about the liberation of Belsen concentration camp. Yeo-Thomas became so distressed and his reaction to the apparent apathy of the rest of the audience was so violent that they were asked to leave the cinema. In addition to the regular nightmares that he suffered, there was a seemingly mundane but very tangible after-effect of his captivity. He developed an eating disorder and, having always been a gourmet, after the experience of starvation he now turned into a gourmand. He would get up in the middle of the night to raid the refrigerator for any food he could find there, and he was soon transformed from being undernourished and thin into an almost portly figure.

Commendably, senior SOE officers recognized all the difficulties he was experiencing and sought to protect him from increasing demands that he write reports. Acknowledging that his 'psychological condition is, naturally enough, very bad indeed', they decided 'not to badger him to produce stories and reports until AQ/MED [SOE's medical officer] is willing that this should be done'. SOE continued to monitor Yeo-Thomas's health and, in particular, his mental stability. He made good progress through September, 'regaining much of his former confidence and he himself states that he feels better', but the doctors felt that Yeo-Thomas was not ready to write reports as 'this would undoubtedly stir up some of his psychological symptoms'. By the end of the month, permission was given for Yeo-Thomas to go to Germany to assist the Americans in their war crimes investigations, but with the proviso that George Whitehead accompany him as a 'minder'. The two left on 7 October and returned three weeks later. SOE's medical care continued and, at the end of November, a leading neuropsychiatrist was able to report that Yeo-Thomas would make a complete recovery, although he still required six weeks' out-patient treatment and should not be demobilized until this had been completed.

While Yeo-Thomas edged his way to recovery and endeavoured to clear up the loose ends of his service with SOE, the first accounts of his epic story began to appear in the press. On 24 July, Dismore confirmed to his superiors that Yeo-Thomas had given his assent to the publication of his letter from Buchenwald. Surprisingly, this was released under the auspices of the Admiralty, through the office of Commander Ian Fleming[4] of the Naval Intelligence Department, and extracts soon appeared in service bulletins. The national press quickly picked up the story and the *Daily Telegraph* of 11 September 1945 bore the headline: 'British secret agent tortured in Buchenwald –

Human 'Guinea Pig' took name of cremated Frenchman'. Understandably, Yeo-Thomas's name was not mentioned. Similar reports appeared on the same day in the *Daily Express*, *Daily Mail*, *Morning Advertiser*, *Daily Sketch* and the *Daily Herald* – 'The man who wrote it is alive this morning. But his identity will never be made known. He is a British Secret Service agent and will remain as Mr "Y" to all but a handful of British agents who alone know his name.' The *News Chronicle* indulged in more fanciful speculation than the other newspapers and printed the misleading statement that the agent was 'One of Britain's most successful Secret Service men, who had done much work for Naval Intelligence'.

As the remarkable story of Yeo-Thomas's wartime experiences began to be known, SOE addressed the sensitive and contentious question of seeking official recognition for his bravery and dedication. Within days of his return to London, SOE staff were compiling a citation that Lord Selborne intended to submit to Churchill (taking great pains to remind the Prime Minister that he had already met Yeo-Thomas over the question of the allocation of aircraft). In a memorandum from V/CD to A/CD of 17 May 1945, Sporborg stated that:

> He [Selborne] has instructed me to ask you to do everything possible to expedite this. Incidentally, I think SO [Selborne] fully intends to regard an application for a George Cross as a "piss aller" [*sic*] and to go all out for a Victoria Cross in the first instance.

Sadly, Selborne's hopes were not realized. Whitehall committees and boards found no provision in the regulations for the award of a Victoria Cross and felt it necessary to consider the sensibilities of the various ministries. It was noted in unofficial discussions that the War Office might prefer to confer an OBE (Mil), while the Air Ministry would favour a DSO. One august body at the War Office felt it appropriate to voice the opinion 'that there was no case for either the Victoria or George Cross'. A repeat performance of the fiasco that had surrounded Yeo-Thomas's Croix de Guerre and Military Cross began to loom large as pen-pushers and bureaucrats sat in judgment, seeking to weigh protocol against some abstract, empirical gradation of courage.

There remained those, however, who were determined to mark Yeo-Thomas's singular efforts with an appropriate decoration and, on 11 February 1946, Lord Selborne was able to write to him: 'I have heard a bit of news last night which caused me a lot of pleasure. It is not adequate to congratulate you but I merely say that no honour was better deserved, and this is one of the greatest honours that an Englishman can receive.'

The honour to which Selborne referred was the George Cross. On 23 September 1940, King George VI had announced the creation of a new award for gallantry. Initially intended to recognize 'acts of the greatest heroism or of the most conspicuous courage in circumstances of extreme danger' performed by civilians, it was also awarded to members of the armed forces 'for supreme gallantry not in the face of the enemy'. It is a little hard to comprehend the logic behind placing Yeo-Thomas in this category for he was rarely out of sight of the enemy for much of the war.

On 15 February 1946, the night before the gazetting of his George Cross, a press conference was held at the Air Ministry, with Lord Willoughby de Broke in the chair, and the citation for Yeo-Thomas's award was handed out to those present:

The KING has been graciously pleased to award the George Cross to:

Acting Wing Commander Forest Frederick Edward Yeo-Thomas, M.C. (89215), Royal Air Force Volunteer Reserve.

This officer was parachuted into France on the 25th February, 1943. He showed much courage and initiative during his mission, particularly when he enabled a French officer who was being followed by a Gestapo agent in Paris to reach safety and resume clandestine work in another area. He also took charge of a US Army Air Corps officer who had been shot down and, speaking no French, was in danger of capture. This officer returned to England on the 15th April, 1943, in the aircraft which picked up Wing Commander Yeo-Thomas.

Wing Commander Yeo-Thomas undertook a second mission on the 17th September, 1943. Soon after his arrival in France many patriots were arrested. Undeterred, he continued his enquiries and obtained information which enabled the desperate situation to be rectified. On six occasions he narrowly escaped arrest. He returned to England on the 15th November, 1943, bringing British intelligence archives which he had secured from a house watched by the Gestapo.

This officer was again parachuted into France in February, 1944. Despite every security precaution he was betrayed to the Gestapo in Paris on the 21st March. While being taken by car to Headquarters he was badly 'beaten up'. He then underwent 4 days' continuous interrogation, interspersed with beatings and torture, including immersions, head downwards, in ice-cold water, with legs and arms chained. Interrogations later continued for 2 months and Wing Commander Yeo-Thomas was offered his freedom in return for information concerning the Head of a Resistance Secretariat. Owing to his wrist being cut by chains, he contracted blood-poisoning and nearly lost his left arm. He made two daring but unsuccessful attempts to escape. He was then confined in solitude in Fresnes prison for 4 months, including 3 weeks in a darkened cell with very little food. Throughout these months of almost continuous torture, he stead-fastly refused to disclose any information.

On the 17th July, Wing Commander Yeo-Thomas was sent with a party to Compiègne prison, from which he twice attempted to escape. He and 36 others were then transferred to Buchenwald. On the way, they stopped for 3 days at Saarbrucken, where they were beaten and kept in a tiny hut. They arrived at Buchenwald on the 16th August and 16 of them were executed and cremated on the 10th September. Wing Commander Yeo-Thomas had already commenced to organize resistance within the camp and remained undaunted by the prospect of a similar fate. He accepted an opportunity of changing his identity with that of a dead French prisoner, on condition that other officers would also be enabled to do so. In this way, he was instrumental in saving the lives of two officers.

Wing Commander Yeo-Thomas was later transferred to a work kommando for Jews. In attempting to escape he was picked up by a German patrol and, claiming French nationality, was transferred to a camp near Marienburg for French prisoners-of-war. On the 16th April, 1945, he led a party of 20 in a most gallant attempt to escape in broad daylight. 10 were killed by fire from the guards. Those who reached cover split up into small groups. Wing Commander Yeo-Thomas became separated from his companions after 3 days without food. He continued alone for a week and was recaptured when only 800 yards from the American lines. A few days later he escaped with a party of 10 French prisoners-of-war, whom he led through German patrols to the American lines.

Wing Commander Yeo-Thomas thus turned his final mission into a success by his determined opposition to the enemy, his strenuous efforts to maintain the morale of his fellow-prisoners and his brilliant escape activities. He endured brutal treatment and torture without flinching and showed the most amazing fortitude and devotion to duty throughout his service abroad, during which he was under the constant threat of death.[5]

Reports of the award appeared on 16 February 1946 in all the national newspapers. The *Daily Express* set a peculiarly downbeat note with: 'Man who made dresses wins GC', while the *Daily Mail* recalled the publication of the letter from Buchenwald with 'Yeo-Thomas who was yesterday revealed as "Agent X".'

Six weeks after the announcement, on 26 March 1946, King George VI decorated Yeo-Thomas with the Cross at an investiture at Buckingham Palace.

Even heroes had to be demobilized and, a couple of days after the press conference, Yeo-Thomas left the Royal Air Force, having already taken his leave of SOE on 14 January. He had kept in touch with Molyneux throughout the war and accepted the option of taking up his job in the rue Royale. He returned to France and the world of *haute couture*, but a brief note in his diary said it all: 'First day at Molyneux – Hell of a lot to do – feeling lonely and depressed. Wish I was back with Barbara.'

The following days were not much better and, although he was kept busy, usually working late into the night, he wrote that he was 'bored by the work but never a moment's peace' and 'feel browned off'. He later summed up his feelings at this time: 'Back to dresses . . . and all the futility they represent. I packed my uniform away, and put on the white collar and the neat business attire once more . . . and heard anew "My dear, how too, too divine", "Wasn't it dreadful, during that beastly war, I had to go without at least a dozen dresses a year, even though I did manage to buy a few coupons on the Black Market. But, just think how difficult it was to get stockings, I don't know how I put up with it, I really don't." I saw fat, blousy, ill-bred women, accompanied by bloated husbands or substitutes, come in and buy the most expensive gowns and fur coats, with the blood money their profiteer males had sucked up, profiteering whilst we were fighting for their unworthy loathsome hides.'

His frame of mind was not helped by his separation from Barbara and, as he had done during the first months of their courtship, he scrupulously recorded in his diary the letters and telephone calls they exchanged. She had stayed in London to clear up outstanding matters and then took a job at a country club in Northamptonshire, where Yeo-Thomas was to join her if, as expected, he could no longer endure Molyneux's. The plan was changed, however, and instead of his returning to England, in March Barbara followed him to Paris. There was no getting away from the fact that Yeo-Thomas's experiences and their fourteen-month separation had affected their relationship. No woman could have fulfilled the ideal that Yeo-Thomas had created during his torment. Meanwhile, Barbara had to confront the problems of living with a man whom she still loved, but who had discernibly changed. While she wanted to put the war behind them, Yeo-Thomas remained fixated by it, both because of his fame and the rawness of his memories. Matters were not helped by her having to build a new life in a strange environment where she was still far from fluent in the language. Furthermore, her domestic status caused difficulties, even in the supposedly more liberal moral climate of France. She remained Yeo-Thomas's common-law wife, while Lillian refused to grant a divorce and continued to live in the same city. To

compound these difficulties, Yeo-Thomas's health remained uncertain and he was constantly prey to a host of ailments.

To all intents and purposes, however, they remained the golden
couple fêted in London and Paris. In France, Yeo-Thomas stayed in
close touch with his former friends in the resistance, many of whom
were now at the centre of political life. They wanted to mark his
contribution to France's victory and sought to honour him with,
arguably, the most prestigious of the wartime decorations, the Croix
de la Libération. On 7 June 1945, he was recommended for the
award, which had been specifically created for those who had done
most to achieve France's liberation, either on the battlefield or in the
resistance. Yeo-Thomas seemed an outstanding candidate, but the
application was turned down and he had to content himself with
becoming a member of the Légion d'Honneur. There were only
three British recipients of the Ordre de la Libération: George VI, Sir
Winston Churchill and a George Taylor. The last named appears to
have been chosen to represent British endeavour during the war, a
national honour accorded to the 'unknown warrior'.

Post-war France was not merely a place of parades and medals. The
dark side was just below the surface, as recrimination set in and the
investigation of suspected collaborators took place throughout the
country. In the main, Yeo-Thomas concerned himself with positive
deeds, such as securing compensation for the victims of war, rather
than seeking out miscreants. His correspondence is full of letters from
individuals asking his help in clearing their names, having been falsely
accused of wrongdoing, and others seeking his support in their appli-
cations for a pensions. In spite of the work that this entailed, he
delighted in being able to help. Among those seeking his assistance
was Arthur Dietzsch, who had first written to him as early as 20 July
1945. Yeo-Thomas did the best he could for the Buchenwald Kapo
and even recommended him to Thornley for possible employment by
SOE, but this suggestion was not taken up; on the contrary, Dietzsch
had been arrested by the Allied authorities at Bielefeld in December
1946. In spite of all Yeo-Thomas's efforts, there was too much
evidence indicating that Dietzsch had collaborated with the camp
authorities in maltreating the inmates and, on 14 August 1947, he
was sentenced to fifteen years' imprisonment. However, Yeo-Thomas
did not forget Dietzsch's part in saving his life and he wrote to
General Lucius Clay, the Military Governor of the US Zone of
Occupation, asking for clemency. This was not successful but, in the
event, Dietzsch was not obliged to serve his full term of imprisonment. On his release in December 1950 he wrote to Yeo-Thomas,
who responded by sending him money and presents and helped
secure him employment. The two men continued to keep in touch

into the 1960s, with Dietzsch invariably the supplicant and Yeo-Thomas endeavouring to provide money, advice and support.

However, Yeo-Thomas had a long memory for those who had crossed him. There is no record of when he learnt the news that his old adversary, André Lemonnier, had survived the war. The last he had seen of him was in 1944 when they had both been taken to Fresnes and he had managed to broadcast the news of the Frenchman's treachery around the prison. It transpired that Lemonnier had been sent to Dachau concentration camp, from where he returned to France in April 1945, and questions about his dubious wartime activities had been revived. Following a denunciation, he was brought before the *Juge d'Instruction* in Le Mans, but, following various enquiries, the authorities decided to let the matter drop. However, word reached José Dupuis, Bernard Josseaume and Yeo-Thomas of his reappearance and they wrote a letter, affirming their accusations of Lemonnier's treachery. Such was the gravity of their allegations that, at the beginning of 1946, Lemonnier was arrested and charged with '*intelligences avec l'ennemi*'. His partner in crime, Edmond Vacher, was traced to the Bordeaux region, where it was learnt that he had had the audacity to rejoin the resistance for three weeks at the time of the Liberation.

The two men were brought to trial at Angers in July, where they confessed their guilt and Vacher deposited 200,000 francs with the court as repayment for the money he had stolen in Paris. Their confession did not prevent Yeo-Thomas being called as a witness. Wearing his RAF uniform, 'his chest covered with medals',[6] he briefly recounted his initial connection with Lemonnier and the subsequent confrontation in Misselwitz's office. When asked to comment on this statement, Lemonnier declared: 'I am sorry. I wanted to protect the colonel. I was afraid of him. I am sorry to have betrayed his trust because I admired him.' In reply, Yeo-Thomas pithily commented: 'You have a funny way of showing it. You are unforgivable.'

Surprisingly, the two defendants had managed to compile a reasonable selection of character witnesses and, before the court finally passed its judgment, reiterated their regret. Their admission of guilt meant that the best they could hope for was a lenient sentence, but the judge's ruling reflected the gravity of the charges laid against them:

> The court has condemned Lemonnier to a sentence of hard labour for life and Vacher to ten years' hard labour and a ten-year restricted access order. Furthermore, the court has inflicted a lifetime of national shame on the two condemned men and has confiscated their assets.[7]

While France sought to inflict retribution on prominent collaborators, such as Pétain and Laval as well as small fry like Lemonnier and
Vacher, the Allies had set about bringing the leading Nazis to justice.
The trial at Nuremberg of the twenty-two major Nazi leaders began
in November 1945 and lasted until October 1946, with all but three
of the accused found guilty. Further war crimes investigations turned
their attention to the concentration-camp system. Buchenwald had
been liberated on 11 April 1945 by a reconnaissance battalion of the
US 6th Armoured Division, part of the US 3rd Army. The soldiers
were ill prepared for the horrors that confronted them. A few days
after the liberation of the camp, the American wireless reporter Ed
Murrow broadcast a harrowing account of what he had seen there: 'I
pray you to believe what I have said about Buchenwald. I reported
what I saw and heard, but only part of it. For most of it, I have no
words.'

Almost two years to the day after the camp's liberation, the local
ss commander, SS-Obergruppenführer Josias Erbprinz von Waldeck-
Pyrmont, and thirty members of the camp staff were brought to trial
before a US Military Tribunal at Dachau concentration camp, near
Munich. On 15 April 1947, Yeo-Thomas was called to give evidence
for the prosecution. Under the steady questioning of Prosecutor
William D Denson, Yeo-Thomas delivered a restrained, almost dis-
passionate account of his experiences in the camp. He described
specific acts of brutality that he had witnessed and was able to identify Pister, Dietzsch and others among the accused in the courtroom.
The various defence counsel found it difficult to unsettle him and
sought, somewhat lamely, to question the accuracy of his testimony.
The best that Pister's lawyer could offer was a series of smokescreen
questions about Yeo-Thomas's background and status as an enemy
agent.

A few months later, he returned to Dachau under very different
circumstances. This was for the trial of a group of German special
forces personnel, including the notorious SS-Obersturmbannführer
Otto Skorzeny. An early recruit to the Austrian Nazi Party, Skorzeny
had joined the Waffen-SS in March 1939 and went on to serve with
distinction in this élite unit during the initial major campaigns of the
Second World War. A huge, six-foot-four-inch man with a distinctive
duelling scar on his cheek, Skorzeny developed a reputation as one
of Germany's most resourceful and adventurous soldiers. In April
1943, he was ordered to form a special forces unit, Jagdverbände
502, but the efficacy of this formation proved, in large measure, to be
frustrated by conflicting vested interests within the German High
Command. However, Skorzeny was soon to achieve his greatest
triumph in September that year with the spectacular rescue of Benito

Mussolini. The recently deposed Italian dictator was being held at an apparently impregnable hotel in the Abruzzi mountains. On 12 September, Skorzeny led an audacious glider-borne *coup de main* party on to the mountaintop and stormed the hotel. Taken by surprise, Mussolini's guards immediately surrendered and then, at great risk to himself and his VIP, Skorzeny accompanied his charge off the mountain aboard a light aircraft. Never one to shy away from publicity, Skorzeny was determined to deliver Il Duce to Hitler personally. The Führer was understandably delighted and awarded Skorzeny the Knight's Cross. Thereafter, Skorzeny was at the forefront of many of the Third Reich's special operations, including a trip to Vichy in November 1943 to assess the necessity of kidnapping Pétain or at the very least preventing his leaving France. Among these operations was a series of stratagems in support of the German Ardennes offensive of December 1944. Skorzeny had formed groups of English-speaking German commandos, dressed in American uniforms, to spread alarm and confusion behind the Allied lines. Both at the time and subsequently, rumours abounded of Skorzeny's intention either to assassinate or kidnap General Dwight D Eisenhower, the Supreme Allied Commander, at his headquarters near Paris. After initial success, the German advance petered out and, by the first week in February 1945, the 'bulge' in the American lines had disappeared. Following the failure of the offensive, Skorzeny was engaged upon a variety of increasingly desperate tasks, including helping to establish an Alpine Redoubt from which the war would be maintained, making preparations for a Nazi resistance in Germany following an Allied victory and, allegedly, even masterminding an escape plan for Hitler himself. As it transpired, Skorzeny had no intention of continuing the struggle after the German surrender and, on 16 May 1945, more than a week after the end of the fighting in Europe, he gave himself up to American forces in Austria. If some of the first American soldiers he encountered were unaware of his reputation, others soon realized the importance of their captive and the next day he was intensively interrogated by four officers of the US Counter-Intelligence Corps.

Slowly the Allied policy on enemy war crimes began to take shape, and, after the leaders of the Reich had been brought to book, the trials of some of the lesser lights were prepared. The charges subsequently laid against Skorzeny and eight others were that they had 'ill-treated, tortured and killed American prisoners-of-war, whose names and numbers are not known', and furthermore that they had ordered German personnel to wear enemy uniforms. The trial began at Dachau on 18 August 1947, with Skorzeny and the other accused being represented by Colonel Robert D Durst, assisted by Lieutenant-Colonel Donald McClure, Major L I Horowitz and three German lawyers. It was decided that Skorzeny alone would give evidence on behalf of all the prisoners.

The prosecution, led by Colonel Albert H Rosenfeld, began by calling a motley collection of Skorzeny's former associates, but most of the charges steadily fell away before Durst's cross-examination. Eventually, the only substantial accusation remained that of fighting in enemy uniforms, in contravention of an annexe to the Hague Convention of 1907. Putting Skorzeny on the stand, Durst encouraged him to reveal that the inspiration for his Operation GRIEF during the Ardennes offensive and, in particular, the use of Allied uniforms, came from an analysis of similar Allied stratagems. After two days of Skorzeny's testimony, it was evident that too great a burden of his defence lay in his own version of events. Then, to the astonishment of the prosecution and even the defendants themselves, Yeo-Thomas was called as the first witness for the defence. The RAF officer appeared the most unlikely choice imaginable, having suffered terribly at the hands of the Germans and having already given evidence against his tormentors at the Buchenwald trial, but Yeo-Thomas was unequivocal in his denial that Skorzeny had acted inappropriately. Furthermore, he was emphatic that he himself had carried out similar 'crimes' to those alleged to have been perpetrated by the accused. His plan to rescue Brossolette from Rennes prison offered the perfect example:

Durst:	Did you obtain German uniforms for this purpose?
Yeo-Thomas:	Yes.
Durst:	How were they obtained?
Yeo-Thomas:	The details I could not tell you. I gave instructions to obtain uniforms by hook or by crook.
Durst:	Did you also contemplate the use of German insignia?
Yeo-Thomas:	We contemplated everything that could be used to ensure the success of the operations.
Durst:	Insignia of rank or other insignia?
Yeo-Thomas:	Absolutely.
Durst:	Did you also plan to go armed?
Yeo-Thomas:	Certainly: we had to dispose of the guards.
Durst:	Precisely what do you mean by that?
Yeo-Thomas:	If necessary, kill them. We couldn't take prisoners.[8]

Yeo-Thomas faced each question with his own characteristically unflinching candour. It soon emerged that it was Durst's intent to complement the admission of Allied use of enemy uniforms with a more general recognition that skulduggery and 'dirty tricks' had been employed by Skorzeny's adversaries. Yeo-Thomas was asked to out-line the nature of the instructions that he received from his superiors: 'We were given assignments to do and we were told, "Go ahead and do them. We don't want to know how you do them; but if you get caught that is your pigeon; we shall disown you."'[9]

To clarify the picture further, Yeo-Thomas affirmed that Allied agents carried firearms, and in order to prevent discovery would 'bump off the other guy'. Although the prosecution had sought to offer objections on several occasions during Yeo-Thomas's question-ing, they declined to cross-examine him.

Skorzeny later wrote his own précis of Yeo-Thomas's evidence: 'The statements of this officer gave the court a most comprehensive picture of the courageous deeds performed by the British during the war. Disguise was certainly not barred, and all means were considered fair to obtain the gear required for that purpose! I felt sorry that I could not shake his hand when he said: "Gentlemen, Colonel Skorzeny and his officers have always behaved as gentlemen."'[10]

However, as a mark of respect and, no doubt, gratitude, as Yeo-Thomas stepped from the witness stand, Skorzeny gave a muted order to his co-defendants and they stood to attention and bowed to their saviour.

Skorzeny's acquittal did not ensure his release, and in November he wrote to Yeo-Thomas giving him his latest news, namely that he and his adjutant Radl were still under US Army custody. They had been moved to Oberursel where they were assisting the US Army Historical Division in its research into the course of the war and, in particular, into the rescue of Mussolini. He concluded his letter by reiterating his debt of gratitude: 'Let me say it once more, Sir, how very much we appreciated your help in this hard trial we had to stand. I was specially impressed by the fact, and I will never forget it in my life, that you as an officer of a former enemy country were so helpful to an officer of "the other side".'

Yeo-Thomas did not reply until February 1948, when he apolo-gized for the delay, brought about by the fact that Skorzeny's letter had taken six weeks to reach him. He stated that he needed no thanks for doing his 'duty to be fair and behave as I am sure you would have done had the positions been reversed'.

As spring came and the historical work ended, there still seemed no prospect of Skorzeny's release from the prison at Darmstadt, especially as each rumour or scare over the resurgence of Nazism brought Allied intelligence officers flocking to him to carry out further interrogations. Nevertheless, he was able to keep in touch with Yeo-Thomas and, in April, proposed a scheme that former soldiers of Britain, France and Germany should attend a conference to debate the current state of European affairs. This brotherhood of the battlefield appeared to be little more than the product of a prisoner's overactive imagination and there is no record that Yeo-Thomas made reply, but he continued to remain something of a mentor for the SS man and the latter wrote again from his internment camp, this time desperately seeking advice as to what he should do. Yeo-Thomas's reply was short and to the point: 'Escape.' Skorzeny took him at his word and, on 27 July 1948, with the connivance of his friends on the outside, he made a successful breakout. He laid low for almost a year, during which time he is alleged to have renewed contact with Reinhard Gehlen, a former associate and a leading member of wartime German military intelligence. Gehlen was now employed by US intelligence agencies to reactivate his old networks of agents and deploy them against the Soviet Union and their Eastern Bloc partners. In February 1950, Skorzeny caused a major stir in France when he was photographed by chance in Paris. He soon vanished from sight and went to ground in Germany with the assistance of the US intelligence services. Later that year he obtained a 'Nansen' passport (a special document issued to the stateless) in the name of 'Rudolf Steinbauer' and took up residence, along with several other former luminaries of the Third Reich, in the politically benevolent atmosphere of Franco's Spain. Here he still nurtured plans of an anti-communist pan-European army that he felt was particularly needed given the recent outbreak of the Korean War. While he sought to develop these schemes, he also maintained his extensive business contacts and achieved significant success in helping to resuscitate trade between Germany and Spain. Although Skorzeny appeared to exhibit a reasonable level of business acumen, it is believed that his evident wealth was derived in large measure from the substantial sums of money that his adjutant, Radl, had received from SS-Oberführer Josef Spacil, who had ransacked the Reichsbank headquarters in Berlin in the closing days of the war. On 27 April 1945, Spacil had handed over substantial sums of cash to Radl, which the two men had then hidden prior to their surrender. This financial windfall was one topic that the SS men had refrained from discussing with their captors, and it seems certain that it constituted the nest-egg for Skorzeny's diverse post-war activities, both in his business dealings and the funding of escape lines to assist former Nazis on the run.

Skorzeny's whereabouts and activities continued to be both the subject of great press speculation and of significant interest to Western and Soviet intelligence agencies. From his first interrogation in May 1945, Skorzeny had offered his services to the Allies in any future struggle against the Soviet Union and communism. He had helped Gehlen train and run agents behind Soviet lines and was, of course, exceptionally well connected with post-war right-wing European movements. Because of his special relationship with Skorzeny, Yeo-Thomas was asked by British intelligence to renew contact and visit him, 'with the specific aim of pumping him'. He visited Madrid in February 1952, and it is clear that their conversation consisted of far more than wartime reminiscences. Skorzeny outlined the extent of his diverse business and political activities, including his connections with some former leading lights in the Nazi war machine. Much of their talk centred on the military threat from the Soviet Union and the possible contribution of former Wehrmacht and SS elements in the event of a Third World War. To this end, in 1951, Skorzeny had met with a representative of the US State Department, who had proposed that he organize escape lines to assist US airmen shot down over Germany, develop a network of clandestine wireless operators and form groups of anti-Soviet partisans. Skorzeny commented that he felt most of these proposals were impractical. (Even so, the Western Allies went on to develop a complex organization of 'stay-behind' groups, ready to operate as resistance/guerrilla movements in what might have become Soviet-occupied territory.)

Yeo-Thomas continued to keep in touch with Skorzeny and appears to have had a genuine respect, if not admiration, for him. During the 1950s and early 1960s, he sought to help secure German citizenship for Skorzeny, to assist him in locating a publisher for his memoirs and, in 1961, offered his help in rebutting defamations of his character that appeared in French newspapers. In a letter to the *Daily Express* on 7 May 1952, he once again affirmed his stance on Skorzeny:

> . . . to round off the Skorzeny controversy: I went to Germany for his war trial, although I had never met him, because I was asked to testify in his defence. He was accused of sending his men behind the Allied lines in Germany in American uniform. Well, we had used German uniforms and papers ourselves and that is no crime. I have heard German generals and princes at similar trials claim that they were simply carrying out orders from above. But Otto Skorzeny took full responsibility for everything his junior officers had done. He was the only German I knew who had the guts to do so. I take my hat off to him. His trial and acquittal proved him to be a good soldier who pulled off first-class jobs. He fought a good war. I would be glad at any time to have a man like Skorzeny as my commanding officer.

By the summer of 1948, life at Molyneux had become too much for Yeo-Thomas. His celebrity status doubtless enhanced the company's image, but also had the effect of encouraging Molyneux's jealousy of his employee. Furthermore, Yeo-Thomas's health had begun to deteriorate and he became prone to blackouts. Relief appeared to be at hand when one of Molyneux's clients, Aileen Plunket, the divorced granddaughter of the first Earl of Iveagh and thus a member of the Guinness family, offered Yeo-Thomas the position of estate manager at Luttrellstown Castle, outside Dublin. In spite of his complete lack of experience of such work, this new challenge appealed to Yeo-Thomas and, although Barbara felt sure that there was a hidden agenda behind the divorcée's generosity, she gave her approval. He therefore resigned from Molyneux, leaving after the presentation of the summer collection in August, with the face-saving explanation that he 'has been ordered by his doctor to take a year's rest and he plans to spend it in the English [sic] countryside'.[11] At first the break from the world of *haute couture* and the conviviality of Irish life appealed to Yeo-Thomas. He was made Vice-President of the Dublin branch of the RAF Association and gave well-attended lectures to raise funds to purchase decent premises for it. However, he gradually found himself being asked to become a companion or consort to his employer, a role that was not of his choosing. Consequently, he asked Barbara to leave her job in Paris with the cosmetics firm Elizabeth Arden and join him in Ireland. If two were rather uneasy company at Luttrellstown, the arrival of Barbara ensured that three were distinctly a crowd, and amid arguments and recriminations the Yeo-Thomases left Ireland and returned to France.

Then, in the most dramatic circumstances, Yeo-Thomas was given the opportunity of tackling a new and exciting challenge. In November 1949, the body of Edward de Murault, the Paris representative of the Federation of British Industry, was found in his car in the Champs Elysées. He had died from a blow to the head. The men responsible were eventually arrested and brought to trial and, when the fuss and furore surrounding de Murault's murder had calmed, Yeo-Thomas was offered the job of replacing him. His business experience and unrivalled connections at all levels of post-war French life made him an obvious choice and, amid some crass newspaper announcements ('Dressmaker, Saboteur, Trade-booster' – the Continental edition of the *Daily Mail*), he took up the post on 8 February 1950. This was to be no sinecure, however, as Sir Norman Kipping, the Director-General of the FBI wrote: 'This was a job for which he was ideally fitted. It was not only his wartime heroism, but also the quiet authority and confidence it had given him that commanded the respect and affection of all his innumerable friends,

British and French alike. As an interpreter of political, economic and industrial developments in France, he was intelligent and farseeing and his friendships there ran throughout society from the very top to the bottom.'

Yeo-Thomas's own description of his job in 1952 offered a rather more precise impression of his day-to-day duties:

I help British industrialists to find agents for the sale of their products in France. If they already have agents here I try to help them – the agents – to improve their sales. I advise FBI members who have difficulties with licences. If an FBI member wants confidential information on French firms or business individuals I try to get it. If a British firm thinks of opening a branch or subsidiary in France, I explain the legal and other formalities, the taxation and so on. I keep FBI members informed on changes in Customs and other duties affecting imports; give warning – when I can – of impending commercial restrictions. I report to the FBI on French trade conditions and the imports policy.

He found his work at the FBI stimulating and worthwhile. Furthermore, the return to Paris and his new job helped to complete the restoration of his relationship with Barbara. They were more in love than ever and led a life of domestic contentment in his father's old apartment in the rue des Eaux. They were both too strong-willed for there not to be the odd fiery moment, and Yeo-Thomas's spend-thrift nature obliged Barbara to perform wonders with their finances. She was also ever mindful of the need to monitor his health and was concerned that many of the ghosts of the concentration camps were still with him. Therefore, after discussing the matter with his doctors, she prompted him to write an account of his wartime experiences. It was hoped that this would prove a therapeutic experience and exorcise his horrific memories. Numerous newspaper reports had already described his adventures, and a radio dramatization of the latter part of his story entitled *The Undefeated* had been broadcast on the BBC Home Service on 30 November 1947. He had no real expectation of writing a bestseller, but felt that it was a story worth telling and hoped to use any royalties to help resistance charities.

Various other people had already urged him to write his story, including Bruce Marshall, a wartime intelligence officer who had been seconded in May 1943 to RF Section. Marshall had served with the Royal Irish Fusiliers during the First World War, then worked in France as a chartered accountant. In the inter-war years he developed a career as a more than moderately successful novelist. He had met Yeo-Thomas in Baker Street, during one of the latter's brief periods in

London, and learnt a little of his character and activities. They met again in 1946 at the Officers' Club in the rue Faubourg St Honoré, when Marshall raised the question of a book chronicling Yeo-Thomas's exploits. He subsequently claimed that, on this occasion, Yeo-Thomas had asked him to write it, but nothing more came of the 'agreement' until, in May 1950, he was contacted by John Pudney of the publishers Evans Brothers. Pudney informed him that he had just signed Yeo-Thomas to write his book and requested that he assist the author. Marshall's subsequent claim to have written the book is, to say the least, a little disingenuous, for even he conceded that 'Tommy wrote out his story in his own words. Every evening for four or more months he sat down at his typewriter as soon as he had returned from his office and, because he has a good memory, gave me the facts.' Thus, Marshall's task was to edit Yeo-Thomas's script and imbue it with a little literary style, but in so doing he greatly reduced the original's energy, sense of tragedy and, above all, searing honesty. Furthermore, he loaded the book, *The White Rabbit*, with his own religious obsessions and, although it was described as being 'told' by Yeo-Thomas to Bruce Marshall, the ponderous moralizing clearly bears the hand of the latter. One of Yeo-Thomas's wartime comrades-in-arms, Maurice Braun, described it thus: 'And once again, this whole extraordinary odyssey was recounted to us by a third party, Bruce Marshall, Yeo-Thomas staying discreetly in the background, the unique hero of an autobiography narrated by someone else.'

The book appeared on 30 April 1952, accompanied by an extensive publicity campaign during which Yeo-Thomas and Marshall undertook numerous interviews with the media. It was a phenomenal success with the public and sold 50,000 copies within its first six months. Whereas most of the reviews were full of praise for Yeo-Thomas's extraordinary story and Marshall's prose, Guy Ramsey, in a review in the *Daily Telegraph* (2 May 1952), wrote: 'The book is polyphonic: the carping of the author providing a counterpoint to the horrible, horrifying, yet fundamentally ennobling story he has to tell. The quality in Marshall, the Christian, can be defined best by saying he is obsessed, even possessed by a holy hatred; the quality in Yeo-Thomas, the pagan, by a refusal ever to despair.' Similar views were expressed by Laurence Thompson in *Tribune* later that summer: 'It is a story which should be told, however badly – I would argue that it could not possibly be told badly – by the man himself. Marshall cannot leave it alone, he cannot understand that the biographer's first duty is to get his own damn ego out of the picture.' Regardless of these criticisms, the book became a classic of the Second World War genre, with its position confirmed in September 1954 with the publication of a paperback edition. It proved to be a runaway success and sold out almost immediately. The publishers had to restrict deliveries to bookshops, and undertake a massive reprint later that year. It also achieved greater currency in France with the publication of a French-language version that boasted an introduction written by Pierre Brossolette's widow, Gilberte.

Early in 1957 the press reported that Anthony Bartley, a film producer and former RAF officer, had bought the film rights to *The White Rabbit*. It was not mentioned that they had been acquired in large measure because of Yeo-Thomas's insistence that his story be spared a Hollywood treatment. As a result, he and Bruce Marshall concluded an arrangement with Bartley and his associates which, ostensibly, guaranteed his wishes, but meant he did not receive the much higher fee he might have expected from an American film studio. Thereafter, the film trade press was awash with speculation and hyperbole. Bartley, his associate Brian Kingcombe, Jack Trevor Story and, later, Leo Marks (the erstwhile head of SOE's code and cipher section) were all credited with working on a script. Meanwhile, the list of actors mooted to be in the running to play Yeo-Thomas included Richard Burton, Kenneth More, Richard Todd, Rex Harrison and Cary Grant.

By 1960, the film had still not been made, but it was reported that plans were now being masterminded by Spyros Skouras, the President of Twentieth-Century Fox. Such news was hardly to Yeo-Thomas's liking and he was far from pleased with the apparent failure of his former RAF colleagues to protect his interests. Then, in the spring of 1961, speculation about the project was revived with the British actor Kenneth More tipped for the lead role. More already had a string of war films to his name, among them a celebrated portrayal of the RAF fighter pilot Douglas Bader. In March and April, More was interviewed by the press and expressed his admiration for Yeo-Thomas, 'the bravest man in the world', and exhibited a refreshingly honest anticipation of the pitfalls ahead. 'The chap's still alive – he's sixty now and working on some trade job in Paris – and there are bound to be problems when we meet. There always are when an actor plays a living character.' In fact, Yeo-Thomas and Barbara were reassured to learn that More had won the part, admiring his past performances and, most of all, his 'Britishness'. Problems arose over the ownership of the book's copyright, however, and in 1962 More stated that, having wasted a year of his life waiting for plans for the film to come to fruition, he reluctantly had to concede that it would never be made.[12]

Yeo-Thomas's unique position as a British subject with access to the highest circles of French political life was of great advantage in his work at the FBI. It also made him a more than useful adviser to a range of British diplomatic personnel. Among these was Stephen

Hastings, a member of the Secret Intelligence Service, who was posted to Paris in 1954. In his memoirs,[13] Hastings recalls that his period of service in France was marked by three 'dramas': the Hungarian Uprising, the Suez Crisis and the political upheaval in France that led to the return to power of de Gaulle. Understandably, Hastings was most concerned with events in France and was a keen observer of the political strife that almost propelled the country into civil war in May 1958. He had met Yeo-Thomas soon after his arrival in France and noted that the latter was 'deep in the confidence of the Paris Gaullistes, and gradually through him I met a number of his friends and contacts'. As French politics rocked from one political crisis to another, in large measure occasioned by conflicting opinions over the ultimate fate of French Algeria, the intrigue in Paris and Algiers began almost to rival that experienced during the German occupation. Hastings recalls visiting Yeo-Thomas at his apartment and being shown a list of *messages personnels* and telephone numbers that his host was to transmit to callers.[14] The SIS man assumed that the messages were connected with a Gaullist conspiracy, but later concluded: 'They meant nothing at all, but did serve to increase the general excitement in Paris and to persuade the Government that the paras were on their way.'[15]

With the passage of the years, Yeo-Thomas increasingly became a revered embodiment of Anglo-French amity. He was a regular presence at resistance reunions, memorial services and British Legion functions in France and Britain. He remained very close to his comrades-in-arms of the RAF Special Duty Squadrons and, when they formed a 'Tempsford Association', he accepted the invitation of Group Captain Ron Hockey, the former commanding officer of No 138 Squadron, to be their guest of honour. In an interview in 1953, he said that if he won the lottery he would give the money to the widows and orphans of the pilots who dropped agents in France. He also dreamed of buying a cottage in a country village as a rest home for his wartime friends – then, correcting himself, said: 'Better than a cottage I'd take a quiet country pub that had a spare room or two for old pals . . .' A particularly poignant moment came in June 1957 when the Queen Mother unveiled a commemorative plaque at Dorset Square. This was followed by a lunch at 10 Downing Street that was attended by many of the leading Gaullist personalities and surviving SOE luminaries.

Not all wartime memories were so sweet. In 1958, there was a growing debate over SOE's wartime activities and, in particular, various aspects of F Section's operations. Yeo-Thomas had long harboured a personal feeling of resentment that F Section, headed by Colonel Maurice Buckmaster, had secured preferential treatment from the SOE administration. The two men had not got on during the war and their relations did not improve after it. In the late 1950s, various authors criticized Buckmaster's leadership and investigated several controversies concerning alleged double agents and the section's apparent disregard for the fate of its captured agents. As Yeo-Thomas had reported during the war on one of the leading figures, Henri Déricourt, and had intimate knowledge of the F Section agents in Buchenwald, he was inevitably drawn into the dispute. Such was the level of acrimony that, in the spring of 1959, he even contemplated ceasing to wear his George Cross as an act of protest over some of the politicking within former SOE circles.

Such unpleasantness compounded and accentuated a growing feeling of regret and disappointment at the failings of post-war society. In the early 1950s, he had written of his sadness at the country's rejection of Churchill in the 1945 election and began to question the purpose of his own sacrifice:

> Well it is over now. I have my memories, something no one can take away from me. I am a bitter man now, but I have known real happiness as well as real sorrow and excruciating suffering. Knowing men like the many I counted as my friends in those hectic and dangerous days has made me richer than the veriest Croesus. Often, though, I envy them, for they gave their lives willingly, gladly, and they died happy, for they died with an ideal, with the feeling that they had sacrificed everything for something good, something enduring. They did not live to see the sham that it all was, to see the wasting of all their efforts, the shameless scramble for personal satisfactions.
>
> So, I exist, but most of the aim has gone out of my life. It is a hollow mockery of what I had visualized, and I am constantly sickened by what goes on around me.

These feelings seem to have returned by the early 1960s, although it is uncertain whether this was a consequence of his advancing years or a more fundamental questioning of social values. Whatever the motives, he did not pull his punches when giving a candid interview to the *Daily Express*:

> The gilt has worn off the gingerbread . . . I mean it just hasn't happened has it? I look around me. I see a world which has returned to its old brutalities. And it hurts. I hear young people say that England has had it. Down the drain. I'm all right Jack. It shakes me. Sometimes it hurts so much that I wish I could have died after my escape from Buchenwald in '45. It's not easy

for me to tell you a thing like that. But it's true. I wish, sometimes, I had died then. We knew we had won the war. It was the
most completely satisfying feeling I've had in all my life. I am,
you know, since you ask, a terribly disappointed man.

Hardly surprisingly, these pessimistic sentiments elicited a flood of
letters from readers seeking to reassure Yeo-Thomas by expressing
their admiration and support for him.

His melancholia may also have been due to a significant deterioration in his health. Although he had prided himself on his stamina and
fitness before the war, following his brutal treatment at the hands
of the Nazis, he suffered one illness after another. Predictably, he
shrugged off his persistent headaches thus: 'I cannot remember a day
since the war when I have not had a headache. But there were so
many people worse off than I am. I survived. They did not.' In 1960
he began to experience difficulty in keeping his balance and a loss in
manual dexterity. Usually so confident a driver, he unaccountably hit
a pair of gates when arriving at a dinner engagement with Barbara
and, thereafter, his driving grew steadily worse until he had to stop
altogether. He went for medical tests and was diagnosed as having a
serious kidney complaint. He had suffered from kidney stones during
his incarceration in the concentration camps and, in the absence of
proper treatment, his kidneys had been badly damaged. He was
admitted to the King Edward VII Hospital in London and found
to have high blood pressure. Although he was put on a course of
medication that eventually was to rise to a daily intake of eighteen
different pills, his health continued to worsen. He was not a good
patient and, if not closely watched, was prone to spit out his medication when those caring for him were not looking.

In April 1963, the *Evening Standard*'s Paris Correspondent, Sam
White, visited Yeo-Thomas and wrote describing his degeneration:
'He is a man without any religious beliefs, but he endured suffering
like a man of faith. He has been unable to work since last December,
but he carries on working from his flat.' Although paying tribute
to the Federation of British Industry for reassuring Yeo-Thomas
regarding his continued employment, White reported that Barbara
had taken a part-time secretarial position (they needed the cash
for doctors' bills), but that left her free to nurse him for the rest of
the day. White recognized that his final statement might 'cost me
Yeo-Thomas's friendship', but nevertheless concluded: 'We award
gratuities to victorious generals. Why not a gratuity for a man who
fought and won battles alone?'

Yeo-Thomas's French comrades-in-arms took the opportunity of
making what they must have feared was a final act of tribute to his

contribution to the liberation of their country. On 22 July 1963, in accordance with instructions issued by Général de Gaulle himself, Yeo-Thomas was presented with the insignia of Commandeur of the Légion d'Honneur. Jean Sainteny, the Ministre des Anciens Combattants et Victimes de Guerre, carried out the ceremony at the Yeo-Thomases' rue des Eaux apartment before a collection of many of the latter's closest friends. These included Généraux Koenig and Valin, Gilbert Renault and, of course, Dewavrin, who doubtless endorsed Sainteny's assessment that Yeo-Thomas was *le symbole de l'amitié franco-anglaise* ('the symbol of Anglo-French friendship'). It was reported that Yeo-Thomas wept at the occasion, had difficulty in standing unaided and struggled with his memory. Koenig, one of de Gaulle's most trusted allies during the war and the head of the Forces Françaises de l'Intérieur, later recalled more elegantly that many of those present were struck by their friend's condition: 'The skeleton was thinner, the man clearly exhausted. He was starting to pay dearly for the tortures endured eighteen years before.'

Yeo-Thomas's health continued to deteriorate. Thanks to a French government pension, Barbara was able to give up her job and nurse him full-time. He became bedridden, and only occasionally lucid. He had a brief remission following treatment by the Swiss doctor, Professor Niehans, but this proved to be only temporary. It was almost a blessed relief when, on 26 February 1964, he suffered a massive haemorrhage and died, with Barbara at his bedside. During the following days the newspapers in London and Paris were full of tributes, although some journalists could not help claiming spurious scoops. Audrey Whiting of the *Daily Mirror* wrote that she had known the 'insignificant-looking, rubicund little man', claiming somewhat naively that: 'I was probably the first person to whom he described in detail his dramatic years of espionage – and ultimate capture and torture by the Germans.'

The funeral was held in the pouring rain on the morning of Saturday, 29 February 1964 at the British Embassy Church in the rue d'Aguesseau. Those who attended included the British Ambassador Sir Pierson Dixon, Généraux Weygand, Koenig and a host of his friends and former comrades-in-arms. Air Commodore A L Winskill, the Air Attaché, who, as a wartime pilot had been shot down over France and helped by the resistance, gave a short address. Fittingly, Général Koenig was chosen to present an oration. It set just the right tone of respect, admiration, tribute and explanation, calling Yeo-Thomas 'an Englishman of France and one of the truest friends of my country . . . Few men, Mr Ambassador, will have done so much for my country. Be persuaded that France cannot and would not wish to forget the memory of a companion so understanding, so ardent, so effective in this most painful of struggles; a struggle that France brought to her Allies' doorstep in order to win back her independence along with her freedom. What a tremendous example of the Anglo-French brotherhood-of arms!'

Koenig took the trouble to address his concluding words to Barbara. He sympathized with her in her grief and affirmed that such was the love felt for Yeo-Thomas by those present that there was a host of others who shared her pain. His action was all the more considerate given her own uncertain position in law. Even after more than twenty-five years of separation, Lillian persisted in maintaining her position as Madame Yeo-Thomas, and posted her own death notices for Yeo-Thomas in *The Times* and French newspapers, alongside those placed by Barbara. A report in the newspaper *Libération-Champagne* stated that Yeo-Thomas's ashes would be interred in the Père-Lachaise cemetery in Paris but, in accordance with his wishes, they were quietly brought back to England[16] and laid to rest in the Glades of Remembrance at Brookwood, Surrey.

A memorial service was held at St Clement Dane's, the RAF church in London, on 30 April 1964. His British friends, family and comrades-in-arms paid their tributes and, fittingly, it was Sir James Hutchison of RF Section who gave the address. Typically, he spoke briefly, knowing that those present were fully acquainted with Yeo-Thomas's virtues: 'You will have known then a giant in courage, in fortitude, in loyalty, in resourcefulness and in patriotism.' He was also at pains to pay tribute to Barbara: 'I have spoken of loyalty – to his friends and to his country. But there is another loyalty which I know that he would have wanted me to mention; the loyalty and devotion of Barbara to him and, through him, to us. For it was her love and care which preserved and comforted him for so long. We who admired and valued Tommy owe her a great deal.' He concluded by paying tribute to Yeo-Thomas's role in sustaining Anglo-French relations: 'We, on both sides of the Channel, are linked and must continue to be linked by the sacrifices and grandeur of men like these. Let us at least keep the lamp of his memory burning bright.'

POSTSCRIPT

In the early 1990s, during and after the Gulf War, the British public rediscovered an interest in the heroics of its armed forces and, in particular, those soldiers and airmen subjected to the most brutal of Iraqi interrogations after their capture. Once again British forces were confronted by a violent, totalitarian regime apparently capable of perpetrating a limitless range of torture. The prospect of being taken prisoner was frightful and events to justify these fears.

The SAS and RAF aircrew who fell into the hands of the Iraqis were, in spite of being in uniform, in a similar situation to Yeo-Thomas. Their captors wanted cooperation and, in particular, information. Unlike Yeo-Thomas, however, the amount of intelligence that the prisoners needed to conceal was limited. Details of the SAS's plans to attack Iraqi missile sites were soon out of date and many of the technical specifications of the Tornado bomber were freely available in open publications. Having held out as long as their training demanded, the soldiers and airmen were able to provide sufficient co-operation to ensure their survival. Like Yeo-Thomas, they have told their stories to produce bestsellers, which have fascinated the public and delighted their publishers.

The epithet 'hero' has been bestowed on them, not by themselves or their services, but by the press and publicists. Regrettably, in recent times, the media has, in large measure, debased the word, with headline labels, such as 'Falklands Hero in Bank Hold-up'. However, by the same token, we should not forget that, following the Second World War, there was an equally inappropriate dilution of the meaning of the word. The media, doubtless encouraged by the authorities, sought to represent that all British officers behaved on every occasion with exemplary courage. It could not be countenanced that there might be gradations of valour descending, finally, to cowardice. Yet such a distortion of the variety of human behaviour was manifestly wrong, for, while it sought to protect society from admitting the fallibility of its soldiers, sailors and airmen, it also detracted from the remarkable bravery of its real heroes. By denying the existence of one of the extremes of behaviour, post-war writers diminished the qualities shown at the other end of the spectrum.

It would be easy to see Yeo-Thomas, like the Gulf War heroes, as simply a man of his time, one of a pantheon of British Second World War heroes who, brought up with a belief in King and Country, found their apotheosis in a crusade against the tyranny of Nazi Germany. While acknowledging that each generation needs to discover its own heroes, some set standards that are timeless. Yeo-Thomas is such a hero.

FOOTNOTES

Chapter One

1 According to Forest Yeo-Thomas, a greatuncle, F A Yeo, had been Mayor of Swansea.
2 Tuchman, *The Guns of August*, pp229–30
3 Anoui, *Monograph on Military Personnel and Related Records of the War Department 1912–39*, p315
4 The Red Army continued its advance to the very outskirts of Warsaw before Pilsudski engineered a masterly counter-attack and drove the Bolsheviks into retreat.
5 Martin and Koda, *Haute Couture*, p24
6 Yeo-Thomas had boxed for the US Army in an Inter-Allied Championship in 1919.
7 Churchill, *The Gathering Storm*, pp 271–2
8 Bernier, *Fireworks at Dusk*, p311
9 ibid.

Chapter Two

1 Ellis, *The War in France and Flanders 1939-1940*, p29
2 The sugar that Yeo-Thomas had introduced into the fuel tank would have caused his adversary's car engine to seize.
3 Following Finland's refusal to accede to Soviet territorial demands, on 30 November 1939 the Red Army launched an invasion. Although the Finns defended stubbornly, it was an unequal contest. Support for Finland captured the popular imagination in France and, perversely, Daladier made bellicose statements about granting military aid. Britain did not share his enthusiam for this adventurous and ill-advised scheme and, on 13 March 1940, Finland and the Soviet Union signed a peace treaty.
4 Spears, *Assignment to Catastophe*, pp184–5
5 Zamoyski, *The Forgotten Few*, p121
6 Smith, *Action Stations* Volume 3, p209
7 No other reference has been located to confirm Yeo-Thomas's conversations with MI9; they do not appear in any of the other files consulted, nor his own writings, nor has Barbara Yeo-Thomas any recollection of them. The evidence is far from conclusive but it cannot be discounted that Yeo-Thomas was seeking to indicate to Keswick that he was a man 'in demand' and therefore a worthy candidate for SOE.

Chapter Three

1 West, *Secret War*, p20
2 Pimlott, *Hugh Dalton*, p296
3 A fifth, AMF, was later to operate from Algiers.
4 Michel, *Cinquantenaire de l'Ordre de la Libération*, p17
5 In a subsequent broadsheet, de Gaulle added the famous phrase, 'France has lost a battle; she has not lost the war.'
6 Piquet-Wicks, *Four in the Shadows*, p70
7 Foot, *SOE in France*, p153
8 Sweet-Escott, *Baker Street Irregular*, pp179-80
9 'Passy', *2e Bureau Londres*, p65-6
10 SOE Archive
11 ibid.
12 Hutchison, *That Drug Danger*, p80
13 Piquet-Wicks, op. cit., p70
14 Molyneux had managed to leave Paris before the German occupation and was living in London.

Chapter Four

1 Also known as *Zone Non-Occupée* (ZNO) or Unoccupied Zone
2 Darlan's ambivalent presence soon disappeared from the drama. On 24 December 1942 he was assassinated in Algiers by a twenty-year-old member of the resistance.
3 Foot, *SOE in France*, p118
4 Recollections of Barbara Yeo-Thomas. It is sometimes easy to forget that, although Yeo-Thomas spoke English without a trace of a French accent, occasional blemishes occurred in his use of the language. On one occasion, when discussing bomb damage in London, he corrected Barbara for pronouncing 'debris' in the French manner.
5 Renault's associate, François Faure.
6 Rémy, *Memoirs of a Secret Agent*, p238
7 'Passy', *10 Duke Street*, p66
8 At this time, on Bastille Day, 14 July 1942, de Gaulle's movement changed its name to France Combattante (Fighting French) in order to help identify itself with the resistance in France who were, by definition, not 'free'. However both names continued to be used.
9 'Passy', *Missions secrètes en France*, p74
10 ibid.
11 'Tommy Rabbit' was a long-time pet name, and therefore, when later asked for a codename, Yeo-Thomas proposed 'Rabbit'. As this had already been assigned elsewhere, he chose 'White Rabbit', unaware of the frenetic personality of the Lewis Caroll character. As it transpired, this was to become his most famous codename, although it was the one that he used the least.
12 The excitement proved too much for Hutchison, who left his briefcase in the SIS car, which returned to London the next day. It was not until

the following afternoon that he realized his gaffe and ordered Piquet-Wicks to retrieve it. Luce returned it safe and sound but a memo had to be submitted chronicling Hutchison's forgetfulness.

13 Manhès was subsequently sent to Buchenwald concentration camp from which he returned at the end of the war.

14 Beaufils's clandestine activity on behalf of the Communist Party continued after the war, and in 1977 he was exposed as a Soviet agent.

15 In April 1942 Général Henri Giraud had escaped from German captivity and had been touted by American officials as a likely alternative French leader to de Gaulle.

16 'Jargon' was being recalled because, as Courtaud later wrote: 'He was a brave lad but not suited to the obscure tasks that we had to offer him. He was undisciplined, refusing to carry out orders and, more seriously, he drank, pouring forth remarks that were extremely dangerous for the service. I had spoken to "Alex" [Alphonse Tanguy] about this and we had got to the point of contemplating doing away with him if he did not change and we couldn't find another solution. Fortunately, "Passy" came to France. I handed the case over to him and he took him back with him to London. A murder had perhaps been avoided as well as serious compromise for the network, which could have resulted from this officer's indiscretions.' ('Jacot', *Souvenirs d'un autre temps*, p115.) Courtaud records that 'Jargon's' real name was probably Jordin or Jourdain and that, once removed from the clandestine life for which he was ill suited, he went on to serve France well.

17 Courtaud's post-war account offers a different description of the arrangement of the passengers. However, it seems likely that Yeo-Thomas and Dewavrin would have remembered their own flights more precisely than an agent who arranged many such operations during the war.

18 Yeo-Thomas never saw Ryan again and his memories were not of the happiest, recalling: 'The American officer I brought back from France, and to whom I had lent my lucky pullover, never returned it, nor did he ever give me any sign of life. I was most annoyed.'

Chapter Five

1 Hutchison was to get his wish and left RF Section to train as a JED-BURGH. Having subjected himself to a somewhat unnecessary and unconvincing operation to change his appearance, he parachuted into France as Colonel 'Hastings' shortly after D-Day.

2 Hutchison, *That Drug Danger*, p83

3 The betrayal of Moulin has become one of the causes célèbres of French history. It is widely held that René Hardy was responsible, for, although he was twice tried and acquitted by military tribunals after the war, the burden of evidence still seems to point directly to him. Hardy had been released by the SD shortly after his arrest but then neglected to inform his comrades of his capture. Although some were surprised that he should have been asked to attend the meeting at Caluire, this was not in

itself suspicious. However, Hardy was to achieve the distinction of being the only person to escape Barbie's clutches when he broke free as he was being led out of Dugoujon's house. Passersby later found him suffering from a bullet wound in the arm and took him to hospital. Before he could be eliminated by members of the resistance who had decided on his guilt, he was transferred to a German military infirmary. Miraculously, Hardy's astonishing luck had still not deserted him and he managed to escape from detention, displaying a series of feats of great athleticism in spite of having his arm encased in plaster. He remained at liberty in the South of France and Paris for some time before reaching North Africa where he joined the Free French administration.

4 Dank, *The French Against the French*, p156

5 Prophetically, his personal report on completing SOE's Beaulieu course included the comment: 'Outwardly he is the complete man of the world; nevertheless it is possible that he might not prove very practical when faced with a difficult situation.'

6 There was to be a tragic postscript to this idyll, as Yeo-Thomas was to recall after the war: 'Of the thirteen men who spent that day together, only three are alive today. The Mas [farmhouse] we were staying in was attacked by a strong German detachment, some months later; all our companions were there, and they put up a terrific fight, killing many of the enemy, before themselves being overpowered, only two of them survived, one with thirteen bullet wounds in his body, the other with half a dozen bullets through his stomach, and one arm blown off.'

7 This is not the last we will hear of Vacher, for he appears again later in the narrative.

8 He later claimed that he had been caught stealing stationery from the Kommandatur as a prank. Threatened with imprisonment, he agreed to work for them in return for his liberty.

9 Lemonnier features again in Yeo-Thomas's story.

10 One can only assume that Yeo-Thomas had satisfied himself that it was no longer under surveillance.

Chapter Six

1 Hutchison had now moved on and his place, having briefly passed to Bickham Sweet-Escott, was taken by Dismore, a former journalist who had joined SOE in October 1941. Dismore had initially served in West Africa and had taken part in the spectacular Operation POSTMASTER in January 1942, when SOE operatives seized two Axis ships from the neutral port of Fernando Po in Spanish West Africa. Although perhaps not enjoying as close a relationship with Yeo-Thomas as Hutchison, Dismore's sound knowledge of SOE made him a capable replacement.

2 The question of Yeo-Thomas's decorations dragged on for several more months. In January 1944, SOE resubmitted an application for the award of a Military Cross for his work on the SEAHORSE mission for reasons that were separate from the award of his Croix de Guerre. This was finally gazetted on 14 March 1944. A recommendation for a Bar to his

Military Cross for his work on MARIE-CLAIRE was put forward by SOE in April and the award was gazetted on 16 May 1944.

3 Air Historical Branch, *Special Duty Operations in Europe*, p83

4 ibid., p86

5 Dismore acted as his Conducting Officer.

6 Lostrie was subsequently to operate in the Loire region with resistance groups.

7 Bingen had stepped into the breach following the arrest of Bollaert, and acted as his stand-in until the arrival of Alexandre Parodi in April. Bingen then went to Clermont-Ferrand on 10 May to use it as a base for his activities after the invasion that was expected any day. He was almost immediately betrayed by a double agent in the pay of the Germans who had penetrated the local network. After a failed attempt to escape, Bingen took his suicide pill.

8 Misselwitz was arrested after the war and, in 1952, sentenced to five years' imprisonment. In 1983, it was alleged that he had not served his sentence and had been employed by the French Security Service, the Direction de la Surveillance du Territoire.

9 Surprisingly, this document does not feature again in the story other than in a post-war SOE debriefing of Yeo-Thomas. In this he referred to having had in his possession a list of rendezvous, but that it was secure for it 'gave the wrong place and the wrong time'.

Chapter Seven

1 Yeo-Thomas later identified this man as Frédéric Martin, alias 'Rudy de Mérode', a Frenchman born in Lorraine who had worked for the Abwehr since 1928. However, Martin's activities, while covering a wide range of disreputable collaborationist activity, seemed to be particularly devoted to extortion and black-marketeering. Although it has been claimed that he was instructed to concentrate on police work early in 1944, there must remain a question regarding the accuracy of Yeo-Thomas's identification.

2 Brossolette, *Il s'appelait Pierre Brossolette*, p235. A further and fascinating insight came after the war when Yeo-Thomas received a letter from a member of the RAF, who wrote:

> I was one of three 'evaders' who were to be evacuated by Lysander . . . scheduled to take place near Vervins. During the delays waiting for favourable weather, I spoke with Brossolette a number of times, the conversation mostly being 'shop'. Being then somewhat ignorant of the form, I asked him the procedure he advocated in case of capture. In reply he showed me the ring he was wearing, unscrewed the top and showed me the cyanide pill. The pill somehow got dropped on the floor and rolled under some furniture. A brief search was made but it could not be found and, as Brossolette did not appear very concerned and there were more important matters on hand, nothing further was done.

> Later I heard of the capture and tragic death of Brossolette . . .
> Speculation is idle but nevertheless fascinating, and whether subse-
> quent history would have been altered had the pill not been lost I
> don't know, but there is the story for what it's worth.

3 José Dupuis conducted her own investigations at the hospital. Her
informant stated that Brossolette had arrived in a coma suffering from a
fractured skull and broken arms and legs.

4 Michel Pichard was later to suggest that the German interrogators were
rather more sophisticated than it at first appeared. He wrote to Barbara
Yeo-Thomas: 'One rather important point I have (almost) established is
that the Germans started by asking mostly questions to which they knew
the answer. This helped determine if the agent had broken down or not.
Yet, they were subtle enough to let the agent (temporarily) believe he
had fooled them. This is what happened to Tommy when he gave his
most inaccurate description of myself. This was in March 44, . . . and the
Gestapo (or SD) had circularized my exact description in March 43: I
have a copy of it.'

5 Although Yeo-Thomas wrote of this meeting after the war, this
encounter does not appear in any contemporary report or debriefing seen
by the author.

6 Like several other captured members of the resistance, Delimal took his
'L' tablet while in captivity at the rue des Saussaies.

7 Michel Pichard wrote after the war that Brigitte Friang denied that
Alavoine had the chance to write a note and therefore he must have confessed to the rendezvous when questioned by the Germans. Pichard
explained Yeo-Thomas's belief in the existence of a note thus: 'Tommy
chose to accept Guy's [Alavoine's] word about it (and I trust that Guy
would be honest about it) or because he chose to give this explanation
about his own arrest in order to minimize Guy's responsibility.'

8 Suni Sandöe was deported to Ravensbrück in August. She survived the
war and later returned to Denmark.

9 Manuel vanished after a few weeks. After the war, he was reported to be
living in Colombia.

10 He had received a wireless message from one of de Gaulle's representatives, Maurice Bourgès-Maunoury, advising him of Yeo-Thomas's
arrest.

11 The note reached London and, together with many of Yeo-Thomas's
artefacts, is currently on display in the Imperial War Museum, London.

12 The Simon brothers, Luquet and Deschamps, were sent to Germany
where they died in captivity.

Chapter Eight

1 The official history of SOE's work in France categorically states that
Starr betrayed Southgate. On the other hand, after the war, Starr
claimed that he had not implicated his friend and that Southgate had
blamed another agent's indiscretion for betraying him. Moreover, he

implied that Southgate had adopted a similar level of cooperation with his captors as Starr had himself.

2 Although the number of men in the party is constant in all sources, the names and spellings appear in different forms. A contemporary German list does not include the 'Corbusier' in Yeo-Thomas's memoirs, but there is a Marcel Keunen (not to be confused with 'Kane'). Similarly, there is a discrepancy on the lists between a Henri 'Heusch' and a Henri 'Reusch', but they are obviously one and the same.

3 Cave Brown, *Secret Servant*, p583

4 ibid.

5 ibid., p584

6 The British subsequently learnt that, apart from German inmates, different nationalities within the camp were given a letter indicating their country of origin. They therefore requested that they be given a letter to distinguish them from the German prisoners and 'Es' were provided.

7 Burney, *The Dungeon Democracy*, pp14–15

8 ibid., p18

9 Pickersgill (ed. Ford), *The Making of a Secret Agent*

10 Hackett, *The Buchenwald Report*, pp277–8

11 Burney, op. cit., p38

12 Balachowsky's would-be employers at the Pasteur Institute falsified his papers in the hope that this would save him from execution.

13 *The Buchenwald Report* states: 'Post-war reports identify this as an RAF raid' (p95) but, as Yeo-Thomas recalled, it took place in the afternoon, and it would therefore appear to have been an American effort.

14 *The Buchenwald Report* gives their numbers as 82 Americans, 50 British, 25 Canadians, 9 Australians and 2 New Zealanders

15 This may have been a note sent via one of Hessel's contacts.

16 In his evidence to the trial of the Buchenwald personnel at Dachau, Yeo-Thomas stated that Dietzsch had told Wilhelm that he would give Peulevé the injection and feigned doing so.

17 After the war, Yeo-Thomas visited Chouquet's widow.

Chapter Nine

1 The Weiss's survived the war.

2 Two and a half years later, Birchall sent the print to Yeo-Thomas as a keepsake.

3 Interview with Joan Morrison.

4 Dodds-Parker, *Setting Europe Ablaze*, p205. The second book, *From the Red Army to SOE* by L H Manderstam, an SOE staff officer with the African and Russian Sections, offers such a fanciful and inaccurate account that it does not bear repetition.

Chapter Ten

1 Eventually an exception was made and, on 28 June 1945, Yeo-Thomas was given the rank of Acting Wing Commander, after Sporborg had lent

his weight to the application stating that it was 'not a mere "stunt" or desire for aggrandisement of Yeo-Thomas himself'.

2 Whitehead had already carried out an investigation into the fate of the CITRONELLE mission, of which Hubble had been a member.

3 Another paper among Yeo-Thomas's files is a 'List of Stores to be taken on Mission THUG'. The title alone betrays his intent, as does the following:

> 2 Silent Stens + 300 rounds ammo each
> 2 carbines + 100 rounds ammo each
> 2 Welrods + 50 rounds ammo each
> 4 .45 Colt + 100 rounds ammo each
> 4 Holsters and belts for .45 Colts
> 4 prs handcuffs
> 4 Locking knives

4 James Bond's creator.

5 The citation is not without errors and confuses the chronology of Yeo-Thomas's escape.

6 *Courrier de l'Ouest* 29 Juillet 1946

7 ibid.

8 Foley, *Commando Extraordinary*, p174–5

9 ibid., p175

10 Skorzeny, *Skorzeny's Special Missions*, p213

11 *Women's Wear Daily*, 7 July 1948

12 More was eventually to get his wish to play the role of Yeo-Thomas, albeit in a BBC television version of *The White Rabbit*. However, contractual difficulties remained and the programme, with a script written by Michael Voysey, was broadcast once in 1967 and not seen again.

13 Hastings, *The Drums of Memory*

14 Hastings states that he passed on the messages after Yeo-Thomas had fallen asleep. Barbara has no recollection of these events.

15 Hastings, op. cit., p178

16 With the assistance of Jacques Foulquier, formerly of Gleina, but in 1964 Conseiller Municipal de Paris, Président de la Commissaire Départmentale de la Police.

GLOSSARY

AASF	Advanced Air Striking Force
Abwehr	German Military Intelligence
Advanced Air Striking Force	Component of the RAF based in France in 1939/1940
Agents de liaison	Members of the resistance acting as couriers
'Armée Secrète'	'Secret Army' organized by the French resistance to assist in the liberation
Bachelier ès lettres	French Arts degree
Baker Street.	Primary location in London of SOE's headquarters
BCRA(M)	Bureau Central de Renseignements et d'Action (Militaire)
BEF	British Expeditionary Force
BOA	Bureau d'Opérations Aériennes
Bureau Central de Renseignements et d'Action (Militaire)	Free French Secret Service
Bureau d'Opérations Aériennes	Resistance organization coordinating clandestine air operations between Britain and France
CDLR	Ceux de la Résistance
Ceux de la Libération	Resistance organization especially active regarding intelligence, escape lines and the 'Secret Army'
Ceux de la Résistance	Resistance organization with wide-ranging support
CFLN	Comité Français de Libération Nationale
CND	Confrérie Notre Dame
CNR	Conseil National de la Résistance
Comité Français de Libération Nationale	Provisional Free French administration established in North Africa
Confrérie Notre Dame	BCRA/SIS intelligence network
'D-Day'	The date (ultimately 6 June 1944) of an Allied invasion of France
Dead-letter drop	Site for the clandestine delivery and reception of messages
Délégué Militaire Régional	Resistance leader appointed by de Gaulle to coordinate the formation of a 'Secret Army' in the regions of France
Département	Region of France administered by a préfet

GLOSSARY

Below.

DF	SOE section organizing escape routes out of occupied Europe for agents
D/F	Direction-finding
DMR.	Délégué Militaire Régional
D/RF.2	SOE symbol for Yeo-Thomas
F Section	SOE 'Independent' French Section
FAAP	Forward Air Ammunition Park
FANA	Intelligence liaison section of the Front National
FANY	First Aid Nursing Yeomanry
FBI	Federation of British Industries
Feldgendarmen	German military police
feldwebel	German sergeant
FFC	Forces Françaises Combattantes
FFI	Forces Françaises de l'Intérieur
Forces Françaises Combattantes	Fighting French Forces – alternative name for the Free French
FN	Front National
Forward Air Ammunition Park	RAF establishment in northern France
Franc-Tireurs et Partisans	Communist-led resistance organization
Free French	French organization based in London under de Gaulle (also known as the Fighting French)
Front National	French resistance organization drawing its support from a wide spectrum of French society with its leadership dominated by communists
FTP	.Franc-Tireurs et Partisans
Groupes Mobiles de la Réserve	Vichy rapid deployment police unit
Gendarmerie	French paramilitary police force
Gestapo	*Geheime Staatspolizei* – German security police
GMR	Groupes Mobiles de Réserve
Halifax	Four-engined bomber used by the RAF's Special Duty Squadrons to drop agents and supplies to the Resistance
Hudson	Two-engined light bomber used by the RAF's No 161 Squadron on larger pick-up operations
JEDBURGH units	Teams of Allied soldiers parachuted into France to assist the resistance support the Allied landings
Légion des Volontaires Français	French volunteers serving with the German forces on the Russian Front
Le Tout Paris	Fashionable Paris
Libération	Resistance organization with a politically diverse base of support

Libération Nord	Resistance organization based in the Northern Region of France
Luftwaffe	German Air Force
LVF	Légion des Volontaires Français
Lysander	RAF light aircraft originally intended for army reconnaissance, but ideally suited for landing and picking up personnel from fields in Occupied France
maquis	Rural resistance fighters
message personnel	Simple phrase broadcast by the BBC that conveyed a coded message
MI5	British Security Service
MI6	British Secret Intelligence Service
MI9	British secret service dealing with the escape and evasion of Allied personnel in enemy territory
NCO	Non-commissioned officer
OCM	Organization Civile et Militaire
ODMR	Officier Délégué Militaire Regional
Office of Strategic Services	US intelligence and special operations organization
Officier Délégué Militaire Regional	Resistance leader appointed by Free French in London
Organization Civile et Militaire	Influential resistance organization drawing its support especially from members of the military and civil service
OSS	Office of Strategic Services
Playfair	A substitution cipher
Préfet	Senior civil servant
RF Section	Section of SOE liaising with the Free French
RF/P	SOE symbol used by Yeo-Thomas
SD	Sicherheitsdienst
Secret Intelligence Service	British secret service, also known as MI6
Service du Travail Obligatoire	Mandatory Work Service
Sicherheitsdienst	Intelligence service of the Nazi Party
SIS	Secret Intelligence Service
SOE	Special Operations Executive
Special Operations Executive	Secret British organization formed to create and aid resistance movements against the Axis powers
SS	*Schutzstaffel* – originally Hitler's bodyguard and subsequently in control of the Nazi security and intelligence apparatus
STO	Service du Travail Obligatoire
STS	SOE Special Training School

WAAF	Women's Auxiliary Air Force
Waffen-SS	Military branch of the SS
Wehrmacht	German armed forces
Women's Auxiliary Air Force	Women's branch of the RAF
W/T	Wireless telegraphy
ZNO	*Zone Non-Occupée*, the area of France administered by the Vichy Government under the terms of the armistice
ZO	*Zone Occupée*, the area of France under German occupation after the armistice

SELECT BIBLIOGRAPHY

The primary sources for this work have been Yeo-Thomas's own papers, diaries, letters and writings. These have been supplemented by information drawn from the SOE archive and a variety of personal papers, letters and memoirs of former members of SOE and the French resistance.

Air Historical Branch, Special Duty Operations in Europe, Air Ministry, London, 1946

Allen, Robert S, *Patton's Third US Army*, Manor Books, New York, 1974

Azéma, Jean-Pierre, François Bédaria, Robert Frank (eds), *Jean Moulin et la Résistance en 1943*, Les Cahiers de L'Institut d'Histoire du Temps Présent, Cahier 27, Paris, 1994

Bernier, Olivier, *Fireworks at Dusk*, Little, Brown and Co, Boston, 1993

Bertram, Barbara, *French Resistance in Sussex*, Barnworks Publishing, Pulborough, 1995

Brossolette, Gilberte, *Il s'appelait Pierre Brossolette*, Albin Michel, Paris, 1976

Burney, Christopher, *The Dungeon Democracy*, Heinemann, London, 1945

Burney, Christopher, *Solitary Confinement*, Macmillan, London, 1952

Cave Brown, Anthony, *The Secret Servant*, Michael Joseph, London, 1988

Churchill, Winston S, *The Second World War*, Volume I, *The Gathering Storm*, Cassell, London, 1948

Churchill, Winston S, *The Second World War*, Volume II, *Their Finest Hour*, Cassell, London, 1949

Cobban, Alfred, *A History of France*, Volume III, Pelican, London, 1988

Cookridge, E H, *Inside SOE*, Arthur Barker, London, 1966

Dank, Milton, *The French Against the French*, Cassell, London, 1974

Deacon, Richard, *The French Secret Service*, Grafton, London, 1990

de Cheveigné, Maurice, *Radio Libre*, privately printed, nd

de Gaulle, Charles, *The Call to Honour*, Collins, London, 1955

de Gaulle, Charles, *Unity*, Weidenfeld & Nicolson, London, 1959

Dodds-Parker, Douglas, *Setting Europe Ablaze*, Springwood Books, Windlesham, 1984

Ellis, Major L F, *The War in France and Flanders 1939-1940*, HMSO, London, 1953

Feig, Konnilyn G, *Hitler's Death Camps*, Holmes & Meier, New York, 1981

Foley, Charles, *Commando Extraordinary*, Longman, Green and Co, London, 1954

Foot, M R D, *Resistance*, Eyre Methuen, London, 1976

Foot, M R D, *Six Faces of Courage*, Eyre Methuen, London, 1978

Foot, M R D, *SOE*, BBC, London, 1984

Foot, M R D, *SOE in France*, HMSO, London, 1966

Foucher, Dominique and Roselyne Augustin-Pellecchia, *Jean Moulin:*

Unifacteur de la Résistance, Ville de Lyon/Centre d'Histoire de la Résistance et de la Déportation, Lyon, 1993

Geraghty, Tony, *March or Die*, Grafton, London, 1986

Gilbert, Martin, *Road to Victory*, Heinemann, London, 1986

Guillin, François-Yves, *Le Général Delestraint*, Plon, Paris, 1995

Hackett, David A (ed), *The Buchenwald Report*, Westview Press, Boulder, 1995

Hardy, René, *Derniers Mots*, Fayard, Paris, 1984

Hasquenoph, Marcel, *La Gestapo en France*, Editions de Vecchi, Paris, 1975

Hasting, Stephen, *The Drums of Memory*, Leo Cooper, London, 1994

Hawes, Stephen and Ralph White, *Resistance in Europe: 1939-1945*, Allen Lane, London, 1975

Höhne, Heinz and Hermann Zolling, *The General Was a Spy*, Pan Books, London, 1973

Horne, Alistair, *To Lose a Battle*, Macmillan, London, 1969

Hutchison, Sir James, *That Drug Danger*, Standard Press, Montrose, 1977

Infield, Glenn B, *Skorzeny: Hitler's Commando*, St Martin's Press, New York, 1981

'Jacot' (Olivier Courtauld), *Souvenirs d'un autre temps*, privately printed, nd

Kedward, Rod, *In Search of the Maquis*, OUP, Oxford, 1993

King, Stella, *Jacqueline*, Arms & Armour, London, 1989

Kogon, Eugen, *The Theory and Practice of Hell*, Secker & Warburg, London, 1950

Linklater, Magnus, Isabel Hilton and Neal Linklater, *The Fourth Reich*, Hodder & Stoughton, London, 1984

Littlejohn, David, *The Patriotic Traitors*, Heinemann, London, 1972

Longmate, Norman, *How We Lived Then*, Arrow, London, 1973

Manderstam, L H with Roy Heron, *From the Red Army to SOE*, William Kimber, London, 1985

Martin, Richard and Harold Koda, *Haute Couture*, Metropolitan Museum of Art, New York, 1995

Mengin, Robert, *No Laurels for de Gaulle*, Michael Joseph, London, 1967

Merrick, K A, *Flights of the Forgotten*, Arms & Armour, London, 1989

Michel, Henri, *The Shadow War*, André Deutsch, London, 1972

Michel, Michelle, *Cinquantenaire de l'Ordre de la Libération*, Musée de l'Ordre de la Libération, Paris, 1990

Minney R J, *Carve Her Name With Pride*, George Newnes, London, 1956

Morgan, Ted, *An Uncertain Hour*, The Bodley Head, London, 1990

Noguères, Henri, *Histoire de la Résistance en France* (five volumes), Robert Laffont, Paris, 1967-1981

Overton Fuller, Jean, *The Starr Affair*, George Mann, Maidstone, 1973

Ozouf, René, *Pierre Brossolette*, Librairie Gedalge, Paris, 1946

'Passy', Colonel (André Dewavrin), *2e Bureau Londres*, Raoul Solar, Monte Carlo, 1947

'Passy', Colonel (André Dewavrin), *10 Duke Street*, Londres, Raoul Solar, Monte Carlo, 1947

'Passy', Colonel (André Dewavrin), *Missions secrètes en France*, Librairie Plon, Paris, 1951

Perrault, Giles, *Paris under the Occupation*, André Deutsch, London, 1989

Pichard, Michel, *L'Espoir des ténèbres*, Erti, Paris, nd

Pickersgill, Frank (ed George H Ford), *The Making of a Secret Agent*, Goodread Biographies, Nova Scotia, 1983

Pimlott, Ben, *Hugh Dalton*, Papermac, London, 1985

Piquet-Wicks, Eric, *Four in the Shadows*, Jarrolds, London, 1957

Porch, Douglas, *The French Secret Services*, Macmillan, London, 1996

Pryce-Jones, David, *Paris in the Third Reich*, Collins, London, 1981

'Rémy' (Gilbert Renault), *Memoirs of a Secret Agent of Free France*, McGraw-Hill, New York, 1948

'Rémy' (Gilbert Renault), *Le Livre du courage et de la peur* (two volumes), Aux Trois Couleurs & Raoul Solar, Paris, 1946

'Rémy', (Gilbert Renault), *Comment meurt un réseau*, Raoul Solar, Monte Carlo, 1947

Richards, Brooks, *Secret Flotillas*, HMSO, London, 1996

Rings, Werner, *Life with the Enemy*, Weidenfeld & Nicolson, London, 1982

Russell of Liverpool, Lord, *The Scourge of the Swastika*, Cassell, London, 1954

Sayer, Ian and Douglas Botting, *America's Secret Army*, Grafton Books, London, 1989

Sayer, Ian and Douglas Botting, *Nazi Gold*, Granada, London, 1984

Simkins, Peter, *World War One*, Colour Library Books, Godalming, 1992

Skorzeny, Otto, *Skorzeny's Special Missions*, Panther, London, 1959

Smith, David J, *Action Stations*, Volume III, Ian Allan, London, 1981

Spears, Major-General Sir Edward, *Assignment to Catastrophe*, The Reprint Society, London, 1956

Stafford, David, *Britain and European Resistance*, Macmillan, London, 1980

Sweet-Escott, Bickham, *Baker Street Irregular*, Methuen, London, 1965

Thomas, Jack, *No Banners*, W H Allen, London,1955

Tuchman, Barbara, *The Guns of August*, Dell, New York, 1963

Verity, Hugh, *We Landed by Moonlight*, Ian Allan, London, 1978

Watt, Donald Cameron, *How War Came*, Heinemann, London, 1989

Werth, Alexander, *France 1940-1955*, Robert Hale, London, 1957

West, Nigel, *Secret War*, John Curtis/Hodder & Stoughton, London, 1992

Wilkinson, Peter and Joan Bright Astley, *Gubbins and SOE*, Leo Cooper, London, 1993

Zamoyski, Adam, *The Forgotten Few*, John Murray, London, 1995

Selected British and French newspapers, magazines and journals

INDEX